THE *John Howard Griffin*
READER

The JOHN HOWARD

GRIFFIN

→ *Reader*

SELECTED AND EDITED
BY BRADFORD DANIEL

With photographs by the author

HOUGHTON MIFFLIN COMPANY
BOSTON : 1968

Books by John Howard Griffin

The Devil Rides Outside: Nuni:
Land of the High Sky: Black Like Me

First Printing w

I think of the people who tell me they *have* to write because they have so much to tell the world.

I write not because I understand anything and want to expose, but because I understand nothing. I experience newness every day and write of it as the first tasting of passionate interest. I write in order to seek understanding. I write because I ask constantly "why?" Will I ever know? Other people seem to. Others understand. Others even speak with authority about the great mysteries of almost everything.

> — John Howard Griffin
> Journal entry of Easter, 1951

FOREWORD

———————————————————————————————————————➤

WHEN I first approached John Griffin about the possibility of compiling a representative collection of his writings, he lit a cigarette and mumbled something that sounded like "a writer ought to write and not allow anything to be published until after his death . . ."

I contended that this was wrong.

I told him that his work should be better known, that it should be objectively studied and edited in chronological order. I knew of the thousands of people who swell his lectures into standing-room-only audiences all across the country . . . and in the summers, all across Europe. I knew, too, of the unbelievably heavy mail that he receives almost daily — letters asking advice on inter-racial problems, letters seeking aid in writing or suggestions on religious matters, letters requesting reprints of this or that article that he has written, letters asking for more information on his life and work.

I told him it was important to present a coherent picture of his work. This only embarrassed him. John Griffin is not a man who likes to discuss writing. He is not a "Literary Man," and he avoids the notions and nonsense that center around the "Literary Man." He believes firmly (and here one could echo the words of the iconoclastic William Faulkner) that a writer *should write* — should write every day, each and every day, that a writer should create and let all that follows rest on the work. Fame is an absurd word to John Griffin.

Why then his lectures? This is another matter. Unlike most novelists (at least in our time) Griffin has gone out on a limb. He has devoted himself to a crusade against bigotry and racism because of deep philosophical and religious convictions.

He speaks out against injustice. He names the evils and wrongdoers and attempts at patient and loving length to help correct these wrongs. For he was blind for well over a decade. And while he was blind he learned at devastating levels of thought and torment that a person cannot be judged except on the basis of his individual worth as a human being. A blind person cannot see pigmentation. A blind person cannot readily perceive if a man is a Jew or a Negro or an Indian. A blind person can only react according to the goodness that he feels in another human being.

After he had regained his sight, Griffin, a southerner, disguised himself as a Negro in the Deep South in order to gain insights for his study on racism that eventually was to become *Black Like Me*. Violent reprisals followed the publication of this book. Threats of castration and death. Threats against him, his family, his relatives, his friends. Threats of homes being burned in the night and bombs planted. Finally, out of fear for their children, Griffin and his wife left their home in Mansfield, Texas, and took refuge in Mexico. All this because he had told the truth as he had seen it, because he had said let us correct the evils that are among us. Were these *unreasonable* words?

In Mexico, tensions vanished and Griffin began work on a cultural history of the Tarascan civilization. After a year, trouble struck again in the form of Communist activity in Morelia, the capital city of the state of Michoacán, where the Griffin family lived. Anti-American demonstrations were fostered, mainly through indoctrinated university students. Griffin was asked to investigate these by the American Embassy. One night the inflamed mobs marched up the hill toward the small American colony. Women and children were moved back into the hills to a Benedictine monastery for the night while some of the men kept watch with their Mexican and Tarascan friends. The mob was finally turned back when Federal troops were ordered in. Knowing that other reprisals were sure to follow, most Americans, including Griffin's family, left. Griffin stayed behind alone to finish his research. He documented the financing of various student groups by two secretaries of the Russian Embassy and revealed that the series of crises were an attempt to break the government of Lopez Mateos by killing tourism and discouraging American capital investment. The Mexican government expelled the two members of the Russian Embassy, public sentiment shifted and parent patrols became active in protecting schools and churches from further rioting.

As a result of the time involved in such endeavors, Griffin has not published as much as some of his contemporaries. Nevertheless I was convinced that a *Reader* of Griffin's work should be brought out, to be a continuation in some ways of the work that *Black Like Me* had started.

The Devil Rides Outside, his first novel, was hampered by the fact that it was the first book published by a new Texas publisher. A small group of people, mainly Texans, had read his historical study, *Land of the High Sky*. It had been written for a special audience at a special time and had a limited circulation. And what of his articles that had been published by newspapers and magazines? They should be brought back.

I wanted to bring all this scattered material together and correlate each section with Griffin's life and circumstances at the time the particular work was being written.

Griffin's life has been an extraordinary one. As an adolescent he traveled to Europe to be educated. He worked in a mental hospital that was experimenting with music in the cure of mental illness. He became a member of the French underground during World War II. At twenty-one he was a recognized authority on Gregorian chant. Having to flee Europe or risk capture by the Nazis, he returned to the U.S., served in the American Army Air Force, and because of his proficiency in languages he was assigned to Pacific islands inhabited by aborigines. (This experience led to the writing of *Nuni* while his earlier musical education at monasteries in France surely influenced *The Devil Rides Outside*.) Wounded by an exploding bomb in the war, Griffin lost his eyesight. When it was restored ten years later, he saw his wife and two oldest children for the first time.

The Devil Rides Outside and *Nuni* appear here in condensed form. In both books I have inserted explanatory passages to bridge the gaps in the story and so both novels can be read as complete entities. Explanatory passages have also been placed between the selections taken from *Black Like Me*.

Griffin's extensive work in racism is represented. Even before the publication of *Black Like Me* he was actively involved in this field, especially in working on research projects concerning the alarmingly high and increasing suicide rate among Negroes. For his dedicated efforts to alert the world to the destructive cancers of racial hatred and bigotry he has received the National Council of Negro Women's Award, the second *Pacem in Terris* Award (the first recipient was the late John F. Kennedy), the *Saturday Review* Anisfield-Wolf Award, and the Christian Culture Series Award. A film version of *Black Like Me*, starring actor James Whitmore in the title role, was released in 1964.

"Sauce for the Gander," a classic short story that has been praised throughout the world, is included along with other short stories. Selections from *Land of the High Sky* constitute another section, and selections from his current and future work are presented in "Work in Progress." A portfolio of thirty-two portraits make up "The Salt." Although Griffin's photographs have appeared in many national and international publications, "The Salt" combines for the first time a sizeable array of his contribution to the art of portrait photography.

Numerous critical studies and evaluations have been written about Griffin's work since the publication of *The Devil Rides Outside*. Definitive is Maxwell Geismar's essay, "John Howard Griffin: The Devil in Texas," which Mr. Geismar has graciously brought up to date with a "Postscript" written especially for this book.

I know as I type these last words that my work is finished. For the better part of two years I have persevered because I wanted John Howard Griffin's work to be read, to be studied, to be heeded.

Griffin's writing can best be described in Griffin's own words. In a letter to his friend Decherd Turner of Southern Methodist University, in 1959, Griffin wrote:

> You will have solved what little secret there is to my writing if you just realize that this, what happens here tonight, is the whole source. I escape from time. I come here to this barn studio and am alone and I listen to Bach or Mozart as another listens to another wisdom, and it tranforms me, and the writing, no matter how carefully planned, is basically nothing more than the overflow of this great love which causes men to throw out all the paraphernalia of what is in favor of what ought to be.

For their cooperation during the time it has taken to prepare this book, I would like especially to thank Paul Brooks and Mrs. Ruth Hapgood of Houghton Mifflin Company. To many others, too numerous to name individually, who gave assistance and encouragement, I am deeply grateful.

Bradford Daniel

Texas / Mexico / California
Summer, 1967

CONTENTS

PART I

Introduction

——————————————————————→ John Howard Griffin: The Devil
in Texas *by Maxwell Geismar*

The Men From the Boys

JOHN HOWARD GRIFFIN: THE DEVIL
IN TEXAS *by Maxwell Geismar*

$\longrightarrow$

JOHN HOWARD GRIFFIN is the Texas novelist who lost his sight in World War II, and who just recently regained it. The two novels written during the period of his blindness are remarkable and original documents. Nothing like them has been written in American fiction of the modern period. For sheer talent, power and virtuosity of craft, Griffin ranks very high among the new writers; but he has deeper powers still than these, and more interesting facets in his temperament and work. It is another ironic commentary on the literary quarterlies and popular press of the present day that he is virtually unknown to many readers.

The Devil Rides Outside was first published by Smiths, Inc., in Fort Worth, and perhaps because of this never achieved the recognition which it deserved. But the novel is odd enough in its own right to perplex the audience which might ordinarily welcome another story of Christian redemption. This is, to be frank, a category of books to which I am ordinarily averse. What we need now, in an epoch of underlying fear and hostility, is perhaps a few less Christian converts and a little more Christian morality. Part of the *Devil*'s distinction is that it embodies a true Christian ethic, set against a background of pagan human nature — and it is hard to say which element in the novel is more disturbing. (The paperback edition of this book by a devout Catholic writer was banned in Detroit by Catholic censorship organizations, and its validity as a work of art had to be guaranteed later by the United States Supreme Court.)

But it *is* a work of art just because it is perplexing, disturbing, eloquent, and entertaining. The hero-narrator is a young American, educated in France, who arrives at a Benedictine monastery in order to study the Gregorian chants. It is autumn, and he is appalled by the damp, the coldness, the dirt, the poverty and what he feels to be the asceticism of a vestigial medieval order. There is the daily routine of the monastery which is intolerable, and wonderfully well described. The hero is filled with anger, disgust and loneliness. He misses his girl in Paris, all the comforts and luxuries of city life — of modern life. He feels shut off, isolated, "out of all time." The animal-like eating of the monks, in a society cut off from all feminine grace, is repulsive.

There is the automatic "reader" at mealtime who recites the tortures of the Benedictine nuns at the hands of the Indians — until the monkish audience begins to giggle. There is the "malevolent crucifix" over his cot while he reads and studies to avoid the "nightmares of carnality." And then, slowly revealing itself in the narrative, there is the childlike manner, the great learning and the great humanity of the individual Benedictine brothers. "Here you must develop a new standard of facial judgment, for these are men of great intelligence without appearing in any way intelligent, according to outside standards." This human understanding and companionship is the hero's only consolation for all his misery — it is indeed the spiritual state of mind which this misery is designed to create. "God makes suffer only those whom he loves." And still the hero yearns for Paris, life, and his girl — "to be happy and shallow!"—amidst the silence of Compline, the adoration of Vespers.

During a bout of illness, he reads and reflects upon Gide, the prophet of modern homosexuality, on Fabre and Valéry. He follows in his mind or on his radio the music of Kotzebue, Viardot, Stravinsky; and considers the nihilism of the Dada movement, of surrealism, cubism and existentialism. "After all the intellectual searching one is offered only two obvious solutions: the *néant* of daily life on a level plane of mean juices, or the grace of mystical renunciation of the ego, opening floodgates of satisfaction in the denial of satisfaction." And yet, "No! To hell with the must and musk of sanctity!" the hero cries. He complains that even in his dreams a buxom country lass has refused him her favors. Winter has arrived at the monastery. It is bitter cold; the outside toilets do not work. Yet this confraternity of sacrificial ascetics consider the increase of their daily suffering as a further tribute to God, the body's pain exalting the spirit and the mind. In this regime of primitive communism a warm bath, a forbidden luxury except in case of special need, becomes a kind of subdued group orgy among several of the monks. The simple-minded hog-tender, Brother Placide, who nurses the hero back to health with complete devotion, resists even this temptation. "He is nothing," the hero reflects, "but he is already in Heaven."

There is a series of brilliant and funny episodes with the village taxi-driver, Salesky, an avowed hedonist and accomplice in sensuality. "What's your favorite way of making love, M'sieu?" he says. Father Clément, the hero's confessor and spiritual guide in the history and meaning of the Benedictine order, is mildly disturbed by all this preoccupation with chastity, which is a preoccupation with the flesh and lust, when, after all, there are so many other human failings. "My lechery is purer than my prayers, and more respectable," the hero says. And directly after this comes the encounter with the mysterious widow from Paris.

Can anything so natural and necessary, so friendly and exhilarating and comforting as making love, can it be really so evil? "Ah, that's pretty, for example," says the widow while she watches the hero relaxing in the bathtub. "You're suffocating me, my friend," she says drowsily after the act of her "seduction" has taken place. There is both an intensity of sexual emotion in this scene and a warm play of domestic comedy that may remind us, as it were, of D. H. Lawrence and of Jane Austen. Shocking thought! and this hero, too, returns to his monastic cell full of remorse for the communal life which he feels he has betrayed. "Stripped of its suggestive elegances, I have done nothing more than sleep with a woman. Nothing more than that. Only my guilt remains. In the chapel below, as I undress, many men pray. Men who have cared for me when I was sick. Men who share their food and goods with me. Men who are my brothers. . . . The pleasure of the many sacrificed for the pleasure of self. All that thrown away for the filthy little heats of holding a woman's naked buttocks in my hands."

This is rather hard on the charming widow; and these accents of disgust, self-laceration and failure are symptomatic in the novel. The raggedness and turbulence of the outside world are contrasted with the inner peace of the monastery, the devotion to spiritual works, the consuming fire of total purity. The sexual act is described recurrently as "hasty," "peremptory," "fumbling." And yet it is so necessary, so desirable, so inevitable; chastity is impossible! The novel's action swings out from the divine purity of the monastic world, which the hero so yearns for and cannot achieve, to the little French village nearby — and to the nether regions of the flesh and the ego. Already the hero has met the evidences of this lower "worldly morality" in the peasant family of Chevissiers who have refused, out of ignorance and avarice, to call a doctor for their dying child. Madame Renée, one of the great ladies who run "the sordid affairs of the village," has connived with them to get the dead girl a proper Catholic burial, and then has blackmailed the parents in order to get money and food for herself.

This provincial French village life, whose atmosphere is rendered quite as brilliantly and vividly in *The Devil Rides Outside* as is that of the Benedictine monastery, may remind us in turn of a Kafka nightmare with some Rabelaisian touches. In this close, narrow, stifling little scene of scandal, intrigue, malice, of petty power, jealousy, fear and suspicion, Madame Renée is the devil who rides outside of the monastery walls. She persecutes the Paris visitor, Madame Vincent, for yielding to the hero. She wants to drive out of the valley Salesky's mistress and the two illegitimate children. She tries to destroy the impending marriage of her unfortunate son, Michel, who is struggling to escape from her imperious and avaricious dominion. She wants complete control of the hero himself, through feeding, nursing and "protecting" him, and then by gradually offering her body to him under the most "respectable," moralistic and lascivious auspices. With her devouring ego and vanity, her wiles and then with her aging and helpless passion for the young American stranger, she is a remarkable literary portrait.

But this mother-son, mistress-lover relationship has some very grotesque aspects. If Madame Renée is at once the hero's satanic adversary and the cross he must bear, he allows himself to be entrapped by her salacious advances of the flesh not altogether unwillingly. Rage as he may at her infamy — "The remarkable goodness of Christians!" — he is drawn back to her in a mixture of attraction and repulsion.* It is only when he is on the verge of actually yield-

---

* Certain aspects of this relationship may remind us of Stephen Crane's early novel, *George's Mother*. This is a direct mother-son story, where the older woman uses

ing himself, indeed, that he escapes from this odor of musk and rottenness, of moral evil and physical corruption at the highest peak of "village" society, and finds relief in the company of the farm women. There is another bout of illness, and he recovers from fever to find himself being nursed and bathed by the aged Mother Nourrie. Like the Paris widow, she admires "the charming sight," and openly regrets the hero's return to modesty. "Bye-bye sweetness, bye-bye, young fatness, bye-bye, nice thing, bye-bye, pinkness, bye-bye, prettiness, bye-bye fresh garden, bye-bye —" So she chants, and the shocked hero is yet drawn to "this laughter, this pagan health." Just so, he is openly drawn to the "devil odors" of the young Christianne at an orgiastic village dance. And thus *The Devil Rides Outside* really moves on three levels of human or historical development: the primitive level of the senses, the medieval Christian level of spiritual renunciation, the "modern" level of worldly society.

There is also the obvious fact that in this novel by a young Texas writer there is hardly a reference to twentieth-century American life. And the provincial French life of the narrative is still essentially feudal and peasant. When the dark-hued Doctor Castelar reproaches the hero for being, with all his wild outcries of lust, an essentially pale and weak young man, restrained, inhibited, "good in a small little mean way," the Griffin narrator agrees. "I think you're right, Doctor. . . . I'm the type who'd make. An impeccable clerk. Or a good politician. I write a nice neat hand. I can speak several languages. I'm soft. Where I should be hard. I know this. And I loathe it. I'm the sort of person I can't tolerate. What do I do but take up space? Fill the sewers? Vote like everyone else? Some day produce my share of children? Who'll be like me? Without understanding. Without ever understanding."

This is hardly a flattering view of either modern life or the modern protagonist. And does this haunting self-image account in some part for this hero's aversion to the narrow mediocrity — the "sor-

---

the wiles and strategies of her very dependence, and where the rebellious son threatens, bullies, repudiates her, and then capitulates in much the same way as the present hero. But Crane's tale dealt only with emotions, of course, while Griffin, by projecting this oedipal love-hatred into foreign circumstances, achieves a far greater boldness of insight and intimacy of detail. It is the real thing, and is this type of human entanglement really so unusual? It is common in our fantasy life at least.

did affairs" — of even his little foreign village? Is this the impelling force behind his hatred of conformity and social compulsion in any form — legitimate and sharp as the satire is? Is it perhaps behind his wild carnal urges, and his recurrent and repentant moods of ego-renunciation, total purification of the flesh and a purely ascetic exaltation? In the same remarkable scene with the demonic Doctor, where both protagonists become drunker and drunker as their discussion ranges more widely, Castelar finally admits that the search for God is the best of all the many narcotics. (Like his generation, the Griffin hero also believes that self-expression is no longer possible in the movements of social reform or social revolution.)

What is certain, at least, is that the cards are stacked here, as to both modern society and the values of common ordinary life.

The central dichotomy of utter purity (goodness) in the monastery and prevailing evil, or mediocrity, in the village surely represents an author's yearning rather than an established fact. (Yet Griffin's talent as a novelist can make both sides of this chasm equally interesting.) Even the village priest, Father Sauvac, is presented in a not altogether flattering light. In the battle with Madame Renée — "a woman literally eaten up with pride; a woman in love with herself" — the priest operates with worldly wisdom, rather than Christian humility. Outside the monastery, too, in the sway of Catholicism's temporal authority, we see the evidences of clerical superstition operating on the village people in terms that the Benedictines would hardly tolerate. ("Surely one little heathen smuggled into heaven can do no harm," the hero thinks, in the struggle over the church burial of the Petite Chevissier.) Beneath the great abstractions of God and Art, all purely human motives and actions are bound to be imperfect. So, too, in the central thinking of the hero (and the author?), human morality is viewed as another absolute.

When a man can act "without the risk of another's judgment," we are told, then only is he real; and this is a commendable if a difficult standard of behavior. On the other hand, the tolerant and highly flexible moral judgments of the Benedictines proceed from the fact that in their orbit "there are no illusions to be destroyed — nothing that is forbidden." These saintly monks have indeed become brothers in "the search for the infinite" — but is there no brotherhood possible within the ordeals of the finite? It is the same Doctor Castelar (whose name suggests social caste as well as moral heights) who declares that "Man is basically an entity, complete unto himself, who has become dependent on society." And this striking statement may represent either the climax of spiritual aspiration or the deepest and darkest depths of man's primitive fear. The central psychological concept in *The Devil Rides Outside* is indeed that of the stranger, the exile, the solitary hero who struggles against not merely an imperfect but a hostile society. Beneath this chronicle of divine love, there are echoes of that somber and savage Darwinian cosmos of "dog eat dog" which for a while, earlier in the century, dominated American thought and art.

Yes, and maybe within the psyche of this estranged and gifted young American artist himself — conversant as he also is with Cocteau and Apollinaire, Huysmans and Mallarmé — there are still other ambiguous strains. The great charm of many of the sexual scenes in the novel is due to their direct infantile fantasy quality. The element of voyeurism is strong here, and how much washing and bathing, dressing and undressing, the forbidden (and delightful) fondling of child and nurse, and the incestuous physical contact of what is also, in effect, mother and son. This is beautifully done in the story, and is true at least to some of the deepest levels of the male psyche. But what is curious is the mixed tone of all the later, or more mature, sexual episodes. There is the enormous power of the sexual drive, and the immense revulsion either during or after the sexual act. Torn away from Christianne's alluring embraces, the hero reflects that after all, "with her needs and stinks," she is nauseating, impossible. After each episode with Madame Renée, in which the hero submits to her increasingly bold and lascivious advances, he despises himself more. "But in my mind I smell the unbearable reek . . . the stench of myself."

The final, most intimate moment of this terrible (and ridiculous) seduction is centered around "the detested goal" — the breast and nipple which Madame Renée exposes and offers to the hero. In a brilliant prose passage of mixed sexual desire and antipathy, the hero has visions of twisting bellies, "in a gigantic serpentine voluptuousness," of "strong legs, of distorted buttocks, of insatiable, slavering vaginas." Here, too, the novel expresses boldly some of the deepest and most discordant elements of the so-called "masculine revolt" — the modern fear of an insatiable, all-devouring feminine sexuality (though literature has many earlier examples of what is essentially a psychobiological rather than a chronological sexual attitude). And what one notices also is that these powerful sexual drives, and equally powerful repulsions, are concerned always with lust and carnality, for good or for evil, rather than with mature sexual love. The hero's "passion" for Madame Vincent has only one direct sexual encounter in it, and then, burdened with guilt, relapses into a "pure" and a doomed friendship. The true sexual currents of the novel are divided between the phallic worship of the peasant women and the repressed, sinful, provocative puritanism of the aging Madame Renée.

For the literary temperament behind this novel, too, the monastic order must surely have an immediate appeal. Feudal and medieval in its thought, it is also close to the nursery world of childhood in its order and authority, in its spiritual serenity and "innocence" — where every "sin" is directly known even before the assuaging process of the confessional, or repentance and absolution. When Madame Renée leaves the village, spring returns once more to the Benedictines. "The air is mysterious, full of fragrant balm. . . . . All France bows to the pre-Easter season with music." So the novel ends with the Christian theme of resurrection and rebirth (though the restless spirit within the monastery walls will not be content to stay there). And whatever the mysteries and enigmas which lie behind John Howard Griffin's tale, it is brilliantly told, and absorbing to read.

The Devil Rides Outside is indeed, along with James Jones' *From Here to Eternity* and William Styron's *Lie Down in Darkness*, among the three best novels of the decade 1950 to 1960.

In a curious way, incidentally, this mystic and religious writer, so remote from his own time and place, is directly linked to the other leading talents of his day. If Griffin's touch is less subtle and tender than William Styron's, if it deals with bolder themes in broad and heavy colors, he is surely aware of that lost world of infantile sexuality which is here described in terms of both pagan laughter and Christian horror. And in one respect, what else is Griffin's Benedictine Brotherhood but a highly refined, intellectually and spiritually sublimated form of the military son-horde in which James Jones' restless anarchs also found their true home and refuge? And Griffin's second novel, *Nuni*, in 1956, was both completely different from his first one, and yet, psychologically and esthetically, a revealing supplement to it.

The new hero is an English professor at a small Southern school whom a plane crash lands as the sole survivor on a South Sea island. We learn that as a placid-looking adolescent he has spent "the secret hours of the solitary night," reading the medical chronicles of Paré, the venerable sixteenth-century Flanders surgeon. In the separate life of this night-borne child, he remembers also the modern American Dr. Chase's *Receipt Book and Household Physician*, describing how young boys must train themselves with much exercise, hard beds and cold baths for the ordeal of "vigorous manhood and virtuous marriage."

In a tiny room at Poitiers (where the author transports the personal retrospect of his shipwrecked or planewrecked hero during the first days of solitude on the island) he had felt the necessity to make:

> . . . some sudden bold choice between the animal and the spiritual. His soul desires to enfold another in the ancient dream nurtured in him by Dr. Chase — the dream of health and homemade yeast bread, but his body drags the dream down into a swampy vision of a whore's belly, seen again and again in devastating reality of touch and sight. He smells the reek of humanity, seeing it only as frailty, and he hates it with all of his love, his body and soul distilled into a concentrated essence of loving.

Loving, indeed, or hating? — this reek of humanity within himself, this whore's belly which is opposed to the dream of health and yeast bread, in the hidden depths of this adolescent protagonist? "It is decency, mediocre decency and not love, decency that binds me and will not let me break way," this earlier hero had written in his journal, still divided between the hope of heaven and the desire for hell. Oddly enough, during the first few days of despair and solitude on his lonely island, he cannot bring himself to remember his wife, his home and his children: the ecstasy which he has created in his mind from the "dullness of familiarity."

But this tantalizing glimpse into the origins of *The Devil Rides Outside* is all that we get in *Nuni*. Amidst the dazzling coral, the overpowering sun, the hallucinations of nourishment and water, the dreams and nightmares of tulips and giant purple grapes, Professor Harper is rescued by a curious and merry black child, and by an old black patriarch with a club. The tone of the narrative is reminiscent of Jack London's tales of the South Sea savages, along with something else. When the hero starts learning the primitive and guttural tribal language — "Taeega . . . Angua Kulangu . . . Kmai Kakosekani . . . Augoo-ah!" — these phrases which he repeats to himself in fear and panic are close to a sort of black Swiftian baby talk. And what Harper notices immediately is the contrast between the blank, inhuman eyes of the patriarch Tombani and the expressive young eyes of the child. "What has happened between childhood and age to glaze those of the old man?"

This is the real point of *Nuni* on its first level of import. The novel is a brilliant satire of a tribal culture whose whole aim is to suppress every human emotion. Tombani is a hostile old man whose eyes are indeed dead to affection, "eyes that speak only in degrees of contempt." Enforcing the tribal mores with his heavy club, this "black ball of whimsy and caprice" is without a trace of interest in his fellow human beings. And what mores! As the hero gradually learns the tribal language, he discovers the names for all parts of the body except the intimate parts, which are completely taboo. The normal functions of the body must never be witnessed under pain of death — though everybody is completely naked and completely sexless. Mating is "zagata" — no good — though it is necessary for the bearing of children. Sex is considered painful and unpleasant, to be consummated as a duty to society. Indeed, the sexual act means the loss of virility for the man who performs it.

"It is good to be with a woman," says the ignorant hero to the child Veedlie. "Taeega!" he screams. "It is bad, bad." Nuni is a world without love. The voices of the tribesmen are compounded of rage and anger. In the course of the hero's education, Tombani electrifies the air "with his thunderbolts of abuse and insults, telling me of my insignificance . . . of my worthlessness." This education is a form of brainwashing, and gradually Harper realizes that "no one here cares in the slightest for my existence." The village called Vanua is hidden in the jungle foliage near the bank of a swift-flowing silent river. The tribal huts are dark chambers of animal stench, the food is comprised of sour-tasting vegetable roots. The single recreation is the elaborate ceremony of betel eating, which casts the men of the tribe into a drugged stupor for hours. But there is the freezing pool into which, at appointed intervals, the tribe plunges as a unit, to recover its "normalcy."

The faces of the people are "tattooed black masks, not human faces, masks with yaw sores around their eyes, stoic masks, cold and feelingless." The women, who are perhaps the saving element in all societies, are here "untouchable . . . disinterested, dulled by dusts of resignation." And Harper feels his own stability of character beginning to disintegrate under the tribal pressures. "We leave you in sunlight," says the witch Rauka to the corpse of Maigna, "and we go back and wait in shadow" — while the tribe howls in savage derision at a sudden mishap to one of the body-carriers. Nightmare imagery and a nightmare tale: at the mid-point of the narrative *Nuni* is a novel which rouses all kinds of dark shadows in our mind. While Harper, giving up hope and pleasure, is lying in a desolate stupor, the little Ririkinger nestles into his chest and gives him the only affection he has met with in the tribe. He looks up to see the swinging genitals of Tombani over his face and the patriarchal club descending upon his head. It is taboo to touch a girl-child.

These children are not given names before the tribal tattooing because so many of them die during it. They are fastened to a stake before the ordeal in order to dull the pain of the cutting; the weaker ones do not survive. When Harper decides to prevent this from happening to Ririkinger, and becomes the direct adversary of Rauka, the tribal sorceress and lawgiver, the central drama of the novel begins. Rauka is hideous, aged, sexless, but cunning and wily — another symbol of odious maternal authority. No wonder that the hero yearns for and mourns over the lost world of childhood: "where all is guilelessness, all is innocence and gaiety," before the advent of maturity, of society, and of what appears always to be in Griffin's work an evil and scheming matriarchy! But just what are the further levels of meaning of a novel in which the stench of "betel-soured closeness" is almost the stench of humanity itself?

In Vanua "all that is right, all that is human, is taboo," the hero thinks. "If I move to counter it, I am clubbed." And there is the description of Tombani's "benign face" as he carries out the tribal "law" — making people into animals. On the surface *Nuni* is a grand vision of human evil which must be placed against the vision of divine good in *The Devil Rides Outside*. (And part of the attraction of this writer's talent lies just in its movement between these polar extremes.) In part, too, the angry satire of Griffin's second novel, the Swiftian tones of repudiation and disgust as well as the language, is certainly directed against the American social values and institutions which are carried to their ultimate point in Vanua. In the portrait of this hostile, angry, taboo-ridden, sexless and loveless black tribe there are obvious references to the darker side of the national spirit.

Yes, and aspects of American life which other modern spokesmen, from the time of Mencken's bitter *Notes on Democracy*, and earlier, have commented on in similar terms. "A man can do anything but beg for that which must be freely given — some recognition that he exists and is known." This lament of the novel's hero, faced with tribal antipathy and indifference, is a familiar refrain in modern literature — or of art, that is to say, in a social environment which has become increasingly scientific, industrial and abstract. The language in Vanua has no past tense, we are told (as Hawthorne and James remarked about the American scene). The tribal legends glorify only hostility, cruelty and rapacity, and there are no words here for "reason, justice, kindness, charity." There is only the monotonous chant of derision which is the tribal form of "education."

In a larger sense, of course, *Nuni* is dealing with the tyranny of all societies: of Society. These are the constraints, repressions and taboos which are always put upon the innocent effusions of the human spirit that wishes to soar and to flower. Here Griffin is joining in a common chorus of the literary voices during the 1950's which beholds the warm and innocent life of childhood constrained into the mold of a civilization which is always repressive and banal. (Ernst Schactel's thesis of "Childhood Amnesia" — the loss between the original vision of childhood, the modes of adult perception — is a key source for all these novels.) How almost compulsively Griffin's novel describes these free, happy and nameless

children, who are then trained in stoic renunciation, who are crucified and cut in accordance with tribal mores, until only the hardiest,
most brutal survivors become the tribal "individuals"! There is the
vivid image of the professorial hero himself, so much like an indignant, outraged, ostracized child-man, who stands apart from the
odious mass of tribal humanity, clutching his yellow buttercup as
the single token of natural harmony and grace. Not only in the
more or less superficial view of "social adjustment," but in the
deeper, more personal psychobiological currents of *Nuni* there is a
fundamental sense of estrangement and alienation. Is the symbol of
paternal authority really that of the ignorant old savage with his
heavy club — a paternal authority, I mean, which is not that of the
Lord himself? On the distaff side, the witch-hag Rauka, though an
"adversary of stature," and in effect a more extreme version of
Madame Renée in *The Devil Rides Outside*, is hardly much better.
And are all the "children," for whom the professorial hero risks his
life in defiance of the tribal taboos, really so defenseless, crucified
and cut?

Here indeed the earlier theme of the isolated stranger and the
hostile universe becomes dominant — a black, savage and threatening world. All the submerged fears, hatreds, aggressions of the first
novel are channeled into a central hostility and alienation. But this
is a familiar phenomenon in literature. The major figures of this
"school" include such varied writers as Byron, Poe, or Melville, as
well as the archetypal Dean Swift himself, or the nineteenth-cen-
tury French decadents whom Griffin knows so well. One notices
the strain of incestuous affection in the present writer's work too, as
well as elements of both the superman and the demonic spirit. Not
all of this anger, rage and cruelty must be attributed to the hostile
outer world. Some — how much? — must reside in the hidden,
fuming, sulphurous psyche of the artist himself. If he seems to be a
born, or indeed a hereditary outcast, so was Lucifer, so was Satan.
From another angle, the nightmare visions of *Nuni* also project
backward into the primitive childhood of the race. (Are children,
after all, so pure, innocent and blameless?) And with this horrid
dream of a "black birth" Griffin has allied himself, even more than
in the earlier conflict of good and evil, with the "dark writers" of
literature. The Devil also rides in Texas.

Perhaps, indeed, the intense struggle to reach God and the orbit of divine love — through the sanctity of monastic renunciation — derives its intensity just from its "diabolical" sources. (The possessed and "puritanical" Hawthorne, who was also conversant with witches, might see the attraction of this theme.) The voodoo world of Vanua is too well described, too vividly and intimately known, *too* familiar! But indeed, how many tantalizing levels of meaning are half revealed in the flickering midnight symbolism of *Nuni* which continually shifts between the personal, the social, the racial. If the primitive tribe of Vanua is meant to describe the worst aspects of white civilization, there may also be a latent content of the South's own deep and abiding fear of, and guilt about, the Negro race itself. How many other young artists from the nether world of Faulkner and Faubus have described so vividly their own terror and isolation among these savage black people?

Yet we must add that it is also the Griffin protagonist who sacrifices symbolically his own daughter in the hope of saving his adopted black child, Ririkinger. This is the final "message" of the tale, and the method through which the outsider regains his own sense of identity, of belonging and of love. In the end the professor tries to humanize both the tribe and himself through the black child, who is indeed the missing "key" of the South's drama, as well as the novel's. On the rational and moral level, nothing could be better than this last gesture on the part of the outcast hero; and at the story's close, as in the Easter music of *The Devil Rides Outside*, there is the scent of flowers and "peace drifts to me on the lively twitterings of birds."

I have hardly had space to stress certain other aspects of Griffin's talent. (The element of broad sexual comedy and devastating social satire is again apparent in the section from his new novel, *Street of the Seven Angels*, published in *New World Writing: 12*, where Griffin's tone is close to Henry Miller's.) This writer is fertile and prolific, as well as bold and sweeping in emotional range, almost to the point of melodrama and farce. Still another novel is awaiting publication, and these works will doubtless sustain our interest in this original and, as I think, large-sized artist, who should be classified meanwhile in the upper bracket of contemporary writing.

❋

Postscript to "John Howard Griffin: The Devil in Texas"
Seven Years Later

Sitting here in my Adirondack study — while in Washington the best of our students and the boldest of their professors are protesting the war in Vietnam — I have been reading over my earlier essay on John Howard Griffin.

It is not too bad, really, and what I am most proud of is that this was probably the first critical essay to acknowledge a powerful new talent in this country — a talent which is still largely ignored by the prevailing literary establishment in the United States. But this is as it should be, of course, for our establishment of teachers, critics and editors, composed of Cold War Liberals and refugees from communism and McCarthyism alike, is dedicated to a "safe" mediocrity: to such writers, I mean, as Saul Bellow, Philip Roth, John Updike, J. D. Salinger, etc.

There is nothing of the safe, the innocuous, the formalistic or the mediocre in John Howard Griffin's work, or in him. He reminds me of a Texas Balzac at times, as he returns the American novel and the American novelist to the great tradition. But also note, as I said around 1958, that he is an absolutely original voice in this tradition; we have had nobody before like John Howard Griffin. I came across *The Devil Rides Outside* in a curious way; it was sent to me in a rather ugly paperback edition by Herbert Alexander, the editor at Pocket Books. The original work, as I learned, had been printed by Smiths, Inc., in Fort Worth, owned by two brothers: not really the cough drop kings, but some local men of wealth seeking southern culture. Partly as a result of this the *Devil* never had any national notice by the commercial press. I read this extraordinary novel as though it had dropped from heaven — for all its demonic undertones — and with all of Edmund Wilson's "shock of recognition."

People keep asking me: what does a critic *do?* and sometimes I am glad to give them Mark Twain's ready answer: "I don't know." I have met a score of persons who, after reading the Griffin essay in *American Moderns,* have gone out to get *The Devil Rides Outside,*

and among these readers I have never met one who was not as astonished by and impressed with the book as I had been. That particular book of mine, *Moderns,* is my critical "best-seller," running up so
far to seven or eight printings — so that I assume there must be
many more readers and admirers of Griffin's first novel, even
though it has not yet been reprinted as a hardcover edition.

I remember too that what I most clearly felt and said at the time
of reading the *Devil* was, according to my more provincial prejudices, the lack of both a "social context" and more specifically an
American social identity. I did not know then that John Howard
Griffin had been almost entirely educated in Europe, that he was a
Catholic convert, that he had trained to become a doctor; fascinated by Gregorian chant, he was a remarkable musicologist, and
that, while relatively unknown in this country, he was on intimate
terms with some of the great figures in European philosophy, art
and music: names both esoteric and celebrated, such as Poulenc,
Reverdy, Lourié, Maritain, Braque. So that, while I had all the
enthusiasm of discovering an "original," John Howard, on his part,
calmly entered upon a dialogue of minds which he, gratefully for
me, has continued to the present time.

But for the American "thing," Griffin's second novel, *Nuni,* was
(apparently) not much more of a help. The story of a professor
cast out among a most savage tribe of South Sea blacks, written in a
series of nightmarish episodes almost like horror slides thrown upon
a white wall — Griffin was still then in his period of blindness —
this little fable becomes more and more impressive to me each year.
(It is not yet even in paperback, where it should obviously be; and
I remember some of Griffin's sedate New England publishers shaking their heads dubiously over this fantastic charade.) For *Nuni,*
written, as I've since discovered, in the depths of Griffin's spiritual
despair, recorded the desperate effort of an isolated human being to
remain himself in the midst of an absolutely dehumanizing society
or culture. Was this parable also, and so deviously, directed at
modern life (perhaps even American society)? And these dark
fantasies of the capricious and savage black tribesmen — did they
perhaps reveal something of the true Southern unconsciousness —
even the expatriated Griffin's — about their Negro kinsmen?

In an odd way, as I have come to see now, *Nuni* was the true antecedent, the necessary revelation, almost the forming force of *Black Like Me*, the book that finally brought John Howard Griffin into the national consciousness. And this famous book, which some might think started out as almost a journalistic "stunt," which ended up as a paperback best-seller with sales of over a million copies, as I have been told, and then became known all over Europe, and then became a famous movie, inaugurated almost an entirely new phase in Griffin's career. Traveling through the South as a Negro, he had, through the dramatic power of his concern and his talent, created a powerful chronicle — and a chronicle which in turn led to the deep involvement of John Howard Griffin, during the last few years, with the cause of the Negro in the South at perhaps the most explosive point in history.

These were years of lecturing at an incredible pace all over the country, and of working in the turbulent South in particular; years, too, of mysterious missions of aid and relief, and of horrifying revelations about the conditions down there. John Howard Griffin was going "American" with a vengeance, and I can think of no other contemporary novelist who has, in this way, committed his total being, his whole life, to what is the primary internal crisis in the national life today. But Howard was still, and primarily, a writer in my eyes, and *there* was the old question. While approving entirely of his moral fervor, and conscious of what a store of information he was gathering about his native scene, and also concerned to see how generous he was, even recklessly so, in the giving of his health, his talent, and yes, his personal safety, to the cause of justice in the South — well, I often rebuked myself for wanting him to finish the three books which he has had in progress during this whole period of crisis.

I had seen two chapters from *Scattered Shadows* in the magazine *Ramparts*. This was the autobiographical account of the period of his blindness, and nothing could be a more fascinating subject, and nothing could have been better than the chapters I read. But where, oh where, was the finished work which, Howard said vaguely, needed some revision — this was some years ago. (I even had a somewhat baroque exchange with his publishers, when Griffin said they had this manuscript or another one in their files, and they returned saying they had it not, and John Howard, then, with Christian charity, saying perhaps they didn't, while muttering under his breath that they still had it.) And a while before *Scattered Shadows*, I had also seen, in the now-defunct *New World Writing* anthology, another chapter from the novel called *Street of the Seven Angels*, which was, to say the least, very handsome writing. But what in turn had happened to this novel also; and meanwhile there was still a third book, *Passacaglia*, about which I had even less information, except that a long time ago it was in "fourth draft."

John Howard Griffin, then, was an original voice and a major talent in our fiction, and I had already planned to include him in the company of Henry Miller and Richard Wright for the fifth and final volume of my series of books on the modern American novel. But to do a major study of a major novelist you must have a major body of work. The truth was that during the long years of John Howard Griffin's involvement with the problems of racism and the civil rights movement; that during all of this, admiring Griffin's activity as I did, and perhaps even somewhat jealous of it, and disturbed by my own passivity and remoteness — that I had still wanted him primarily to finish the three books which have been so long delayed in his literary career.

Any two out of these three books would be bound to be good, I suspect, and even in Griffin's most journalistic work — which he sometimes throws out in a rage of haste and temper — there are passages which remind you of the journalism of a Zola, say, not to mention Balzac again. It is almost impossible for this writer to write badly; the problem is how to get him to write at all. And yet I can resign myself by thinking of those novels — like *Huckleberry Finn*, say; or the tale called "The Mysterious Stranger" — which Mark Twain laid away in his literary storage racks until the impulse compelled him to take them out again, to finish them. Very often the best books are written in this fashion; and meanwhile the great writers go out to waste and to gamble away all their divine talent and time until they are on the very edge of disaster — and writing remains as their single salvation.

For this was just as true of Dostoevski as it was of Twain, Ring Lardner and Scott Fitzgerald and perhaps even Hemingway; all we can do in the end is to be grateful for what they did achieve. But I do not mean this postscript to "The Devil in Texas" to be a kind of nostalgic epitaph for John Howard Griffin's literary career — on the contrary, it is meant as a kind of foreword for the three books due from him which I have mentioned above. Just the other day came one of his marvelous letters, saying it was such a joy to be working at the typewriter again, to be alone once more, to think and brood and muse and "moon about," as Theodore Dreiser said — and to create!

For the writer who does not write, all his life is a slow form of poison; and every good writer knows this, and every writer who is afraid of this spiritual corruption must, finally, come back to his writing. John Howard Griffin has no other choice, really, and it is time for him to resume that solitary (and sometimes tedious) destiny of art which Melville once called the "Hostile Necessity."

In the same letter which I have described above, moreover, Griffin has started talking about his two future novels. (I believe that *Scattered Shadows* is almost ready for publication.) *Street of the Seven Angels,* he says, is based in Paris and deals with the problem of "goodness" — with the malicious doings of a group of religiously-oriented women out to clean up the St. Jacques quarter of Paris of all forms of filth. Hidden in there somewhere at the core is "the demonstration of the self-defeating hypothesis involved in the idea of the compulsory return of the Kingdom of God."

The novel, though never stating this thesis as such, but merely personifying it in the characters and action, thus will deal with the mentality of censorship — the book-banners, the guardians of public virtue, the "sanctimonious serpents," as Gerald Vann called them. Underlying this, counterpointing it, though the two themes never really touch (but in alternating scenes serve to contrast and point up), is another subsidiary plot and list of characters, an essentially somber one. This book is almost entirely written in scenes with very little introspection. It lays the foundation for *Passacaglia,* which comes right out . . . with the idea that morality is an unamiable goal in itself, that it can calcify the soul of the man who aims at the perfection of "routine Christian morality" or "routine Jewish etc. morality" (this is developed in *Street* this far, carried on much more massively in *Passacaglia*). I think that morality of this sort castrates man, prevents him from becoming fully functioning man, and that in fact it is an obscenity; and that in order to move above this routine morality, he must undo the damage, the concretization of soul that can neither grow nor dilate into those areas that in theology one calls sanctity, in psychology integration, in art genius.

The whole thesis of these two novels, so Griffin adds, was first conceived as part of a theological structure, and then transplanted into the form of an artist, a concert pianist, keeping the parallels exact. "*Street* has a large cast of characters and is a brief book in the classical form; *Passacaglia* has a small cast of characters and is a lengthy book in a massive, contrapuntal, continually developing form. Both are novels in which all the themes are hidden in the fabric and structure . . ."

And, as Griffin adds, he has actually been working on *Passacaglia* for nine years, and is still absorbed in it — and furthermore "I never talk about my works." And there you are. For when you can get a writer to talk about his own writing, he is always fascinating to listen to, or to read. All that remains is to get the books into print.

Maxwell Geismar

Harrison, New York
September–October, 1965

THE MEN FROM THE BOYS

——————————————————————————→

Like every published author, I receive a great many queries from all sorts of people about this business of writing. They range from the blunt and businesslike letter I received not long ago from a girl in Portugal who said: "Please tell me how to write a best seller. I want to make lots of money," to another received from a man in Dayton, Ohio, who asked permission to come and see me so we could collaborate on what would surely be a national best seller. He had the plot and wanted me to do the writing. "It can't miss," he said. "It has one murder and two rapes."

In barber shops, on trains, at the supermarket, anywhere a professional writer (i.e., one who makes his living writing) happens to be, the following scene is certain to take place:

"What business are you in?" someone asks.

"I'm a writer," you say.

"Really? You had anything published?"

"Oh, yes . . ." you say, vaguely offended that he has never heard of you.

"Well, I'll say. That's wonderful," he muses. "You know, I've always wanted to write a book."

This even happened to me once at a funeral.

Following this traditional opening, the scene can take on all sorts of variants. If it is a man, he generally has one or two plots worked out and would like to give them to you or possibly allow you to write the story of his life. If it is a woman, the questions are more practical: where can she *find out* anything about writing? If it is a college student, the questions are more intellectual: what do you think about art as a virtue of the practical intellect? — or, where do people get the idea that Faulkner has any talent?

Over a period of years, certain questions keep recurring. I list here the most common ones and my personal answers to them. It should be pointed out that these remarks are concerned exclusively with the writing of fiction.

1. *What breaks do you need to get a book or story published?*

The only break you need is the break of writing a publishable book or story. Many will not agree with this answer, for there is a very widespread belief that in this business it is all a matter of getting the breaks. This attitude is so prevalent that it is worth looking into for a moment.

As we have seen above, nearly everyone considers himself to be a potential author. There is nothing wrong with this except that few of them have any idea of the work involved in producing a story or a book. There are millions of these people who appear to be convinced that being an author is a gravy train, that all we need is our God-given talent, that there is no work to it, and that to be successful the only requirements — other than talent and breaks — are that we have either a low character and a fine vocabulary or a saintly character and an equally fine vocabulary.

From among these millions, a certain number at one time or another dash off stories or books with no technical preparation whatsoever. Indeed, most of them write strictly for the satisfaction not of creating a good work, but of seeing their names in print and being *authors*.

The mailing of a manuscript produces a very peculiar reaction. Here, at this point, there is no longer any separation between the men and the boys, the amateurs and the professionals. The same thing happens to all of us. The moment the manuscript is shipped, it begins to grow in our eyes. It becomes grander, more majestic. Certain flaws about which we have had some doubts are now seen as virtues. As the days pass, this magical reaction grows and so does our pride. We think benevolently of editors with their eyes popping amazement, murmuring to themselves that this is the greatest thing they've seen in months; and we are happy because we know that our talent has made them happy.

Then, when the work comes back rejected because it is dull, badly written, unimaginative or self-aggrandizing, it once again becomes easy to separate the men from the boys.

The professional will respect the reasons for rejection. He may disagree with them and mail the manuscript off to another editor, or he may agree with them and make some changes before sending the script out again. He will never consider it an injury to his honor or talent. He will calmly go on about his work and tell himself that rejections are part of the profession, that he is producing a marketable product and that where one market may not like it, or may be overstocked, another may like it and buy it.

The nonprofessional, however, generally takes these things deeply to heart, especially after having passed through the magical period between mailing a script and getting it back rejected. He falls into the "woman scorned" category. His gift of love and talent has been thrown back in his face. If he is alone when he gets that fateful packet, he is likely to blush, to be humiliated and then outraged. He hides the rejection slip as though it were some scarlet sin from his past. He often writes a wrathful letter to the rejecting editor. If someone asks him whatever happened to that story he sent off he resents it and wonders why people can't mind their own business. He concludes that the publishers are not only monstrously stupid but monstrously cruel as well and that they have taken out their spite on him. It almost never occurs to him that he may have written a story or a book that only he and his mother could possibly cherish. No — he just didn't get a break, didn't know the right people. Even if he wrote like Shakespeare, those crooks still wouldn't publish him. Since the vast majority of manuscript submissions are from such people, there is then this widespread belief that getting a book published is a matter of breaks.

But the happy truth is that publishers welcome with open arms any publishable story or book, no matter how unknown the author may be, no matter what his race, color or creed, no matter if they love or despise him as a man. Every manuscript submitted is read in the hope that it will be the nugget of gold in the slushpile; and when it is, the publisher will go all out for it. The breaks, then, come after publication, not before. There are no strings to pull, nothing to do except produce a worthy piece of work.

2. *What background and education does a writer need?*

This is a strange question because he obviously needs all he can get.

As far as formal education goes, there is a danger to be avoided, the danger pointed out by Goethe of "studying yourself away from life." This is perhaps one of the reasons why American intellectuals rarely become top novelists. Aside from this danger, it is impossible to have too much formative education providing it becomes an enriching background for thinking and not just a vast conglomeration of factual material. One of the beauties in such a field is that although such an education can be helpful, it is not absolutely necessary. I know of at least two people with no formal education whatsoever who are writing superb material. But I should think that minimum educational requirements would be a good knowledge of grammar and syntax, a broad vocabulary and a respect for the exact shadings of words. This is obviously something that you continue to acquire throughout your life. All other subjects — history, English, mathematics, etc. — become vital when they are focused toward the formation of the student and the creative work he will someday accomplish. But if I could advise the study of only one subject, it would be logic. A good foundation in logic not only teaches us to reason toward truth and destroys the element of personal prejudice that can so distort our judgments, but it quickly shows us what propositions are worthless and what ones merit further exploration. This is the finest formation I can imagine for the creative artist, for it virilizes his work and his thinking and supplies it with solidity and authority. Such novelists as Huxley, Camus, Sartre, Beauvoir, Greene, Mauriac, Waugh, Marshall — indeed most of the best of English and French writers — have thorough backgrounds in philosophy, or at least in logic. Very few American novelists have this, and it is one of our weaknesses. I do not mean, by any implication, that we should necessarily write "philosophical" novels. Not at all. I do think that many essentially creative people shy away from the study of philosophy in the fear that it might hamstring them; whereas in reality it would liberate them by providing a larger and broader and more profound view of any given idea, dramatic or otherwise. It helps toward bigness in writing, robustness, fascination — characteristics sadly wanting in our work today. Those anemic intellectuals who have been unable to assimilate properly the burden of their studies are writing shriveled and dwarfed little works. Others are writing bombastic and directionless works, substituting steam for bigness and discipline. Somewhere in between is the mean; somewhere between the precocity of the intellectuals and the grossness of the anti-intellectuals.

Technique is another part of a writer's education and background. In all other arts, it is a foregone conclusion that basic technical matters must be assimilated before creative proficiency is gained. Musicians, painters, sculptors develop their own techniques through endless and intelligent practice, through studies of composition and design and the methods peculiar to their art. The great fallacy in our field, and the reason why there are so many disillusionments, is that few realize the immense amount of work necessary to gain technical proficiency. Most laymen tend to consider that because fiction uses the same medium — words — that is coincidentally used in ordinary speech, they already have the equipment to become writers. Because one is literate, has a good vocabulary and can write a splendid letter is no guarantee that he can sit down and create character, drama, mood, tension and atmosphere. The longer a writer works, the more he respects technique and the more he practices to develop his own until it becomes an integral part of him. Technique consists in the use of all the ingredients of creative expression, varying them, combining them, balancing them, until it becomes a matter of being able to depict vividly and accurately what you wish to depict. Note the difference, for example, between a straight statement: "My grief is tremendous," which is dull and ultimately ineffective beside a similar statement handled by a master technician: "My grief is so great that I wonder at the sun" (Raissa Maritain).

In lecturing around the country to creative writing classes in various universities, I am always surprised to discover that although most of the students have a superior critical appreciation of the functions, ethics and esthetic values of literature, they have no practical knowledge of technique at all. They can discourse brilliantly on Joyce and Eliot and the New Criticism, but if you ask them about basic things like characterization by gesture, posture or clothing, you get quickly the impression that they rather resent your bothering them with such pedestrian details. This is somewhat like studying everything there is to know about a Beethoven concerto with the avowed intention of someday performing it, becoming a great authority on it but not bothering to sit down and perfect the execution of scales, trills, and other points of technique. This augurs poorly for our literary future and explains some of our literary poverty today. On this point, it is a sad truth that most authors do not have sufficient respect, reverence even, for the humbler mechanical elements of their art. They neglect this sort of perpetual apprenticeship and the result is a creation that is born already tired and defeated.

However, technique is never enough; it must never be an end in itself. On the opposite side of the above coin, we read many works that are technically perfect and yet utterly frail. This is like meeting a man who is greatly polished but who has no spirit.

So, although formal education and technique are important, the indispensable ingredient of background education, and too often the most neglected, is that of experience. It is obvious that the broader one's experience is, the more sensations and sentiments and sights and sounds and reactions will be stored in the imagination to be drawn upon in creative work. It is not that we make factual use of the experience — not at all — but rather that we make use of the insights that come to us through experience.

The true writer, like the true painter, is an observer of all things, and quite especially of himself; but of himself in detachment, as though a portion of himself stood away and appraised the rest of him, without self-love or "partiality." If he experiences death close at hand, or the tragic break-up of his own marriage, or suffers any physical or mental discomfort, he has the strange consolation, even while hating the experience, of knowing that all of these things, the seemingly tragic along with the seemingly pleasant, will teach and develop him, and that somehow that teaching and development will come out abstracted and refined as an enrichment to his own creative work. Most of us live too protectedly, have too low an opinion of this vocation to which we supposedly dedicate ourselves. We do not value it enough to live for it. Life must be a continuing education for the writer. We must learn to abstract from every second of the day. Goethe said, "Talent is formed in solitude, character in the stream of life." Character, in this sense, must be fully formed and always in formation in order to render talent fruitful. It will be only partially developed if we live too sheltered and too much involved in the creature comforts.

To the writer, then, all of life takes on a different significance. He no longer acts or reacts in a stereotyped manner. If he is caught in the rain, he does not curse his misfortune as another might. He studies the feel of it on his face, rolling down from his hair, stippling the backs of his hands; he studies its various sounds as it strikes pavement or dirt or the leaves of a tree; he studies its odors and what it does to the colors of things. He does this same thing in all of the circumstances and conditions of his life, both good and bad. Unless he does this he is more interested in himself than in this endless learning process which is the formation of the writer and his greatest wealth.

3. *What is the best way to get started writing?*

I always advise the keeping of a private daily journal in which the writer describes, with total honesty (and with no thought of another's ever seeing it) his feelings, problems, emotions, reactions, random thoughts, temptations and all of the private dramas and dreams of his day; and also all of those striking things he sees and hears and that soon escape the memory unless set down.

This is an important discipline for many reasons. It is writing, gaining facility and technique. And if it is honestly kept, it will have the tremendous advantage of giving the writer a true knowledge of himself, the motives for his actions, the wide range of his spiritual fluctuation. This can be horrifying, sometimes overwhelmingly so, for it is humbling to see oneself without illusions; but it is the old Socratic way to wisdom and compassion.

What has this to do with writing? It has much to do with it, because it allows the writer to create directly and without wending his way through all of the jungles of delusion and self-aggrandizement. The act of creation is far more profound in its sources than most of us consciously realize. It comes up mysteriously from the very depths of a being, and that *sound box* which is the spirit must be tempered and balanced as near as possible to the truth in order to produce the truest work. This is a very important point and one that needs exploration, for it is vital to all writers. The profoundest truth constitutes the greatest originality.

On this point, as any editor can tell you, the reason why so many created works are worthless is because the writer usually values himself above his material and cannot resist showing off. This type is not creating out of dedication to his work, but merely out of dedication to himself; and only mediocrity can come from such an attitude. This type is aiming toward that which is average, rather than the far rarer object — that which is normal. Honesty and a type of selfless self-awareness are remarkable antidotes to the poisons of pride and egotism, and one of the best ways to achieve them, for a writer, is the keeping of a journal in which he submerges himself to the truth, in which he quickly learns the difference between "what is" and "what appears to be."

4. *What are the errors to avoid?*

Avoid the error of setting out to make a story educational. This is a presumption in the first place, and more importantly it starts you off on the wrong foot and is therefore self-defeating. Although every really good story educates, it does so in very subtle ways, by a form of osmosis, never directly. Fiction educates you by making you live through experience and go inside of characters, never by direct teaching. Read *Moby Dick*, for example, and you will know more about the sea in all of its moods than you did before, but you will know it by having vicariously experienced it through Melville's art, not through purposeful teaching.

Avoid the error of basing your work on prevailing literary styles and fashions. If you write to please the critics of the various schools, it is no longer your work but only an adaptation of your work to gain a given portion of your audience. In fact, avoid trying to please any given audience, whether religious sectarian groups, artistic groups or any others who would discourage you from writing as true to yourself and your materials as possible. Any great work is a bold work, and any bold work is going to cause some trouble somewhere. The moment a man begins to fear what his neighbors will think, he is diverting his work from its true channel to a false one. This in no way implies contempt for one's neighbor or for society, but rather respect for the truth of the work. A great enough work can never ultimately offend society, even though society might not agree. By refusing to create inferior works, you show far higher respect for society than it often shows for itself.

Avoid the rush of being in too great a rush, of demanding results too soon. Many authors have written sensational first novels only to discover that they could not sustain their initial success. They had to go to work and learn to do consistently what they did intuitively in the beginning. William James called this tendency "generally an American characteristic," and he advised that "results should not be too voluntarily aimed at or too busily thought of. They are *sure* to float up of their own accord, from a long enough daily work at a given matter . . ."

Avoid the error of basing your hopes on the low level of much contemporary fiction; base them instead on the masterworks of the past and present.

Avoid, finally, the error of attaching yourself too faithfully to a work. The author must be fickle. True, he must attach himself profoundly to a work and immerse himself in it during its creation, but when it is completed he must cast it off and attach himself to a new one. He must not even much care what happens to the old one. The old and poetic idea of works being "the children of one's loins" is not only false but needlessly distracting. It is impossible to dedicate yourself fully to a new work if you have one eye cocked to the reviews of the old one.

PART II

The Devil Rides Outside

Notes

→

The Devil Rides Outside was the beginning.

In the late summer of 1949, in a small room in the barn at Willow Oaks, his parents' farm at Mansfield, Texas, John Howard Griffin started writing. This room, roughly measuring 6½ × 10 feet, or "three long steps each way," as he has described it, was starkly similar to the monastery cells he had occupied at different times in Europe and the Philippines before and after his discharge from the Army Air Force in 1946.

Aside from numerous academic studies he had made, the majority of his other writing had been chiefly concerned with music. A talented musicologist, and at twenty-one a recognized authority on Gregorian chant, he had co-authored a book, *Interpretation of the Ornaments of the Music for Keyboard Instruments of the Seventeenth and Eighteenth Centuries*, with Father Pierre Froger, organist of the Cathedral of Tours, France.

He began writing *The Devil* after a discussion with the literary critic John Mason Brown; Brown had urged that he should write.

> Although I had read extensively in French literature, I had little knowledge of English or American literature, and indeed very little knowledge of literary forms or techniques [Griffin states]. I did, however, have some knowledge of music, and I began to write *The Devil Rides Outside* based on the form of Beethoven's *Opus 131 Quartet* — allowing the themes to develop from fragments.

The book was finished in seven weeks, Griffin writing much of the first draft in French. Due to his blindness, his work schedule consisted primarily of dictating the material into a wire recorder at night and transcribing it himself on the typewriter the following morning. In 1952, after several rewrites, it was published by Smiths, Inc., of Fort Worth, Texas, the initial publication issued by this new company.

The book chronicles the life of a young American, who remains nameless throughout, who comes to a monastery in northern France to study manuscripts of Gregorian chant. The narrative is in the form of a journal of his experiences there and in the neighboring village and town, and takes place between mid-October and the following Easter. It is principally a confession-novel, psychologically evolving the theme of man's struggle with God; the monks at the Monastery symbolize mankind dedicated to God, whereas life in the prejudice-plagued Valley outside the Monastery symbolizes the eternal compromise with Satan — this compromise often parading behind the mask of holiness.

Indeed, *The Devil* is an unusual first novel in a multitude of respects. But the most distinct of its qualities is the deep, prolonged probing into the psychological depths of the sensual and the spiritual layers of man, its religiously agonized search for esthetic and scientific angles of proper perspective, its doggedly spare-nothing pursuit of truth, self-understanding and self-salvation.

In his article, "The Post-Modern American Novel," which appeared in the Summer, 1962, issue of the Canadian periodical, *Queen's Quarterly*, Eugene McNamara wrote that four contemporary American novelists (Griffin, William Gaddis, William Styron, James Purdy) seem "to be creating works which are original in a radical sense." Examining the point that Griffin's heroes undergo torturous spates of self-revelation in an attempt to find the lost Father, the lost Eden or Paradise, McNamara pointed out: "In conventional terms, 'sin' and 'fornication' are equated. But Griffin brings us to a sharp realization that the ultimate sin is the proud insular shutting off of the self — it is the sin of rejecting love." Concluding the essay, he wrote:

> Thus in Gaddis, Styron, Griffin and Purdy, we see the isolation and death of those who cannot love, who cannot take on the responsibility of being human in a total sense, who delude themselves into thinking that their comfortable somnolence is life . . . At any rate, it is a new and frightening world we live in, and these novelists help us to see it accurately, to find ourselves in it. Instead of escape, they offer confrontation.

The young American hero of *The Devil Rides Outside* seldom

attains escape. Headlong and completely devoid of any protective guises — save for perhaps a few unknowing self-delusory maneuvers — he struggles painfully to find values he can live with, all the while thinking the world has put a near-unobtainable premium on values. Repeatedly he seems to ask himself: *Who is God? Who am I? What does He expect of me? What could I possibly do for Him?* And Griffin's understanding of the gigantic tasks demanded for a salvation of self (i.e., in some cases, even a *bare knowledge* of self) forces itself through in ascetic clearness: "To be obsessed with chastity is also to be obsessed with the flesh; to be obsessed with humility is to be obsessed with self-righteous pride; to be obsessed with food is to be obsessed with hunger . . ."

The late, world-renowned Dominican scholar and philosopher, Father Gerald Vann, reviewing the book in *The Catholic Herald* of London on September 25, 1953, was greatly impressed by a non-Catholic's (Griffin at that time was an Episcopalian) knowledge of Catholic thought and doctrine:

> This is an outstanding book, both vivid and subtle . . . a brilliant piece of work; and as a statement of the Catholic view of life, of holiness, of human love and the love of God, it is magnificent. In this respect it is precisely this communicating of an *outsider's inside* knowledge of monasticism that is so compelling. The insider's main criticism here (and, apart from a number of small points, perhaps his only one) would be that the author's admiration and affection have led him to paint a picture in which the real approaches the ideal more closely than is generally to be expected in our fallen world.

The five women in the novel were chosen to illustrate prototypes. Madame Renée is the "Great Lady," consumed with pride; Madame Vincent, the sensual-spiritual; Madame Nourrie is the Mother Earth type; Mademoiselle Marthe, the humanist, intellectual; Christianne, the purely sensual. The hero succumbed to each of these except the pride; she gave him the most difficulty, and his feelings of affection-disgust for her were the most ambivalent of his feelings toward any of the women. When he finally rejected her, he was enabled to resist himself, to stave off temptation for the first time in his life.

All of the women are finely developed and their individual characteristics proportionately blended in consistency to the others. But the characterization of Madame Renée, the protagonist's foremost opponent, is the *coup de maître* of Griffin's achievement in *The Devil Rides Outside*. Certainly she is one of the most notable creations in contemporary fiction.

In his review of October 27, 1952, in *The New York Times*, Orville Prescott wrote:

> And he [Griffin] has created one magnificent full-length character. This is a gruesomely expert study of a hysterical woman consumed by vanity, hypocrisy and old-fashioned meanness. His Madame Renée is a frightful and horrible creature, but never a monster. She is pitifully human, too. Madame Renée is a character such as Balzac would have enjoyed writing about. Any first novelist capable of creating her is blessed with uncommon talents . . .

Two lengthy scenes in the novel are correspondingly similar, even to the point of having identical wording; however, in the whole analysis of the work and its structure, they have altogether different and counterbalancing purposes.

In "13 december," the phrasing is used to describe the protagonist's ecstasy in his sensual encounter with Madame Vincent. In "21 january," on the other hand, the same wording denotes his rapturous delight of a mystical union with the Virgin Mary. The first scene takes place in a hotel room in the Town, the second in the Monastery chapel.

Yet, the climactic descriptions of each of the scenes has nothing really to do with either scene. Griffin originally wrote the scenes as a description of the slow-building orchestral climax in the first section of the Ravel *Concerto for the Left Hand*. The construction could be a description of almost any climax, either sensual, physical, or spiritual.

However, these descriptions, like some others in the book, created a controversy. In their brilliant study of censorship and obscenity, *How To Read A Dirty Book* (Franciscan Herald Press, Chicago, 1966), Irving and Cornelia Süssman lamented this fact:

> . . . For the American Catholic reader, this kind of Christian novel is strong medicine. Groups have banded together to condemn it,

and have torn it apart to seek out and isolate "pornography." Yet priests and religious have praised it, and Father Simon Scanlon, O.F.M., said of this book, *The Devil Rides Outside:* '. . . it is a magnificent book. It is a very powerful story of a young man's struggle with temptation and his search for faith . . . I do not recommend it to pious old ladies or to children. But I have recommended it to young men . . . who are making the same search and fighting the same temptations.'

The book, unrelentingly paced in a first person, present tense narration, carries the reader alongside the nameless protagonist, the nameless Village, the nameless Town, the nameless River, the nameless Monastery, until it becomes overpoweringly obvious that *the reader is the hero, the narrator,* and that this sequence of events that he is imagining (or *allowing* at his reading convenience) to happen to some person in a remote and cold France could, in essence, as easily happen to him; that it is in truth somehow *himself.*

This jolting realization, in its unleashing and presentation, brings to mind the motifs of St. Antony or St. Augustine — or even Walt Whitman. As Whitman put it in his "Song of Myself":

> I celebrate myself, and sing myself,
> And what I assume you shall assume,
> For every atom belonging to me as good belongs to you.

Historically, *The Devil Rides Outside* led a counterattack against book-banners and unjust censorship laws. For years publishers had been vexed by a melange of contradictory interpretations concerning censorship statutes in different states. They had prevailed upon court after court for an answer to the varying rulings, patiently seeking a definitive edict as to which of these laws were right and which were wrong.

Finally, in the spring of 1954, Pocket Books, Inc., publishers of the paperback edition of *The Devil*, decided upon a drastic and daring diplomacy. It was arranged that Griffin's novel would be put on trial in Detroit, where the book had been banned by the city's police censor bureau in order to test a Michigan censorship statute that had been in effect for over a hundred years.

The sales representative for Pocket Books in Detroit sold a copy of *The Devil Rides Outside* to a police inspector and was immediately arrested. He was summarily convicted by the city's lower court and fined one hundred dollars.

After the Michigan Supreme Court refused to hear the case (*Butler v. Michigan*) on appeal, a lengthy series of legal actions followed that eventually brought the litigation before the United States Supreme Court two and one-half years later.

The Supreme Court had never before dealt with a similar matter. Its 1957 decision, a unanimous one, was written by Justice Felix Frankfurter. It declared unconstitutional a section of the Michigan penal code which forbade the sale of any publication *containing* obscene, immoral, lewd, or lascivious material tending to incite minors to violent or depraved or immoral acts, manifestly tending to the corruption of the morals of youth.

In so ruling, the Court invalidated the 1868 opinion of *Regina v. Hicklin*, a case that had been the most enduring guide to Anglo-Saxon jurisprudence concerning censorship and obscenity. This decision, which had been handed down by England's Lord Chief Justice Cockburn, had defined as an obscene libel any work which *contained* words or phrases capable of subverting the young, the weak and the susceptible into whose hands such a work might fall. For over a century this, which was known as *containing statute* legislation, was the basis for most censorship laws.

The Supreme Court ruling, as written by Mr. Justice Frankfurter, stated that the Pocket Books sales representative had been arrested by the State of Michigan because "it made it an offense for him to make available to the general public a book that the trial judge found to have a potentially deleterious influence upon youth. The state insists that, by thus quarantining the general reading public against books not too rugged for grown men and women in order to shield juvenile ignorance, it is exercising its power to promote the general welfare. Surely, this is to burn the house to roast the pig."

He further stated that the law, in effect, was to "reduce the adult population of Michigan to reading only what is fit for children . . . it thereby curtails one of those liberties of the individual . . . that history has attested as the indispensable condition for the maintenance and progress of a free society."

The ruling, besides reiterating that a book should be judged as a whole, and not by any isolated sections out of context, also meant that:

(1) All states would have to revamp any existing *containing statute* legislation similar to the Michigan censorship laws;

(2) Booksellers would be better protected from future illegal incursions;

(3) Writers would have freer, more clearly defined vistas of expression; and

(4) The battle-tattered issues of censorship and obscenity would at last, hopefully, be channeled into a truthful and tenable direction.

The Court's decision was enthusiastically praised in America and throughout the world. The American Book Publishers Council applauded Justice Frankfurter's stern cry for justice and expressed its deep debt to Pocket Books and Griffin for having fought the unprecedented case through to a conclusion.

The text of the selections is that of *The Devil Rides Outside* (New York: Pocket Books, Inc., 1954): "12 october" is from pages 3–9 of that edition; "13 october" is from pages 9–20; "21 october" is from pages 30–48; "13 december" is from pages 111–129; "15 december" is from pages 155–174; "24 december" is from pages 218–223; "25 december" is from page 223; "15 january" is from pages 338–339; "21 january" is from pages 348–359; "28 january" is from pages 377–395; "29 january" is from pages 395–398; "15 february" is from pages 406–443; "23 march" is from pages 494–514; "24 march" is from pages 514–529; "25 march" is from pages 529–537; "1 april" is from pages 556–575; and "6 april" is from pages 575–579.

BOOK 1 — THE CLOISTER WITHIN

———————————————————————————→

1 2 october

"But no, M'sieu," the driver groans, "since our fine government closed the brothels it's impossible."

The taxi moves slowly past outlying houses, following its head-lights in the narrow cobblestone road.

"It's the same in Paris," I say regretfully, "but there they've simply gone into the streets."

"Tell me, M'sieu —" His voice falters.

"Yes?"

"Not meaning to be personal. But the Monastery? You're going there for religious reasons? Maybe to become a —?"

"I'm going there to do some research."

"Ah well, then," he says with sudden relieved loudness, and settles back into the seat. "I wondered, you know. You tell me to drive you to the Monastery and then you ask about girls."

"I guess it doesn't sound right, does it? Tell me, how are the monks?"

"Fine men, M'sieu. You'll like them. But, it isn't there you'll find any young girls, eh?"

"I know. I'll just have to forget that for a while."

The driver puffs a cigarette hanging disconsolately from his lips. "Yes, the only thing our young men can do is keep themselves buttoned tight. I know how it is. I'm not so old as all that. Why, it's a terrible thing for our boys. Look at yourself, M'sieu — a fine young man like you — what can you do? It's impossible." He mumbles to himself for a moment, cursing all governments; then, turning to me, "You're American, aren't you? I can tell by the clothes. Did you have a girl in Paris?"

"Yes."

"How long you been with her?"

"Since before the war."

"You're going to miss her, eh? What's her name?"

"Her name's Lucette," I sigh heavily, "and I'm missing her already."

"That's a nice name, for example," he says, and nudging me in the arm, "I'll bet she's with somebody else this very night."

"Wouldn't be surprised. How far is the Monastery from that little Town back there?"

"About five kilometers, M'sieu. But I drive slow when these damned roads are slick. I put my last penny in this taxicab. You didn't expect to find a taxi in a little hole like this, did you? There's only one other car in the Valley." . . .

He turns into a narrow street. Headlights pass over the tightly shuttered windows and doors of many small houses lining the sidewalks.

"In any case I'll look out for you. If a nice girl comes to Town, I'll get her a hotel room and come for you. And," he adds with great friendliness, "I won't charge you a thing."

"Fine. After a week or so in the Monastery I'll probably be desperate."

"Naturally, M'sieu, naturally — you're young. It's the same with me, though I'm much older than you."

The car slows into a cobblestone square and pulls up before a high stone wall.

"Here we are, M'sieu. Two hundred francs. Call me any time. If it gets too impossible, just call Salesky, eh? I'll find you something . . ."

I step from the car into the deserted square and he drives away in a shifting of gears. I look up at the wall beyond which I am to live for a time, and in the mist-veiled darkness I can't tell where the wall stops and where the sky begins. A heavy door is thrown into relief by the street lamp. Reluctantly I pull the bell chain and hear it ring somewhere within. After a moment I hear approaching footsteps crunching. The door is opened by a black-robed monk who carries a lantern over his arm.

"Good evening, sir," I begin. "I'm expected, I believe. I am —"

The faceless monk nods his head violently and places a finger to his lips to stop me. Taking my suitcase, he motions me to follow him. The door is closed noisily behind us and we walk through a graveled courtyard . . .

I follow him up exposed stone steps, staying close to the wall to guard against falling, for there is no rail. The yellow light from his lantern catches the outline of a squat, doorless opening at the top, through which we stoop to pass. The floors and walls of the door-lined corridor beyond are of rough stone. Our shadows flit beside us along the wall until we reach an open door, which he motions me, with a slight bow, to enter. The door is closed behind us, and a lamp is turned on to reveal a small cell.

"Now, my son," he says shortly, impersonally, "we have put you immediately above the chapel. The only way out is the way we came. On this night table is a card with full instructions as to your activities here. I think it covers everything. You have arrived during the Great Silence which begins at nine-thirty each night, a time during which speech is supposed to be forbidden. If you have any questions please make them as brief as possible."

"I guess I can find everything, sir. If you'll just tell me where the bathrooms are."

The aging monk walks to the window and opens it, pointing out into the dark. "The water closets are in the courtyard. But you are requested not to leave this cell after Compline. If you need it, there is a chamber pot to be used at night. The nearest water for shaving is downstairs to the left of the door. If you feel you can, we ask you to clean your cell every morning. Father Clément will visit you each day." He picks up his lamp and walks to the door. "Good night, my son," he says with sudden gentleness. "May you find happiness here and may God give you peace."

After a time the wind blows in heavy drops of rain, chilling the cell. I turn away to close the window left open by the monk. In this maze of stone corridors and doors, nothing but my lamp burns at this late hour. Desolation of paralyzing loneliness, skeletal, as each passing moment brings thirsts for sounds and lights and noises left only a few hours ago. I must move about, light a cigarette, unpack the suitcase, do small things. The cell is cold and cheerless and smells of damp and mold and age. In Paris this morning, the kiss in the railroad station like all other kisses that follow woman's pleading for man to stay with her. Silence growing in the cold of these cells.

Smoke from my cigarette curls floating on the air. I look at the straw mattress of my cot and at its covering roughness of blanket, and I remember the good bed and white linens of last night . . . And I am sick for wanting the safety of that bed, for wanting to breathe the breath of another and to wake in the night and feel her against me.

But it's time to sleep. I unlace shoes and put them neatly to one side. They sleep in other cells; they sleep in their cots and never know the taste of another's pleasure. Socks are placed in the shoes. The stone floor is cold beneath my bare feet.

I must swallow the night's desolation in small things. Tie and coat and shirt are removed slowly. The cell is small. It won't be difficult to clean. Undo the belt and step from the pants. Fold the pants and put them over a chair. On the washstand a large carafe of water has been placed in a badly chipped porcelain bowl. Next to this on the marble table top is a soap dish in which there's no soap, and to one side, a towel rack on which there's no towel. Drop wrinkled white underclothing to the floor and reach for the blueness of pajamas. There is the night table with its lamp of small voltage and weather-spotted lamp shade. There are some books and the placard of instructions.

The instruction card must be read. It is hand-printed in ink, with a ludicrously shaky cross at the top, and it tells what I must do and where I must be at all times — from the first bells at four in the morning until the last bells at nine-thirty at night. It informs me that I must follow the rigid schedule of the Benedictines, and that I must neither do nor say anything that might provide a disturbing element or distract the monks from their work.

Thunderless night of monotonous rain and of insomnias of newness and loneliness . . .

13 october

I force myself from the cot. It is cold and my legs tremble as I feel about in obscurity for my shoes. It is dark as night. I turn on the dismal lamp. Sounds from below of chanting. I am late, my card informs me, for the early morning offices of Matins and Lauds.

My footsteps sound heavy in the gravel as I walk in the direction of the chanting. The air is chilled and clear after the night's rains and there is no hint in the sky that it's near dawn.

Cold morning before sunrise, and I almost fall from sleep sitting in the faintly lighted chapel. Impression of spaces and heights and heavy gray shadows in the vast interior. Sounds reverberate empty and the monks seem faraway. Hours of praying and chanting and praying. The bench grows hard. I am the only visitor in the chapel. This morning there has been no waking slowly, no smells of coffee, no sleep-drugged belly beside me.

I wait for a long time in a sort of waking sleep, hearing nothing, until the hours have passed and it's time to leave. I follow the monks into a door marked REFECTORY, where breakfast is served on long polished tables. We are given large bowls of coffee which tastes as if it were made of ground acorn shells.

. . . In the corridor leading to my cell, the damp odors of age become almost suffocating. The only sound is the sound of my footsteps and the closing of my door. Alone I walk to the one window of my cell to see a scene below that's like some unknown abstract painting: a foreground of gray Monastery walls cutting at an angle across clear green waters of the River; and on the opposite bank, flat pastures for grazing cattle, in the oranges and blues of early autumn; and far to the background, an undisciplined panorama of many small housetops clustered beneath the protection of high wooded cliffs . . .

They leave me in this cell and pay me no heed. Barren feelings must seek life this morning and remember other lives and lively smells of Paris and the comfort of a girl's smiling.

Idly I pick up the placard of instructions and read it again, feeling that the crucifix tacked to the wall reads over my shoulder. It's an uncomfortable feeling. The thing is evil, shining, dark.

My thoughts are cut short by a knock on the door.

"Come in!" I call out sharply.

The door is opened by a tall, gaunt monk. "I am Father Clément, my son," he says, shaking my hand. His hair is sparse in texture, turning from brown to gray. And his face is warm, as if he expected to be amazed at every instant. "So you are my charge? Why are you here?"

"I'm a musician, Father — a musicologist. I've asked permission to do research in Gregorian chant from your manuscript collection."

"Many musicians have come here for short visits." He lowers himself stiffly onto my cot. "So you are interested in Gregorian chant?"

"Very interested, Father. I've spent several years studying the texts written by your monks. It's always been my ambition to come here. Will I be working with you?"

"No," he says smiling, "you will want to work with Father G'seau. I am here to be of help to you in other ways. Will you want to confess, to take the sacraments?"

"I'm not of your faith, Father. I wrote that in my letter."

"Of course, I had forgotten . . . Well, what do you think of this new home?"

"It's beautiful, Father. I think I'll like it all right once I get used to it. Hope I don't make too many mistakes."

"You will be all right, my son," he smiles, getting to his feet. "I know this is all new and strange to you. Much of it probably seems unnecessary. I shall come for an hour each day to visit with you and to help you with any problems that may arise. But you may call me at any time, if need be. It is almost time for Mass. You will attend our offices, I suppose?"

"Yes, Father. I believe I'm required to live exactly as the rest of you?"

"With the exception," he puts in, "that you are free to come and go as you like. Our life is a great change from what you have known. You are young — you will undoubtedly need to dissipate some of your natural energy by exercising. You can break the monotony by walking in the countryside. Our Valley is quite beautiful this time of year. Now, is there anything else for the moment?"

"Yes, Father — I'm wondering if there's a piano I could practice on around here?"

Father Clément rubs his chin absentmindedly. "I do not really know. The only good piano would be the one at a nearby château. How often would you need it?"

"I'd like an hour a day, Father. But I wouldn't want to impose. I thought perhaps —"

"No, no," he interrupts. "It is not a question of imposing. I shall make inquiries. Now is there anything else? Ah, but there are the bells . . ."

I enter the chapel as the last bell sounds and then dies away to intense quiet. There are perhaps seven or eight others — people from the Village who come in by a public side door. After dipping fingers in holy water and genuflecting, they kneel. Each goes through the same motions, and I can't help but feel they are the motions of parrots. I look through the gloom to see if there are any girls, instinctively seeking to pass the time by looking at them. But they are all old — old women and old men. I wonder what they think, how much they feel. I wonder when they bathed and what they had for breakfast this morning and how they slept last night. I've been here only a few hours, and already those on the outside take my interests. My affection goes toward them, and I think of their mumbled prayers and of how little importance such supplication must have in the counterpoint of a day's livingness. They genuflect and kneel with the wetness of holy water still cooling finger tips. They've done it always, and they'll go on doing it until they die.

Peculiar, indescribable odors of age and mold and humid rock: evocative, sweetened by a permeation of incense from untold numbers of Masses.

From the silence of waiting, and these odors, a cough resounds, suspended lifelessly on air, to be destroyed by the bright-toned baroque organ above us, beginning a work of Landino or Frescobaldi.

By twos, entering from the left, monks approach the altar. Without pomp, as naturally as if they were going home, they amble in. Heads, with cowls lowered, assume different positions: some are buried contemplatively on chests, some are held high, some look straight ahead. All move slowly, in pairs. At the altar, after a profound obeisance, they bow to one another and turn to take their places on the benches at the side.

A final bright chord echoes forward through the chapel. But the sound is not allowed to die. Like a falling snowflake being billowed into the air as it touches earth, that tone, with a soft upswing of unisonal monks' voices, is carried forward into the opening phrases of the Introit.

I forget the parrots. I forget the uplifted eyes and hollow faces. I forget the bitter taste of loneliness. This is my reason for being here. This, at least, I can understand. Many voices in perfect unison, breathing one melody, spreading in an ocean of sound without sharpness, to end again in silence. A fragility of black notes on white paper become tender, awe-stricken chant of adoration.

Intoning voices and a Latin text. Five white-vested celebrants before the altar, and on the altar a myriad of candles. Slow, deliberate, never halting, as a chanted *"Agnus Dei, qui tollis peccata mundi"* enters the filigree, entwining itself into the texture: "Lamb of God, that takest away the sins of the world . . ."

And to the right, smoke from the incense crosses rays of inpouring light and rises to lose itself in the grayness of the ceiling high above.

After Mass the spell of its music lingers with a lightness, a hush, as I walk from the chapel. At such times vision becomes precise and the sky is more vast than ever before and you can see each pebble of gravel at your feet.

I return to my cell where I may lie down and pull the blanket around my shoulders. Footsteps pass in the hall but no one knocks — and suddenly I come to know that this life is too great a change for me. Except for the music it's intolerable. I think of leaving. I think of sleeping alone in this hard cot and am lonely at the thought. If only I had money enough for the return fare to Paris. But another check from America isn't due for over a month. I reject for the moment a desire to write to Lucette for the money. If she can find it, she'll send it; I'm sure of that. But it will take a few days. I must wait. Perhaps the impressions of first hours will . . .

The clangor of small, high-pitched bells awakens me. My instruction card tells me that it's time for the noon meal, and that we have five minutes before entering the refectory . . . Father Abbot takes my arm and accompanies me to my table. As we traverse the long, heavily beamed room, standing monks bow low from each side, holding the bow until we are past.

At a signal from the abbot, a prayer is started. On my plate a large bowl of amber-colored soup sends a fragrant steam to my face. Standing with head bowed, I wait with growing anguish as my soup cools and stops giving up its smoking aroma.

"Amen" is followed by a moment of silence finally broken by a peremptory tap, as Father Abbot strikes his table with a small wooden mallet. This tells us to begin.

I glance about me not knowing what to expect, but not expecting what I see. This is the first time I have observed at close range the assembled monks. Except for their tonsured heads and monastic robes, there was never a more ordinary-looking lot of men. Somehow I hadn't thought monks would look exactly like everyone else. Criminals, we think, look like criminals, and monks should look like saints. Aside from a certain repose of movement and face, these men are indistinguishable from any others. Some are bald and fat, as if they had stepped from the pages of Rabelais or Balzac; some are tall and gaunt; some are ascetic in appearance. All of them eat voraciously and noisily, occupied only with the immediate problem of consuming soup. Somehow it's offensive. The elegances of a feminine society have been long since forgotten and table manners returned to a primitive status.

"All meals except breakfast," my card had said, "are taken in silence. Each day during mealtimes a monk will read from works of special interest, after which he will be served in the kitchen."

We become aware of the reader after a time. He sits high above us in a raised pulpit and reads in a monotonous, chanting style that is at first almost unintelligible. Today he is reading about the missionary sisters in Canada and the cruel manner in which they were scalped by Indians.

With the most serious intent, the thing suddenly becomes uncomfortable. Wide grins can't be camouflaged behind napkins. The panic of laughter grows as the reader goes on. To hear him enunciating the horror of nuns being scalped by Indians in the wilds of that long-ago Canada, reading it in a trancelike, expressionless, singsong voice, as if he doesn't really give a damn who scalped whom, is inescapably ridiculous.

Monks of all ages, wearing blue denim aprons over their habits, appear as a welcome distraction from the kitchen. Without interrupting the reader they gather our empty soup plates onto carts and with quick movements disappear back into the kitchen.

Large, smoking tureens are soon wheeled in. The aproned monks dip great spoonfuls of an indescribable main course onto our plates. It seems to be a combination of meat broths, potatoes, yellow beans and onions, cooked together and mashed through a food mill until it comes to us with the thick, lumpy consistency of gruel. With coarse brown bread we eat a great deal of this mixture.

After lunch we are allowed a thirty-minute free period during which we can relax and talk as we like. No one speaks to me today. The afternoon is spent walking about the Monastery gardens until I think I'm tired enough to sleep . . .

The American remains in the Monastery, awaiting word from the Father Abbot if he will be allowed to stay. His anger grows against the lack of attention he is receiving. Several times he starts a letter to his ex-mistress Lucette in Paris, intending to ask her for money to return. He spends a great deal of time in his cell reading books about the Order of St. Benedict that Father Clément has left him. He feels a growing sense of uncertain peace within the walls, but is repulsed by the bleak conditions of monastic life — the unheated cloisters, meager food rationings, the primitiveness of living conditions.

Plagued by these things and desperately fighting off recurring sexual desires, he walks into the neighboring Town. Returning to the Monastery, later, in Salesky's taxicab, he inquires about the possibility of getting a prostitute. Salesky bemoans the fact that none are available. The American informs the amiable driver that he has decided to leave the Monastery.

A week passes. The bare essentials of the Monastery tear at him. Every morning he works with Father G'seau on Gregorian manuscripts in the paleography room; eventually more monks speak to him during the free periods, although much reserve is still in evidence. In the afternoons he walks to the nearby château of Madame la Marquise de la Roche to practice the piano for an hour; in return for this privilege he gives music lessons to her son, Jacques.

Determined that he is soon going to leave, he makes a more conscious effort to understand the hermetic life of the monks.

2 1 october

. . . After Mass, I walk to the château to give Jacques de la Roche his daily piano lesson. I'm surprised to find him waiting for me on the terrace.

"Excuse me," he says miserably as I climb the steps, "but we're in trouble."

"What is it, Jacques? If I can be of any help —?"

"The Chevissiers — you know, the family who work our farm — their little daughter is ill. I think she's dying, but they refuse to spend a penny to call a doctor. Could you look at the child? You told me you've been a medical student."

"But, Jacques, I'm no doctor. I never got beyond premedical work."

"But don't you see? — they'll listen to you. I may as well admit, I told them you were a doctor. I had to tell them. Please, the child is very sick. You've done some hospital work, perhaps you can at least tell me if it's serious?"

I shrug my shoulders. "Of course it won't hurt to look at her."

"Thanks," he says warmly. "We'd better go on over there now."

We walk in silence through an acre of formal gardens down a rocky hillside into flatlands below. With a flutter of white skirts, a woman approaches across the field. We meet her in the pasture.

"Doctor," says Jacques — and at the word I glance at him sideways — "this is Madame Chevissier. How is the child, Madame?"

"I was just coming for you, M'sieu Jacques. She seems very nervous, but I don't think it's anything. She's been like this before, and after two or three hours she always gets over it."

"How long has she been 'nervous' today?" I ask.

"For over three hours, Doctor. The little smarty, she just does this to get her way."

"May I see her, Madame?"

"Ah, no, M'sieu," she says emphatically. "We can't afford a doctor."

"I won't ask any money, Madame. Come, let's walk over."

She hesitates a moment longer, then reluctantly leads us down the path.

As we walk, Jacques whispers disgustedly in my ear, "These bastards! These ignorant bastards! They've made a fortune from the farm. I know they have plenty of money, for they sell everything on the black market — butter, eggs, meat — things very scarce in the Valley."

When I don't speak, Jacques falls silent, and we walk rapidly until we come in sight of a flat peasant hut made of stone.

"I'll wait outside," says my companion. "I'm afraid I'll get sick if I go in."

"Wait for me here then, Jacques. We may need a real doctor." I turn to follow Madame Chevissier.

The farm wife, dragging a black wool shawl across her shoulders, leads me hurriedly through a grove of boxwood hedge and around the corner of the low, sparsely windowed farm house. Across a flagstone courtyard is the open door. High stone walls enclose the courtyard, open at one end, and as we turn to enter, a flock of blue geese waddle in to be fed.

A room of stone floors, darkened beams, plaster walls, of the style built in the early seventeenth century. Monsieur Chevissier sits on a bench at the table. He is half the size of his wife, with the redness of face that comes from the incessant drinking of good country wine. His back is to the door that provides the only source of light for the somber room.

"Is she better, Jules?" asks Madame Chevissier.

"No, Mama, she's still nervous," he says in a quiet voice.

"The little tease, we ought to give her a good spanking." This is the ironic, gritty talk of a woman who can't afford sick children, who will not admit sickness into her home; but the voice hints anxiety. Enigmatic woman — she has the look about her of work, of inherent goodness, and of the evil of ignorance. Like all such women, she probably dominates her family with a love and an efficiency that knows no fluctuation, no alteration.

"Stand up, Jules," commands Madame Chevissier, "and meet this young man. He's a friend of M'sieu Jacques's come to see the Petite."

"Yes, Mama." He absent-mindedly shakes my hand.

"He says he's a doctor."

"Good. I'm glad you've come, Doctor."

"But we can't afford a doctor," his wife continues. "How much will you charge, M'sieu?"

"I told you," I reply, "I'll charge you nothing. Now, where is the child?"

"She's over here, M'sieu. The little tease, she pulls this nervousness to get her way" — tough, easygoing talk, with a tremble of uneasiness.

We walk to the darkest corner of the room, next to the fireplace. There against walls of ancient plaster a bed is propped high on bricks. On the bed, soundless, lies the naked skeleton of a child. A few dull-blond hairs straggle atop a head bluish in cast. Open eyes stare wildly. The small face is colorless as if in death. Skin stretches taut over sharp cheekbones and the lips are gray. Trembling, with violently jerking arms, she stares without seeing: hideous movements of a puppet, controlled only by a mad puppet-master — epilepsy.

I turn from the child. "How long did you say she's been like this, Madame?"

"For over three hours now, eh, Jules?"

"About that, Mama. Is it bad, M'sieu?"

Without answering I hurry from the house. "Jacques, for God's sake get a doctor. The child's got epilepsy, I think. Anyway, she can't stand much more of this."

"Good Lord! Can you do anything?"

"I doubt it. Hurry, will you?"

He disappears, running down the path toward the château. Impotent ignorance, impotence of ignorance: I know nothing of epilepsy.

Monsieur Chevissier waits at the door. "It *is* bad, isn't it, M'sieu?"

"Very bad. You should've called a doctor immediately."

"She's had these spells before, M'sieu. My wife thought she was just putting on an act because we wouldn't give her the glass of wine she asked for."

"Your wife should be able to see that no one can put on an act like this, and that no child could live for long under such a strain."

Madame Chevissier, hearing us, leaves the child. "You better go now, Doctor," she remarks sullenly. "We can't afford to pay you anything."

"I don't want your damned money! Your little girl is *very* sick. Can't you tell that? Now go sit down — no, get me some clean towels and put some water on to boil."

The child, in a seizure of frenzy, lies on her back. Naked, flesh-less arms and legs dance with uncontrolled movements as if they were detached from her emaciated, colorless body. Gazing unsee-ing, terrified, she makes no sound.

Taking her hands in mine I pull a muslin cover over her body. Despite the chill her hands are moist with sweat, like snakes wrig-gling from my grasp.

The child's body quietens. Madame Chevissier moves to the bed, gently releasing two bodiless arms from the covers. They dance again, jerkily, in the obscure shadows — a ghost dance in the half-light.

The father, seated at the table, is silent. The room is silent except for the sounds of the child's mute struggle, the spitting of water beginning to boil, and the drone of flies aroused by the fire.

On the blackened oak table, still smoking, dinner goes untouched — a large casserole of yellow beans cooked with blood sausages, onions and garlic, and two dusty bottles of red wine, streaked clear and dark where hands have touched them.

Monsieur Chevissier sits dejectedly with shoulders bent, silhou-etted against the incoming rays of dull autumn sunlight — a calm sunlight of halcyon October, making its way across the room as afternoon begins to pass, catching in its light floating particles of dust. An hour has passed with no help.

"The water is near boiling, M'sieu." Madame Chevissier's voice breaks the stillness.

"Dip one of the towels in it," I tell her, "and the other in cold water, and bring them to me, please."

Sounds of water being wrung from wetted towels; drops falling to the floor spotting the dust. She hands them to me and I place the warm cloth over the child's desolating blue eyes, covering much of her body. Madame Chevissier again removes the sheet, exposing skeletal belly and legs.

"Put the sheet back, please."

"If she wets it'll be ruined, M'sieu."

"Put the sheet back," praying for patience as I work, my face close above the child's face, sweat dripping from my nose.

The child begins gritting her teeth, grinding her jaws together, always with the beaten stare of watering, unbeaten eyes that can't see.

"If I'd known you were going to mess up my clean towels, I'd have given you some soiled ones," complains Madame Chevissier.

"Your child is very sick, terribly sick, and you simper about towels and sheets. Now go sit down and don't say another word until I ask you."

An hour of compresses, alternating hot and cold towels. The doctor does not come. In mid-afternoon the spasms quieten, allowing the child's arms to rest, still trembling, on her chest.

Madame Chevissier, honest, expansive, broad, whispers, "Don't you think she's better?"

"Yes, she's still unconscious, but the spell seems to be leaving."

Against hope, I lift the warm wetness of rough towel from her eyes. They don't blink at the light — open, unseeing gaze of terror. Moment of hopeless hope, moment of intense affection for this ugly child who doesn't see me, with whom I work against the terror of death.

Fine line of intensity, bending low over the child's face. Ageless face of age in the body of a ten-year-old. Eyes cowering, hurt. Quiet except for a trembling, a suppuration from the nose — feverish-smelling, fetid — as she exhales white foam. I clean her with a towel. We wait for help. We wait for some sign from the child, alone and far away from us. We are exhausted for her, and we have spent ourselves, for her struggle has been ours from the very beginning. Her teeth grind away until we fear they will crumble to chalk in her mouth.

On the cold air without, honkings of geese become more insistent: maddening animal sounds.

A gasp from the child as her left arm jerks into the air, to fall half-back and be pulled up again on some drunken, invisible, senseless string. Arms and legs tremble, slowly at first as in some macabre dance, becoming more frenzied gradually until the even rattle of her breathing grows labored, until the viscid mucus foams from her nose in gray bubbles to burst on the air. Her head moves slightly from side to side with great rapidity. Repeated short gasps come from her lips as we watch. The climax will take her. We know it but we work doggedly, hoping always that she may dance it out and still live.

Jacques must be driving all over the countryside looking for a doctor. I struggle with her, I fight; and in the frenzy of seeing us, the child and me, losing our hope, I close my eyes, changing towels and uttering wordless, formless prayers, pleading for —

"Do you think I should give her an enema, M'sieu?" Madame Chevissier's voice at my elbow shocks me back to reality.

"No, it would do no good."

"I gave her one before."

"No, I tell you, no!"

Another hour drags past with no change. The spasms come rhythmically in great heaves, with a gathering mucus rattling in her throat which the child can neither eject nor swallow.

No help arrives as the sun pours in a lateral, penciled line across the floor, reaching up and over the table with its cold food, its dust-covered bottles of wine.

Hopeless fatigue, the ache of fighting against something unknown. The nose becomes congested and we try to clean it; but we stop, somehow feeling we are wronging this child. I raise her head, hoping to clear the chest of its caldron of mucus, but she jerks in my arms and I dare not force her frailty.

Flecks of saliva at the corners of her mouth. I feel the weight of my cheeks as I bend forward over the child, wiping foam from her mouth and nose. Awkwardness of convulsions, determined to rack her body still more before tossing it on the ash heap of death.

Again the raucous, matter-of-fact voice at my elbow: "There, the little thing's gone and wet her bed. Shame on you, Petite. Ten years old and you still wet the bed."

"Love of God! Will you get away from here?"

Forty minutes more. Monsieur and Madame Chevissier sit quietly on each side of the table. After so long a time without help, without knowing what to do, gone is the intense desire to make her well, to enter with our bodies into her struggle against the dread puppet-master. Imperceptibly over the hours we begin wishing for it to end; no matter how it ends, we wish that it would end.

Madame Chevissier, alarmed with the passing of time, becomes grim and worried. My anger changes to compassion. We work together now, realizing that we're doing these things only because they must be done. The end of the dance has started. We change towels quietly, without further recriminations. The father remains slumped in his chair, and I sense his embarrassment at his helplessness.

Finally we stop applying the compresses. They're doing no good. We sit and watch the child in her dance of horror. There comes a time in such things when all you can do is wait for the end, almost hoping for the death that will take a child from such murderous supplice. You don't cry then; you wait until death arrives. You wait for it, emotionless.

It is a vacuum, a waiting, and we can't understand it. The interim drags, and we wish for it to end. Without weeping we wait exhausted, suspended in time until death will turn this essence of suffering back to us. Then she'll become something we can understand. Then this thing will be their daughter once more; real in death, allowing them to become normal in reactions of grief.

The sun reaches across the room to the opposite wall, an amber, hazed ribbon pale on the floor — cold sunlight of late afternoon. Somewhere outside a hen chirps lazily. And with another honking, geese crowd round the door, stretching long necks to look inside.

"Feed the geese, Jules, and drive them away," says Madame Chevissier in a weary voice.

Obviously relieved to move about, Papa Chevissier carries a wooden scoop of oats outside, geese noisily following. "Come on, geese," he calls — "Goosey, goosey, goosey, come on over here" — in a cajoling, intimate, nasal voice. Returning the scoop, dusting his hands on corduroy pants, he resumes his vigil at the table beside us.

Turning to his wife, Monsieur Chevissier suggests, "Mama, perhaps M'sieu would like a glass of wine."

"Of course, M'sieu, let me get you a glass."

"Thanks. I am thirsty, and this looks like good wine."

"It's the wine of the country, M'sieu, but not bad. There."

She pours three glasses and we drink, refilling the glasses again and again, trying to ignore the soundless struggle.

A short, gasping wail from the Petite brings us to her bedside; a pitifully human sound — the first human sound she has uttered — giving us hope.

"I believe she's coming out of it, Mama," whispers the father in a cracked, harsh, falsetto voice.

But the face, blue and ashen before, turns red with congestion. Her tiny body, rising from the hips, pulls up and forward as if she were trying to cough. Hands shoot out at crazy angles, to fall and rise back again. A heavy, inhuman sound comes from her lips, and liquid putrefaction pours from every orifice in her body. Her mouth opens as if to cough again, veins in her throat stand rigid, and her empty belly contracts deep under the rib cavity, sucking in. The mouth stays open, braying soundlessly. Toes, blue-veined, curled far to the back, double her dancing feet in the air. And the father, bending low to look up into her staring eyes, sees them stop staring.

"She's leaving us, Mama!" he cries. "Our Petite is leaving us."

Twisted still, movement of a raging ocean gradually becomes calmness of the sea, as muscles stop trembling, as bubbles of evil-smelling foam burst against her nose and stop coming, as her belly rises slowly and grows quiet . . . as her heart stops beating.

In that instant of obvious death I put my hand on her chest, patting it unconsciously, grateful for her — this child who has never known me, whom I have known with such tenderness and intimacy, with such compassion. There is a frantic squealing from the mother, but Papa Chevissier, like me, is grateful that it's over, is filled with the peace of relief for the child. A steady stream of meaningless noise pours from the mother.

Vainly I listen for a last heartbeat, my head on her chest; but the breast is still.

Again the terrible squealing, as if Madame Chevissier were doing it out of respect for the mystery of death rather than from grief. I turn to her.

"You mustn't behave like that, Madame," I tell her gently. "The child couldn't have lived long. She'd never have been well."

"But, M'sieu, she wasn't even baptized. She'll be buried like a dog!"

"She was innocent as an angel. Already she's in heaven."

"No, no, M'sieu" — with an agonized wail — "she'll be buried like a dog. They won't even let us put her in hallowed ground."

Papa Chevissier, patting the corpse, mumbles, "The poor baby, she never had any luck."

Others have heard. Children and farm workers come to weep. Deafening din. Only the father remains quiet. Unconsciously I walk to the table and finish my half-empty glass of wine. The others ignore me. I light my pipe and walk outside.

Later, a new Citroën automobile with a physician's crest on the windshield enters the courtyard. The doctor steps out, and I follow him into the house.

They have moved the child from her bed to the dining table. Older children remove the soiled bedclothing. They wash the dead child on the table, letting her lie there in a pool of water. Her eyes have already been closed, and the skin is bluish in cast. Since she has died with her mouth open, they force the jaws together by tying a towel around her head with a large knot under the chin.

The doctor is furious. "That's right," he berates them, "you people won't call a doctor until it's too late. You're afraid to spend a damned penny, even to save a child's life. Until all of you in this Valley learn to call when you need me, I can do nothing but sign your death certificates. The child is dead. Let that be a lesson to you."

The child lies there naked in the darkening room, the ridiculous dirty towel around her head. She is forgotten for the moment as the group listens humbly to the doctor. A tiny lake of water in her navel, where they have failed to dry her, holds my attention. I soak it up with a soggy towel.

The doctor bends efficiently over the table to sign the death certificate. No one moves in the room. Papa Chevissier's voice, almost inaudible, breaks the silence.

"What caused her to die, Doctor?" he asks timidly.

The doctor hesitates, glancing at the dead child. "It appears she died of brain congestion due to epilepsy," he says wearily.

The sight of the child lying there in a pool of water suddenly sickens me. They talk over her and about her as if she had never been human. I look again at the child, and unable to bear it any longer I slip out the door without a good-bye.

I walk back in a ravishing, low-keyed sunset — in a warm affection for the child. Exhausted from the afternoon with a monster, now become child in death, and made beautiful in the small frame of the understandable. Across fields on a path between patches of fresh-turned soil, as cold evening air moves down.

Jacques and his mother meet me at the château.

"Where did you go, Jacques?" I ask.

"I fetched the doctor but he was on a case, so I came on back here to wait for you. Is the child going to be all right?"

"She died only a few minutes ago."

Jacques's mother looks at me closely. "But, my poor boy," she says sympathetically, "you look exhausted. Come, we can go inside where it's warm, and you can drink a cup of tea while you tell us what happened."

Her words make me realize how unsteadily I stand on my feet, how complete is my exhaustion. I gratefully accept the cup of tea she pours for me, and take a seat near the fire. Briefly I tell them what has happened.

"The most peculiar thing, Madame la Marquise," I add "— and perhaps you can explain this — was Madame Chevissier's wailing about the child's not being baptized. Do you really think —?"

She interrupts frantically, "You mean that child wasn't baptized?"

"No, that's what all the fuss was about."

"Ah, the poor child. I must go to the family, they'll bury her like a dog. Oh, why didn't I see to it that they had her baptized!"

After she has gone to weep with the rest, Jacques mutters, "I should have stayed. In case of a death like this one, anyone can baptize the dead person merely by putting a sign of the cross on his forehead, and saying, 'I baptize thee in the name of the Father, and of the Son, and of the Holy Ghost.' If you'd known that, you could have baptized her yourself. That way, it would have been accepted by the Church and she could have been given a decent Christian burial. Now they'll just bury her anywhere, without a service, and it's a terrible stigma on the family."

"Well, Jacques, couldn't we go back and baptize her now? I mean, if it makes such a difference —"

"No, it must be done within fifteen minutes after the death." He looks at me miserably. "You make me feel like a fool. You see, you don't have our beliefs. These things are important to us."

"Well, it's none of my affair — but it certainly seems terrible to me to deprive an innocent child of a decent funeral just because she hasn't been baptized. I never knew it went quite that far," I conclude heatedly.

"You mean," Jacques put in, "you've been in France all this time and didn't know that?" I shake my head, and he goes on, "I wish I could explain it. Our Church just doesn't believe that anyone can get to heaven till he's been baptized in the Faith. You can't imagine the disgrace this will be for the child's parents. It's the worst thing that could happen to them, almost. Can you imagine having your child buried just any place, without proper last rites?"

"No, Jacques, I can't. And I don't think it's any credit to your Church that such a thing has to be. Oh, well, I don't mean to sound so disrespectful," I add, noticing how much my remark has hurt him. "I don't understand, that's all."

Seeking an excuse to end this conversation, I look at my watch. "Guess I'd better go now. It's almost time for supper and I have a long walk." I rise, and Jacques walks with me to the door.

. . . As I walk down the road, late dusk turns into night. The River and the Valley are quiet and indifferent to my presence. I cross the River with the ever-phantasmagoric vision of snakelike struggles with death which I have shared with a little girl this afternoon.

Welcome sounds of bells from the Monastery, and my footsteps hasten in their direction. There is a strange compulsion to hurry. I feel hungry for food, but even hungrier for the light of the refectory and for the sober happiness of eating with the monks. And suddenly I know that I want their company, no matter how silent. I want to escape the abstraction of unreal death that lingers still, in the reality of eating prosaic food with the monks this evening.

The monks are standing, reciting the opening phrases of a long benediction, as I quietly take my place in the lighted refectory. After the long prayer we begin eating. I wonder at my joy in being back; at the peace which fills me as I eat the food that I have detested before. Even a week ago I should have wanted to get drunk or to get a girl to help me forget this terrible afternoon; but now I want nothing but the warm food and the hard bench and the surrounding monks, and later the rest of sleep in my cell.

With food in my belly I learn anew the completeness of my exhaustion, of my desire for sleep. When we have finished evening prayers in the chapel, I stay only long enough to be told that the Fathers already know of the death of the Chevissier child, as everything is always known within a monastery. Relief that I won't have to relive the experience in the retelling of it.

Without taking advantage of the free period I return to my cell, wash, and put on my pajamas. It is nine o'clock. The signal for Compline has just sounded — a tinkling of small bells, not carrying far beyond the walls.

But the day was too much. I hear the rumble of feet below me, and the beginnings of the night's last service. My legs ache as they relax beneath covers. The child, and sleeplessness of too-great fatigue . . .

But the dissonance of such a day can't be resolved in a few moments. Before the completion of Compline I sleep, to awaken sometime later in the middle of the greatest silence of sleep which surrounds — silence vibrating in soundless intensity from the stone that shelters us. I awake feverish and sick from the wetness of disjointed dreams that fumbled away at crazy angles. In the half-sleep of the torturing dreams, I feel the tightening putrefaction of my chest, and the ache of muscles. The wetness becomes cold, and I roll away from it to the edge of my cot. Momentary thought of the child lying on her bier, with a candle at each end for company. She is alone this night, and with overwhelming suddenness her loneliness becomes my loneliness, and I feel lost and afraid in the dark. Fears become desolation, and I grope in the confusion of inner night for sanctuary, and strange and frightening words halfform themselves in my consciousness. For the first time, a mumbled "*Ave, Maria, gratia plena* . . ." But my face blushes in the dark with the embarrassment of a begun prayer. The words become obscenity in my mind, and I can't go on. . . .

Father Clément informs the American that ugly stories have spread through the Valley that he is a doctor, and that he let the Petite Chevissier die. Explaining that he once attended medical school but never finished, he finds out that the stories have been originated by the Chevissier family and a Madame Renée, one of the most respected women of the Village. Father Clément advises him that such stories could impair his chances of getting to remain at the Monastery, that he could be ruined in the Valley, and that it is imperative that he attend the child's funeral that afternoon.

He learns that the Petite Chevissier is to be given a Christian burial. Joining the funeral procession, he is informed by Jacques that Madame Renée had come and baptized the child after everyone had left the previous night. When the parish priest, Father Sauvac, had inquired if the child were baptized, the family had said yes, not telling when. Jacques tells him the people are now terrified that he will reveal the truth. Jacques further states that if the Chevissiers know he will remain quiet about the matter, they will stop the damaging rumors about him.

The procession reaches the church and the services begin. The event passes without incident. The American assures Papa Chevissier at the cemetery that the secret is safe with him, that he will tell no one; Chevissier promises that the false rumors about his being a doctor will stop.

He returns to the Monastery. No money has arrived from Lucette, so he resigns himself that his stay will have to be longer than he wants. Eventually, he receives permission from the Father Abbot to stay as long as he wishes, to attend any of the classes offered at the Monastery, and to work freely on his research in the library and paleography room.

He tells Father Clément that he will probably leave soon; the priest urges him to take his time in making a decision. When he confides his personal battles with the flesh, Father Clément suggests that physical labor will help and arranges for him to work outdoors with the Father Gardener.

Days of intensified work and study. Weakened with fatigue and the harshness of this new life, he falls ill. He is sick for over two weeks.

Finally, the fevers passed, he gradually returns to his work in the Monastery. The winter pounds with renewed force and discomforts steadily mount, but he attempts to accept the adverse circumstances good-naturedly like the monks.

Mail from America, with checks enclosed, reaches him. It has been forwarded from Paris by Lucette, but there is no letter from her. He goes into Town and cashes the checks. Torn with doubts, he ponders leaving the Monastery.

Encountering Salesky in Town, the taxicab owner entrusts him with a secret. ("I may as well tell you now, for you'll hear it anyway. I have a girl friend on this side of the River — Madame Rouen, she runs a little spice shop. She's given me two children, which is more than my wife ever did. Is it bad for a man to love his wife and yet want children by another woman?")

Explaining that it is difficult to see his mistress because of the gossiping ladies of the Town who make it their duty to keep watch on him, Salesky persuades the American to sit in the cab (thus providing a camouflage) outside Madame Rouen's house. He enters and returns before the American has had time to finish a first cigarette. ("Thanks a thousand times for helping me. It was wonderful — but quick, eh? Quicker than you could have handled it, young buck that you are. I didn't even take off my coat, M'sieu.")

Back at the Monastery, he again considers returning to Paris, alternately accepting and rejecting the idea. Accepting, rejecting, at war within himself. He thinks of Lucette, warm, waiting. But there is warmth in his cell, in these surroundings of dedication. Why leave one warmth for another warmth that is less valuable? he wonders. He knows he cannot leave. Not now anyway.

The malaria returns, but a lighter case this time. The doctor recommends that the American leave the Monastery until milder weather, advises that he find warmer accommodations, better nourishment, and more carefully regulated sleep and rest. Father Clément suggests that perhaps he should go to Paris until the spring. Though sick and exhausted, he protests.

He tells Father Clément of his past life with Lucette, and of his fears that if he returns to Paris he may fall into the old sins again. The priest agrees that he can stay, but that they should investigate the possibilities of finding him warm quarters in the Village. He also tells him of the impending visit to the Monastery of Father Marie-Ornoux ("a celebrated young monk — only thirty-three — of the Dominican Fathers on his way to become a missionary in the desert" and possessor of a "sanctity of the most extraordinary real-

ity") and his traveling companion, Dr. Rafael Castelar, a South American.

Days of doubts and classes in morality conducted by Father Clément. Daydreams and nightmares of carnality.

Father Clément tells him that a small villa in the Village, owned by the Countess de la Villesverte, is available to him if Madame Renée, who oversees the property, approves him as a tenant.

The Father tells him about Madame Renée: the monks have known her for many years; her son, Michel, is a monk at another Benedictine monastery; her other son, Jean-Julian, had been killed in a plane crash in England during the war; she is a woman of the world who has retired to the Village to take her place among the other "great ladies" there. He warns that the so-called "great ladies" have immeasurable influence in the Village and can be vicious.

The American tells Father Clément about being a lookout for Salesky, and of his growing repugnance toward such things. This repugnance that he feels, the priest answers, is proof that he is slowly making spiritual headway.

The Father again urges him to pray. He tries at Vespers later that day, but the coldness and wetness interfere and he fails, realizing that he is simply muttering phrases without any real conviction. But he also realizes that the coldness is a superficial reason — his real attention is focused on a young Mexican girl in the chapel.

After Vespers, he and Father Clément confer with Madame Renée about the villa. (". . . A beautiful woman awaits us. She appears to be middle-aged, with prematurely gray hair framing a youthful, unwrinkled face. Her skin is white and fine, and her expression, dominated by clear blue eyes, is relaxed. She is obviously a woman of the world who knows exactly what she's doing. In a glance we find each other sympathetic. Here is a woman who has had the courage to baptize a dead child. My doubts are resolved with the meeting; and I feel sure her reasons for baptizing the little Chevissier girl were open and honest and good . . . I tell her of my sickness, and of my need for good nourishment. She suggests I give her my ration cards and take my meals with her, sharing expenses. She is the finest cook in the Valley, she admits without hesitation.")

Madame Renée explains that the Countess would want it that way, and points out that she lives just across the street from the villa. The American agrees to this arrangement, and the first of January is determined as the date of occupancy. Madame Renée invites him to come to lunch so that he can sample her cooking and meet some of the other ladies of the Village.

Father Clément's admonition comes to mind and he heeds it. ("I must tell you, Madame, that much as I'd like to be able to visit with the ladies of the Village, I can take off only enough time for my meals each day.")

13 december

The Feast of St. Hilaire. This day of great celebration in honor of our Village patron saint, brings the obsession of cold to our first consciousness. We prepare for a pontifical High Mass, and after the Mass there will be a feast in the refectory for many invited guests.

The atmosphere is festive as a great many men, wrapped to their chins in coats and scarves, stand in the little room of the gatehouse waiting for Mass to begin. Salesky is there looking uncomfortable. Nodding unsmiling in my direction, he looks virginal, as if a smile would be a sacrilege undreamed of in this holy place.

A first timid bell is immediately drowned by other bells, until the Valley is alive with clanging sounds calling Villagers to the feast.

. . . We enter the chapel until it's full, and those who are left go to the parish church. This beautiful Mass with its color, with its rhythm, with its slowness of movement, becomes commonplace confronted by the coughing, noisy Villagers. Calm, measured cadences grow static beneath the paralyzing desire of those present to have it finished, a desire felt by everyone and communicated into the very atmosphere.

The service lasts too long, almost till noon. We pour from the chapel, some to return home for comfortable clothes and a good meal, others to stay for the feast in the refectory.

Possessed by an overwhelming desire to be alone, I walk precariously up the ice-covered steps to await lunch in my cell. The room is clean and bright in its smallness. Decrepit gray walls appear warm, and the crucifix above my cot surveys the scene with its fixed wooden sheen.

Father Clément drops in. "Are you resting, my son?" he inquires.

"No, Father, come in. I'm not doing anything. Won't you sit down?"

"Thank you," he says smiling. "I have been thinking about you. You are too much cooped up here. What are you going to do this afternoon?"

"I don't know, Father. I don't seem to be able to read or put my mind on anything today."

"Then how would you like to walk into Town? There will be no classes and you will miss nothing. You should enjoy the walk. Take an afternoon off, go to the tea shop for a cup of hot chocolate, buy yourself a good dinner. I believe it will be good for you."

"I think I will, Father. Might even go to a movie. But this is a feast day for the monks. Mightn't I bring something back for you?"

"Not for me, my son. But since this is an important day in our lives, perhaps you could bring back a sack of dried dates and prunes which we can divide among the other Fathers and Brothers."

After a feast-day lunch of oysters and lentils and cake, I walk swiftly the three miles to Town.

The enchantment of the Valley is felt everywhere. The streets are almost deserted, and there's no noise. A few children play in the snow-covered square near the public urinal, in which water no longer flows.

And it crashes, this security, giving way to a trembling of loneliness. The day is somber and cold, and the streets are deserted. I am seized by a desire to go into the first store and buy something — anything — so long as I can speak and hear another voice answering.

I walk past windows closed against winter; windows on the sidewalk, curtained, hiding interiors where people read the newspaper and smoke and sleep after a good lunch. And I know exactly how they are inside. I know the carpets, and the chairs, and the tables, and the fringed lamps. And the comfort of comfortable clothes and of cleanliness and of the puffings of full digestion after food.

Things of this life which make it ordinary and real. Things no longer a part of mine.

I stop at the open door of a shop. Sweet, pungent odors of spices and soaps on the cold air of the unheated store. And she is there, an ugly woman behind the counter. I look at her and I want her. I want to have her in a filth as great as the filth of my feelings. But she leans forward, and I know the stink of her fat folds. Without speaking I leave.

But the harm has been done. My legs become weak, and my face burns with the uncontrollable desire to find something to take into a bed. This is played in dissonance against the complete consciousness of what I'm going to do, and of the admonitions of Father Clément. It's too far now — the voice of it is cracked and weak and it knows it's too far. My entrails ache to be back in the safety of the Monastery, and my every wish pulls hopelessly against the inexorable line of my body as it becomes a detached thing ignoring my hopes, my prayers, and my pleadings. I no longer have control over it.

I turn to walk back to the safety of Father Clément, who will know the right things to say to kill this force so much greater than my force.

But the body laughs. The body has no ears and no intelligence, and it refuses to move in my direction. Carrying me along the streets, it seeks its own goal. Through the glass window of the tea shop I see a lone woman seated at a table. Before entering I know in every part of my being that she is there for me, and that it's too late and too far.

I take a table next to hers, and order a cup of chocolate from a woman I don't see. My ears burn. I light a cigarette with shaking hands. I am sick, and my legs ache beneath the table with two refrains: *Know her warmness — Go back, go back.*

This woman is mine already. Already I know how her body will be; how the navel will fold in her belly, and how her legs will have the buttermilk markings of used flesh which has once been firm. For she's not young and damp. About forty, with blond hair swept to the top of her head, and a small Parisian hat.

I smoke and stare, calm on the outside, and she asks, "You're the young man staying at the Monastery, aren't you?"

"Yes, Madame. And I suppose you're here for the Feast of St. Hilaire?"

"That's right. I have a son named Hilaire. The service was beautiful this morning, wasn't it?"

We talk, we look at each other, and as people who want the same thing always do, we let our desires be understood. I play the youth honored to attract her notice — somewhat awkward, seeking to understand these things, honest to a point of high crudeness, and deeply sincere. And she is the perfect counterpart, a widow from Paris — intelligent, helpful, but wanting someone to lean on. A woman confused and alone in the world, who is trying to find the solution to her problems here at the Monastery.

"It must be very difficult, Madame," I say to her, fighting to keep my voice even, "when once you've been married, to get used to living without love."

"Ah yes, Monsieur." She says softly, "It is — very difficult."

"That relationship between a man and a woman can be made such a beautiful thing. I've never been married but I've had many girls, and I know what it can mean. I've always thought of it as a great privilege."

"You're quite a Don Juan, Monsieur. You embarrass me."

"Not a Don Juan at all, Madame. I'm just giving you credit for being what you are — a beautiful woman of the world. But you must forgive me. I'm being honest. I think we both want the same thing, and I think we can help each other. If I'm wrong I apologize."

"You're really very nice, Monsieur" — nonchalantly, with ease and grace of manner. "Perhaps we could have dinner tonight?"

"That would be fine. But look, I must return after dinner and we have an afternoon before us. Let me get a room at the hotel where we can be warm. We can visit there until dinner time."

My eagerness catches her, coloring her throat into a blush with the beginnings of desire. She smiles a yes without answering.

I pay the two checks, take her arm, and we go to the hotel . . . They give me a room with bath and have the grace not to mention that we have no bags.

The room is heated — blessed heat. I help her off with her wraps, with the touches such closeness indicates. We sit on the bed and light cigarettes, feeling frozen feet beginning to come to life. With a loud but honestly felt sigh, I take her hand in my own to study it, and her pressure answers mine.

"You don't know what it means to hold someone's hand again."

"I feel the same way. You're very sympathetic, my friend." She glances up at me — quickly, half-tentatively.

"And you're very beautiful."

We fondle hands and then arms, until words die in a vast, sobbing, all-engulfing joining of our mouths. The approach is forgotten as the kiss becomes its own fever. The feverish intensity of starvation flows out from us and we relax our bodies, fainting against each other in relief as muscles melt and the kiss insinuates itself as a pure line of pleasure between us. The dissonance, the ugliness leave, and a clumsiness of beginnings gives way to the ineffable grace of animal responses. As the soul is purged of its hermetic smallness, of its grit of modesty, the demands of our bodies become more powerful . . .

Squares mist milkily, and from the stillness and the dark the curve mounts immutably rhythmic, in ever-mounting intensity. A new gathering of momentum. And through the darkness an occasional glimpse of concentrated white. Now it begins to grow, this strangeness, turning over and over. Slowly, slowly, turning steadily, and the rhythm follows ever growing. And now from the very bottom of a faraway numbness is the quivering beginning of trembling. It's unbearable. The numbness is punctured. Momentum gathers. And the long sigh, unheard, pouring forth from the edges of consummation. From a distance, far within, curving swiftly now, a fast sighing swaying motion curling over and above and around. Beating, beating against the drum of the being, pounding louder and louder till there can be no more loudness, but increasing steadily into the very pulse of the blood. And now before the eyes, the before-hinted, now-brilliant flashing white, growing and expanding to break spattering against eyelids. And from without, a fog of ever-thickening intensity, sparkling and harsh to imagined sight. Simultaneous welling-up of the heaving exploding brilliance, and the beating, now-pounding rhythm piling sound and muffled obscenity, ever expanding above and around, turning faster and faster above the moaned "No! No!" Tightening of the heartbeat, drawing-up of the ribbon. Ecstatic point between life and death when all becomes hermetic and rigid. The pause in space without pausing in movement. The waiting without breathing. The muffled upward surge of the entire being to the crest of the wave, to the very top. Up and up, soaring high onto the peak of noise and heat. The whirling gyrating splash of warning to the mind. Louder now into the head and the brain. Upheaved violence of the belly. This is the flashing of the stars, the cleansing burning of the insides into fervent ash. And the taste of blood grows stronger on the rigid tongue. Finally the broad expansiveness of union, of man's warmness without pain. Sounds descend thinner, slower, draining away to sighing quiet. And the felt pulse of the rhythm faints away to enveloping blackness. The slow easy downhill slide with a final unheard catching of the breath, leading onward and downward until the curve slows to stop against the dark. And down, down again slantingly, quietly to a depth beneath the seas. Beyond movement to stillness. Then the loosening, the resumption of breathing. Gratitude, and the serenity of silent waters . . .

The gray light of winter's afternoon filters through the dusty lace curtains beside our bed. A rug on the floor has lost its color through wear and the accumulation of dust. It is a thin, pathetic covering for the blackened wood floors . . .

Her eyes open to see a face that has lost its strain, and she smiles. "Are you happy, my darling?" she asks.

"It was marvelous . . . Now, shall I keep this room for a few days? We can come here every afternoon."

"But what about your work at the Monastery? Surely you can't leave that? Didn't you tell me your work was your life, your only passion?"

"Yes, but not all my life. I find I have other passions, too."

"Even so, I don't think we'd better keep the room. I must tell you, as much pleasure as this has given me and as wonderful as it's been, I'm here for another purpose. I'll confess what we've done, receive penance, and make every effort not to do it again."

I shrug my shoulders. "You're probably right. This couldn't be helped today. I know what you're trying to do and I respect you for it. I'm afraid I've set you back. But it's easy to be virtuous once passion is satisfied. I feel pretty Christian right now, myself. But what shall we do when we feel it again? Can what we've done be so terribly wrong?"

"I don't know," she hesitates. "But I'll do as the priest says."

We walk down the carpeted stairs to the lobby. I stop to pay the bill while she waits in the hall near the entrance.

. . . After dinner we walk back to the Village together, in the specter of evermore chilling dusk. The Valley is deserted. Not touching, we walk slowly under the heavy grayness of almost-night, through a countryside crisp and covered with snow.

"Thank heavens you're with me," I tell her quietly. "I'd die of loneliness if you weren't here."

"And I feel the same, my friend. I'm glad we're together."

We walk on in silence, unhurried.

"Tell me what you're thinking?" her voice murmurs from the darkness beside me.

I feel for her arm. "I was just thinking," I say slowly, "it's like we'd never slept together now. We're just as we were when I met you in the tea shop. I've known you in the most intimate way possible, and yet we're like strangers. With other women it's different. Afterward you get more and more intimate, till finally it's no longer exciting. If you were anyone else I'd stop right now and take you in my arms and kiss you. But I don't feel like doing that with you. It wouldn't seem right."

"It's only the night and the cold," she reassures me. "It's so lonely out here in the dark we get wrapped up in ourselves."

I shake my head. "No, it's more than that. It's a feeling I have for you. And yet it's nothing like love. If you should leave tomorrow I wouldn't miss you in the slightest. This afternoon I hated you for being there to tempt me. I just wanted to have you and get it over with as quickly as possible, knowing how much I'd regret it later — not because of what I'd done, but because I hadn't been able to resist the temptation. You see, I'd persuaded myself that that was the sin — not ever being able to resist temptation."

"But you're wrong, my friend. The sin is in us, in what we've done. Like you, I can't feel it was really wrong, but I know it was. We're no different from anybody else."

"We feel the same, don't we? Neither of us understands."

She moves closer to me: instinctive seeking of warmth. "Yes, we do feel the same. You might always have been my lover, for we seem to be much alike. But it's dangerous for us to think like this. We mustn't persuade ourselves that it's right. We have to play by the rules of the game even though we don't understand them."

I say nothing, and she draws still closer to me.

"We're cool now," she whispers, and the night takes her words. "Our passion is spent. While we're in our senses let's make up our minds not to see each other again."

"If you wish," I acquiesce. "Maybe some day I'll learn the reasons. Do you really believe either of us would be better off right now, if we hadn't been together?"

"I don't know — I really don't know. That's what makes it so hard for people like us."

"At any rate I'll never forget you — or what you've done for me."

We are close to the bridge. We walk a few steps farther, then I lay a hand on her arm.

"I think we'd better separate here," I say gently. "You go where you have to go and I'll return to the Monastery. Good-bye, and good luck."

It is dark night. She moves from my touch without saying anything more. Her footsteps take her into the shroud of obscurity, fading away.

A half-chill brings me to my senses. I feel a sudden gladness that the day is gone with her footfalls. I pick up my step and my spirits, and find myself laughing with pleasure and relief as I enter the darkened mass of stone that is home. I walk carefully past the faintly lighted chapel: muffled sounds of Compline, which will be followed by the Great Silence. For tonight, at least, I am safe. No explanations can be asked till morning.

But with my return, returns a remembered promise. It stops my steps and my heartbeat, burning my face in the dark, striking my consciousness and my conscience. The day has made me forget my purpose in leaving the Monastery. They chant their prayer of night and of rest, these monks to whom I'm more devoted than I know; these monks who would have taken such pleasure from the dried fruits I was to bring them. A prune or a fig, with Father

Abbot's permission, would have meant more than can be imagined to these men who have so little.

In the chapel below, as I undress, many men pray. Men who have cared for me when I was sick. Men who share their food and goods with me. Men who are my brothers. Men who have awaited my return and the small pleasure it might bring to a day of celebration. Men who have waited and whose waiting was futile. The pleasure of the many sacrificed for the pleasure of self. All that thrown away for the filthy little heats of holding a woman's naked buttocks in my hands . . .

The next morning the American lies to Father Clément, saying he forgot to buy the fruit. Later, he seeks out the priest and tells him the truth about his encounter with the woman at the hotel.

Father Clément tells him that this is already known. ("Some of our nicer ladies of the Village saw you entering and leaving the hotel . . . they felt it their Christian duty to come to the Monastery and report their findings to Father Dutfoy. According to them we are harboring a true fugitive from Hades in our midst. Father Dutfoy told them that such tattling was extremely distasteful, and that perhaps God in His great mercy might give us the strength not to be perverted by another man's sins.") He also tells the American something he doesn't know: the woman's name is Madame Vincent and that she is from South Africa.

Father Marie-Ornoux and Dr. Castelar arrive from Paris. Father Clément puts Marie-Ornoux in a nearby cell and asks him to spend his spare time in conferences with the American.

Marie-Ornoux comes to the American's cell to talk with him. (". . . His habit is the white robe of the Dominicans, now faded and poor and patched heavily with unmatching white squares. The face is not young, nor is it old. It has no age . . . He smiles continually . . . and his eyes compel me to look at his face. There is a look of fear, almost animal fear: a cringing as from something unknown, like a dog which has been beaten. I instantly feel that it's because he lives in the awe, in the mystery of his great love of God. His is the most ordinary of faces made living beauty through years of seeking nothing but God's will.")

The American tells him of his past life with Lucette, and of his experience with Madame Vincent. Marie-Ornoux gives him a book to read, tells him not to leave the Monastery at present for any reason, but expresses doubt that he can be of real assistance to him. (". . . According to Father Clément you are a man of many knowledges. You have culture and intelligence, whereas I am only a man of average learning.") He tells the American that Dr. Castelar will be better able to help him. ("As you will discover, he is a man of great learning, and most important, a Christian of the caliber that shames all of us. Like many of the really outstanding Christians this is not obvious at first, for he is very rough in speech and much of his conversation is devoted to un-Christian subjects.")

Marie-Ornoux asks Dr. Castelar to spend time with the American. The doctor is in France with the ambassador from his native country of Guatemala. He tells the American that he has been staying at the Dominican monastery in Paris, while his wife and children visit relatives in the south of France. He explains that he is interested in all the monastic orders and is very curious to learn about the Benedictines; his primary interest, he relates, concerns questions of morality.

With Dr. Castelar at Vespers the American notices that Madame Vincent leaves the services early. ("It must already have started for her then — the cold stares, the shaking of heads, the prudish looks of disapproval. Poor woman, her worship is haunted with caution.")

Later, in Dr. Castelar's cell, the two drink wine the doctor brought from Guatemala. They discuss a Maria Blanchard painting that Dr. Castelar bought in Paris. Night falls as they sit drinking and talking of art, literature, music, women. The ordinary boundaries of formality vanish as they drink glass after glass of the heavy wine.

The bell rings for dinner. They decide to bypass eating.

Dr. Castelar asks what is the American's great passion. When he fails to answer, the doctor berates him: (". . . You have no passion. And without passion you're nothing . . . To what heights can you rise? You like my Blanchard. But you don't love it as I. For it makes me live. You like women. But you don't know how to go to the very heights with a woman. Because there are some things

your culture and your intelligence. Tell you are wrong. You're
good in a small little mean way. And what's worse. You're bad in
a small little mean way . . . You must learn to love God. In peo-
ple like you. Who have everything else. Ability, training, knowl-
edge. An immense love of God. Can make these things come to
life. It's the only thing. That can do that.")

    They drink continually. Both are now drunk.

    Dr. Castelar explains that society destroys moral tendency to-
ward right. ("Mistakes aren't permitted us in our youth. So we
grow into this shell of little moral righteousness without having
made the choice. And it becomes a core deeply imbedded within
us. But the body makes demands that can't be denied. As a result
we satisfy them in mean and little ways. And the hard core of our
beings remains as a confusion . . . In order to free ourselves from
these traits . . . drastic steps must be taken . . . It takes an agent
strong enough to soften this deeply imbedded core which is planted
there for society's good, by society, as a block against the moral
freedom to choose for yourself . . . That's why I tell you to de-
velop this passion for God . . . With God, you merely turn the
spigot; and as love for Him grows, as the passion for Him and only
Him spreads throughout your belly, the wellsprings flow and the
being understands. And it keeps you whole. And it destroys only
the bad within you. It's a narcotic in that once you possess it, your
happiness can never again be without it . . . You have no passion
. . . Forgive. I am drunk. I — I have the passion. I'm an intel-
lectual only by excessive effort. I'm a man of action. And sin.
And love. I've done everything . . . I've committed adultery. I've
seduced other men's wives. I've cheated and lied and stolen. But
with all that . . . I'm less bad than you . . . I'm sorry. I don't
dislike you. But I hate what you are. I hate littleness in a man.
And weakness . . . You must draw yourself up to your height and
pity those little bastards who question your 'good taste' in loving
God . . . Imitate these men here, whom we love and admire. In
them you will find strength. Otherwise you may do valuable re-
search, you may do good for the community, but you'll die without
ever having lived. Come! . . . We'll go. I'll find some food. One
of the cafés. It's early. And we'll begin by destroying you. With
the most decrepit and disgusting whore in Town. You will make

love. To her. I'll watch . . . Ah, forgive me. I'm too drunk. To know what I'm doing. I just wanted to shock you. Out of this spiritual. This spiritual vacuum.")

They decide to retire. The American tells Dr. Castelar that he will dream of Lucette. ("And believe me, Doctor. Never will she be so magnificently . . . uh . . .")

During the night the American awakens, nauseated. ("My body is numb. I am well under the covers in the dark night. It's quiet, deathly quiet. Someone has removed my clothing and put me without pajamas into bed. There are no dreams.")

15 december

A hand shakes me roughly from sleep. Father Marie-Ornoux is bending over me.

"People who get drunk in monasteries," he says without anger, "even under a doctor's supervision, are indeed very low."

"I'm sorry, Father, I —"

"But you are hurt, my son! What is it?"

"My arm, I can't move my arm." I groan with pain. "Serves me right. Are you going to send me away, Father? I'm sick with shame. Never have I sunk so low."

"Of course we are not going to send you away. And if you have never sunk so low, then you are better than most of us." He straightens up. "But I must fetch the doctor. He told me early this morning what you did, taking the blame on himself. You were apparently caught off guard by his wine, my son. He assured me, however, that he looked you over after the fall and could find no broken bones."

"We were so drunk he wouldn't have known it if I'd had a broken neck."

"You are a pretty mess. I shall run get him."

His wooden-soled shoes clump through the door and sound echoingly down the hall. In a moment I hear them returning. He re-enters the room with an expression of concern on his fine face, closing the door softly behind him.

"The doctor is not there," he says. "Are you in very much pain?"

"No, it's all right." I smile wryly. "I'm afraid your doctor's a little rich for my blood."

"You must not judge him by this one incident, my son. When you get to know him better you will see."

I shake my head skeptically. "I don't know. His methods are too advanced for me."

"You do not like him?" asks Marie-Ornoux, walking back to look out the door.

"Yes, I like him all right. But he's not at all what you led me to expect. You said he was a great Christian."

"And he is. I told you that he was rough, that he talked a great deal about un-Christian subjects. It is hard for people like us to understand him, I know."

"It's certainly hard," I concede, "for me to understand him."

"But he is a man of immense worth," the monk goes on. "A true mystic and a great Christian. There are not many like him in the world. When you get to know him you will see that I am right." . . .

"What a night! Did we make much noise?"

"A little, but do not worry about it." He smiles, then chuckles amusedly. "You know, it is quite obvious that the doctor shocked you. He shocked me too, at first. But I hardly think it any credit to us that we *are* shocked."

"What do you mean?"

"I have come to look upon him as almost Biblical: the type of powerful Christian who made the early centuries of Christianity a period unequaled in history. We really have become weak, you know. All of us. We place too much importance upon exterior qualities — upon niceties of language and behavior."

"Probably."

"Look at a man like St. Paul, or St. Augustine even. Either of them would make the doctor look like a lamb. I often wonder just how shocked some of our nice ladies' groups, some of our civilized Christians would be if one of the early saints should walk into their midst. They would never recognize him, I fear! For a man's exterior actually has nothing whatsoever to do with his love of God, with his passion for God. The strength which often makes him seem uncouth is the very strength with which he adores. Such a man is —" He pauses, listening to the sound of footsteps outside. "But I believe that is Dr. Castelar now. Wait a moment, my son."

He walks out into the corridor, leaving the door half open. The voices of the two men, the one so gentle and the other so rough, come back to me clearly; and I think over what the young monk has told me, understanding little.

"He seems to have hurt his arm," I hear Marie-Ornoux say.

"Then I'd better take a look at him," replies the doctor thickly.

I glance up as they enter the room. Marie-Ornoux waits at the door. The doctor comes straight to the bed and, without speaking, reaches down and pulls back the covers. He examines my arm and shoulder in silence, then pushes his fist into my abdomen.

"Everything's all right there," he mutters. "Now let's see about the legs."

"It feels like you've just rearranged my insides, Doctor."

"The legs are all right. Now turn on your stomach."

But the effort is too much. I wince and reach for the pain in my shoulder.

"Well, it's the shoulder all right," the doctor announces regretfully. "But only a little break. The bone may be cracked, but it's not out of place. I'll put your arm in a sling till it gets all right." Looking very sour, he covers me again and reassures Marie-Ornoux that my injuries are only minor.

"Then you really think he is all right?" asks the monk. "I must leave you now, but I shall return this afternoon. It is after eleven. Try to fix him up, Doctor."

We wait until his footsteps sound no longer. The doctor appears very uncomfortable.

"It was unforgivable of me, young man," he begins. "Here, let me check you again. I was terribly worried about you last night. You took a nasty fall."

"I'm really not sorry for it, Doctor. We might have chosen a better place, but otherwise it was worth it. We got a lot of things said last night that might never have come out."

He grins. "Did you sleep all right last night?"

"I guess so."

"No Lucette?"

"No Lucette." I shake my head sadly. "Tell me — was that why you didn't put me in pajamas?"

"Of course not. I wasn't in much better shape than you, young man. Consider yourself lucky to have been put to bed at all. I never wear pajamas myself, and in my stupor I suppose it didn't occur to me that you would either. Here, I'll put that arm in a sling. And as penance for my bad shepherd act, I'll be your nursemaid. Where are your clean clothes? In this bag?"

"Yes, sir — some clean socks and underwear."

I get painfully from the bed, but it's impossible to move my left arm. The doctor makes me stand as he puts my clothes on me. When I am dressed he places the arm in a sling, then stoops to tie my shoelaces. He does this simply, impersonally, efficiently, not speaking except for a soft muttering to himself. I look down at his head with its dust-covered beret.

"Such undistinguished work for a man of your reputation, Doctor."

He laughs, still kneeling, bending his head back to look at my face above. "Not at all, my friend. It's man's greatest health to help the helpless. And the lower the task, the greater its value." He gets to his feet slowly — dark, stocky, impersonal — the doctor again. "Now, let's see. You're dressed. Try unbuttoning your pants. Now take them down — and then the underwear. That's fine. Now see if you can put them back."

"What the devil is this for, Doctor?"

"I want to see if you can manage it. Otherwise I'll have to take you to the bathroom. But no, I think you can make it all right by yourself, can't you?"

"Sure. It's slow but I can do it. I think I could get dressed except for the shoes and socks."

"All right. If you need me you can knock on the wall separating our cells. Now, how do you feel after last night?"

"Pretty well. A little drawn in the back of the neck — slightly washed out — but no headache."

"No nausea? The stomach feels all right?"

"Yes, sir."

"You look bad. Come, we'll go for lunch. After that you can sleep."

"I have to go downstairs first, Doctor. Wait for me here."

Yesterday's rain has frozen in the courtyard. Pools of slick ice. The sky is overcast. I go to the kitchen for a carafe of warm water . . . And then I am alone in the courtyard, alone with my steaming pitcher of warm water. Drops of water spilled on the stone floor of the bathroom cubicle are frozen. Water in the toilet bowl is frozen. Crystals of amber urine, like costume jewelry, dot the scrubbed whiteness of the toilet. They melt, dissolve, flow to other ices in the drain as I waste warm water to be rid of their sight. Steam pours from the drain, gradually dissipating itself.

When I have finished I return the empty but still-warm water carafe to the kitchen, and rejoin the doctor.

He leaves me after lunch, and I close my door. The shame of last night's guilt forces me to begin the little book by Grignon de Montfort which Marie-Ornoux left on my night table. But the day is dark outside, and coldness will not be forgotten. The book reads as if it were written by a child, and I lay it aside. I return to my bed to sleep.

. . . The doctor quietly opens my door a few inches. Drugged by the desire to sleep, I don't move. The door closes imperceptibly, and I hear his voice suggesting to Marie-Ornoux that I'm in no shape for a spiritual conference — that I should be allowed to sleep as long as possible.

. . . I climb from the bed fully clothed. It's not difficult to put on my shoes with one hand, but it's impossible to tie them.

Dr. Castelar is in his cell, reading in a chair by the window with his black beret on the back of his head. He looks up as I enter. "So you're awake? And how does it feel now — the hangover?"

"Oh, it's about gone, Doctor. Will you tie my shoes?" I sit on his bed, looking again at the top of his head as he ties the laces tightly.

Without looking up he murmurs, "You know, I've been thinking about last night. I'm really more sorry than I can say. I always get smart when I drink too much. In any case, now that I know you a little better I'm convinced I was wrong in much of what I said."

"No, you were right, Doctor — and you know it. Don't be dishonest out of kindness to me."

"In spite of everything I said last night, I find you very sympathetic, young man." He sits beside me, pulling gloves of brown knit wool over his stiff fingers.

"Thanks, Doctor. I was just thinking the same thing — wondering if two people as different as we could ever have become friends on the outside. Why is it so easy in here?"

He rises to spread a blanket over our legs. "You know, the relationship of man to man is always a peculiar one," he says slowly, with much concentration. "So many intangibles are involved. Man is basically an entity, complete unto himself, who has become dependent on society. Man needs and seeks woman, and we've learned to think of the couple as an entity. But physically this is not true. Man is afraid of solitude and of darkness, both natural to him. We pity the blind, not because they can't see, but because their blindness makes them live in darkness and as solitaries. And yet we often find that the blind man develops a happiness which astonishes us, because he's been forced to revert to a single unit of himself, to live in a manner more natural to his basic character. Man carries within himself these seeds, which are physical and involuntary; and as he's attracted to woman, he is in his innermost self wary of both woman and man. It's this wariness, this never-complete trusting, that keeps man from knowing friendship. But there's also an undeniable element of physical attraction or repugnance involved. Study the great friendships of men on the outside — that of Montaigne and Etienne de la Boétie, that of Joinville and St. Louis, that of Hallam and Tennyson. In each of these there must have been a total sublimation of the physical to a point where doubts could not possibly exist. These friendships were deeply felt. They were a sort of love above love as we think of it. And they were clear and clean and lucid. Once man is sure, this physical barrier developed in society, by society, for the good of society, is destroyed and he can taste something which few of us ever know. Such a depth of moral union between men is almost nonexistent — and we shy from it. In a monastery, of course, the barrier is destroyed. It's understood that man's interest is purely moral once he enters these gates. There's no possibility of physical ramifications."

"But, Doctor," I interrupt, "you think the physical has that much to do with it? I find that hard to believe. Surely —"

"Wait a moment — let me ask you a question. Have you ever

made what you thought was a close friendship with another man? Then have you been separated from this man for a long period? And have you been disappointed to meet him again, finding he has lost the qualities you once found in him?"

I think this over for a moment. "Yes, I believe I have. But on the other hand, I've been separated from other friends to find them exactly as I remembered."

"That's the difference. A youth is a hero worshiper, and hero worship, no matter how innocent, how spiritual, is a sign of physical immaturity."

I make a movement to protest.

He laughs. "You don't believe that? Let me finish . . . Each of us has known this emotion in his life. I remember as a student I formed what I believed to be a deep and real friendship for an old professor of philosophy. Never was I so happy as in his company; and I was actively jealous of other students who took his time. On my return I revisited the old man, only to find him stripped of his former qualities. Time had changed him and me. I left quickly, so great was my disappointment in finding him ordinary and like other men. That's a characteristic of this youthful, and often adult, hero worship. It mingles its roots in the passions, and it will always disappoint."

"I've had a similar experience, Doctor," I admit. "And yet since the war I've revisited former friends who were in school with me, and the feelings between us were unchanged, as if we had never been separated."

"Oh, yes. But that's a sort of comradeship, developed in adolescence, which has no illusions. It's an entirely different, and much better, thing. And those friends will never change. A good criterion is the emotion of personal jealousy. When that enters the picture there's something wrong, and it can result only in fruitless disillusion. When passion enters, no matter how subtly or inoffensively, any permanency is lost. You see, that's why I say there's a fundamental caution between men on the outside which has no place here. Now, is that point clear?"

"I guess so, Doctor."

Marie-Ornoux stands in the doorway. It is late afternoon. The doctor's cell is dark, and the corridor forms a blackness of background for Marie-Ornoux's patched white robe. He comes in and sits with us on the now-sagging bed, and the doctor explains his theory.

"That is very astute, Doctor," he says when the other has finished. "My opinion would be a much simpler one. Of course that barrier is forcibly destroyed here. But you know, I think it is something else too. On the outside, man's privacy is preciously guarded. It is his business, and only his, how much money he has in the bank, how successful he is, and so forth — and these are things by which he is judged. Man always seeks to make a slightly better impression on his fellow man than his condition merits, and he is afraid to let his private tastes be known. Here, of course, the moment you step inside these walls those outside standards are lost. There are no classes here. How can we, who live in poverty, who seek poverty, be impressed with temporal successes? No, that is lost here. The only standard left is man's goodness or lack of goodness, and lack of goodness is regarded as no more than symptomatic. It is understood that we seek the same thing, and only in the purity of our intentions can these barriers fall and man learn to love his brother as clearly and as quickly as it is accomplished here."

The doctor leans far over toward Marie-Ornoux. "That, Father, is probably the real explanation," he agrees. "Goodness to you is the same as health to a doctor. Badness is your equivalent of illness or disease. When we come here our sins, which are our disease, must be explained as symptoms. And as sick people in a hospital will discuss their maladies, so do we here discuss our moral deficiencies. They are no longer to be hidden, but, rather, exposed to care. Is that it?"

"Yes," answers Marie-Ornoux, "that is essentially it. Our young friend here was worried for fear we should ask him to leave. His behavior, bad as it was, is nothing to be hidden. Sending him away would be to us exactly like turning a patient who developed a fever from one of your hospitals, Doctor. And it is this, certainly, that destroys most of the barriers. For as you two discuss your faith, your life, and your sins and weaknesses, with a view to understanding them impersonally and honestly, you automatically discuss very intimate things. You discuss pride, lust, anger; and you expose yourselves as simply as one of the hospital patients would expose his fevers, his pains, his scars. There are no illusions to be destroyed, nothing that is forbidden. Is that not the real explanation?"

"Yes," mutters the doctor, staring at the floor. "You explain much better than I, Father. It's a combination: destruction of the physical element of doubt between men; destruction of a standard of values which exists on the outside; destruction of man's hesitancy to let himself be seen as he is, naked, spiritually naked, so to speak . . . But I'd better leave you two. I know I'm not supposed to intrude on your spiritual conferences."

Marie-Ornoux rises quickly. "No, Doctor," he protests. "I had only a few moments. I must go now."

He walks out, leaving a thoughtful silence behind him. Dr. Castelar settles back and leans against the wall.

"But to get back to this for a moment," I suggest. "If a man thus exposes his sins to another, isn't respect likely to turn into disgust? I don't feel that way with you. But if another man came here — if he were, say, eaten up with stinginess — I should detest him regardless of the intimacy."

"No, young man, I don't think you would. On the outside you would, but not here. You would detest the fact of stinginess, as I might detest cancer. You never detest that which is seeking to better itself, which is seeking cure. You may despise sin, but never the man who provides the receptacle for sin."

I sigh deeply. "These are days of great change for me, Doctor. I've decided to do exactly what Marie-Ornoux asks — even to try reading that book by Grignon de Montfort about *La Vraie Dévotion à la Sainte Vierge*. Do you know it? It's an impossible thing."

"Of course I know it. And I love it. You can't afford yourself the luxury of such sophistication, young man. It doesn't become you. For these monks, and for me, this is very real. I pray to the Blessed Virgin every night. She's my greatest happiness."

"I can't make you out, Doctor. One moment you're a mystic, in love with something intangible to the point of being poetic, and the next moment you want to get me the worst old whore in the Valley."

"Forget that, won't you? I was wrong. But you see, you're obsessed with chastity to a point I can't understand. Why are you putting such emphasis on this particular sin? Is it worse than pride, or avarice, or anger? I confess I take great pleasure from love. It's impossible to be chaste without the grace of God. I can't do it, and neither can you nor anyone else. I must have it — and I'm so accustomed to it that I can't hope to put myself in the watery-eyed category of those who say they don't need it. God will give purity; but this I can't ask. Do you understand?"

"No. It doesn't make sense, Doctor. I know a man can't do without physical satisfaction. Maybe that's why I'm so determined to overcome my slavery to it. But you're a believer. With God's grace you could hope for purity."

Dr. Castelar, his face pursed with distaste, lights a strong French cigarette. "I know it doesn't make sense," he continues, talking as if to himself. "You with your fine mind seek consistency. But things are rarely consistent. I've prayed for purity. I worship God as a great sinner. I've begged Him to take my sins from me, no matter at what cost. He's the one sure thing I have, and I love Him to a point of self-annihilation. How I long for this! But I'm too little within God to merit it, to be what I so desperately want to be. But I do know His love, I know it; and with that, my friend, nothing is wasted. Nothing on this earth can harm me. That's why I'm happier tying your shoelaces than I would be between the legs of the most beautiful woman in France. That's why I'm a doctor. If I had been chosen by God I'd be happy as a monk or a priest. But I'm an ordinary man with the blood of my country, which is a savage blood. And God has been content to give me this love without the grace to be sinless. He has left me ordinary . . . ordinary . . . I have nothing to be proud of except my love for you and all the 'yous' of this earth. And my love for God. And my hope to give of myself in His name. To help the helpless. To find my place in heaven one day."

His face is immobile. He looks at me, breathing a deep sigh of profound discontent. I say nothing.

"Humph — it's too bad these concrete dreams come so seldom. I — I wonder at my place in the world. I love God like the saints, with all my passion and my happiness. I should have been chosen. But the thing doesn't make sense. It must not be in the measure of our sin, but rather in the measure of our love, that we base our hope. What's wrong with this?"

I can't answer. He goes on speaking.

"No one knows. No one questions God's way. I wait to find out. But my love is no less great. I produce children without actually wanting them, to pay — and to pay strongly — for the love I give my wife. I could prevent this easier than many men. But I can't bring myself to do it. It's against nature, and anything that's against nature is detestable to God. I'm not a good father, not a good husband. But look, my friend, there are other things more important. My family is a convenience, the result of my libido. I married a woman because we slept well together. I married her for physical satisfaction. But my happiness is not there — my happiness is in my sacrifice. I have everything most men want — money, social prestige, success in my field, a good bed — but these things are as dust to me, for I know what I am. I remember that the Indian women with whom I have lain were born as I and will die as I, and that the children they have by me can never be my equals. What makes these changes? I understand nothing of them. No, my only hope is that the chance will come. We stand around and wait for it, wait for the change to take place, for a man to become his pride. My obsession is with death — to die a martyr, a Christian. It's so easy that way. And my only gift, the only moment of this life which is really happy, is when I can make the gift of myself — my knowledge, my education, my comforts — for another in the name of heaven. If I pervert you to drunkenness it means nothing — the passing of a few moments no more bad than good. But if I, who have performed the most delicate of operations in the most modern of hospitals, who know the secrets of human anatomy — if I can give you a bath, or dress you, or do the most menial tasks for you while you are without the use of your arm, then I am happy and my life begins to make a little sense."

The room is dark. Pulling the blankets from his lap, the doctor rises to turn on the lights. The sound of Vespers reaches up through the floor. The glare hurts our eyes. In another voice, a voice brought into reality, he asks, "Do you want to go to Vespers?"

"No, Doctor, I think not. And why don't you turn off the light?"

He presses the switch, again throwing the cell into the half-light of an early winter's evening. Snow, frozen to his window, obscures any view. He crosses the dim light and sits heavily beside me, covering himself again.

"This is a new world here, Doctor," I say to the dark. "One I've never known — more real, more sharply defined. And I envy you your life, my friend. No matter how confusing it seems, it's straightforward and clear — and it makes sense, somehow. Whether or not I ever believe, I'll never forget what you've told me."

There's an embarrassed silence. I stir my numb legs beneath the blanket.

"Ah yes, young man," Dr. Castelar recovers himself. "I wish I had something to offer you to drink, but I'm afraid of the wine for you now. Have one of these terrible cigarettes with me . . . We sit here, you and I, and we're absorbed in each other, seeking warmth, sharing a closeness of body heat; and the interests of each are in the other . . . But you will go far beyond me, my friend — far beyond if you'll open your eyes and forget all the bylaws of life to learn again from new foundations, without the stultifying background of tailored opinions of behavior. People who can go straight to God, and who know what they're doing, become a law unto themselves — much more severe, but also much more real and satisfying. It's for the emotional, the instinctive, the unenlightened men that we must pass rigid social laws, for like the cenobites of early days they would have their cake and eat it too. These people — and each of us is in part such a man — will have a certain amount of concrete virtue, but the virtue is generally lost in the pride of it. The world is full of them. It's they to whom we refer as 'unenlightened' or 'instinctive.' They take responsible positions and are considered people of virtue, because they so consider themselves. But is sin in a man nullified by simply ignoring it, or by replacing it with another? Can there be any virtue in not committing fornication if you masturbate in its place? And how many who stoutly defend their ability to remain chaste out of strength of will, delude themselves by this substitution of the one for the other? If such were chastity it would indeed be a simple matter. That's the great sin of many of us, I think. We have a convenient criterion of morality which is not basically honest. I've seen people show marked admiration for a woman who doesn't smoke, or a man who doesn't drink. It appears to make little difference how stingy, how uncharitable that man is. If he doesn't smoke or drink he is a nice man, one to be admired. And we're even more dishonest when it comes to ourselves. Anyone who has a sense of perspective, and who lives with himself, must know of the countless private actions and thoughts which plague all of us daily — unspeakably pornographic and unnatural for the most part. We have them unless we convince ourselves differently; they are ours. And yet we would condemn them in another. It's like the old swimming pool story. You urinate in the pool without any qualms, and yet you'd report anyone else you caught doing such a thing; you'd have him thrown out of the pool and fined for committing a public nuisance, when you had just finished doing the same thing with perfect impunity yourself." He laughs, looking at my confusion. "So I hit you with that one, eh? Who hasn't done the same thing? It just never occurs to us that anyone else would do it. We're geniuses for excusing ourselves. It's pretty much the same with everything. You say to yourself, as does everyone else, 'Well, it isn't right, but it won't hurt if *I* do it.' You see, that's what I meant by clearing the mind."

I squirm on the cot, and he asks, "What's the matter? Am I talking too much?"

"No, not at all, Doctor." It is dark in the cell. His teeth show white in the anonymity of obscured facial features.

He continues, "I was going to say that one of the primary values of confession is that we confess simply to our Father in charge, with the firm instruction never to offer mitigating circumstances, never to place the blame on another's shoulders. This is very healthful in making us see our part in the system of guilts. You must learn to think this way. Either you do a thing or you don't, but if you do, then accept the fact without excuse. A great step forward which is always made in these monasteries is the realization that we ourselves are so inadequate, it would be a presumption to judge another. It's a clarity of perception more than anything else, I think, that you get here. These men have reached a point of such scrupulous purging of every fleck of sin, that they regard their souls with microscopic consciences; and since they strive for a perfection which is above the human, their humility must forever grow as they see that the ideal is always far beyond their potentiality for realizing it. They don't occupy themselves with the little goodness they've accomplished, but instead with the deficiencies that remain to be cleared up. That's why humility is one of the keystones of the monastic life and why pride is one of the most detestable of sins; for pride implies a lack of basic honesty, a blindness of the spirit. It shouldn't exist in any man, and when it does it should be stamped out at all costs."

I ask, "Do you really think pride is the worst of all sins?"

"Yes, I do. It destroys the soul more surely than any other sin, for it's an intangible, and those who have it are rarely conscious of its existence within them. You know when you commit the others; you know when you sleep with a woman, or when you become angry, or envious, or stingy. But pride blinds you not only to itself, but to all other sins as well. What's the most despicable person you know? Why, it's the man who can never say simply, 'No, thank you, I don't care for a drink,' but instead declares with a flush of superiority, "no, thank you, I don't drink," or, 'I don't fool with women,' or, 'I don't smoke.' He's a paragon of virtue who's reduced to a nothing by the moral castration of pride — pride in the ability he has to stand alone and above poor bastards like us. That same man is also 'good.' He's good because on page four of his little spiritual codex it says that 'goodness' must make up so much of his life. He'll help anyone in his class, and give an occasional basket to the poor but 'deserving' — always deserving — people of his community. And he'll return home to his good wife and say, 'Ah, but it makes a man feel good to help others.' But if you're drunk, or if you're some poor beggar who's got himself rolled by a whore, then he won't soil his hands on you, he won't weep or waste a prayer on you. He'll despise you, despise whoredom and drink, and forget his own inadmissible fevers of the past. As long as that pride exists he can't love God, he can't be in love with God abjectly and profoundly. No, he gives God a firm handclasp and goes on not doing the things that are done. He's happy in a mean way, for he denies what's always there."

"I think it goes beyond that, Doctor," I object. "You've painted a true picture of me. I'm exactly like that. But it's simply that such things don't enter the heads of people with backgrounds like mine."

"I paint a true picture of myself too, my friend. It isn't pretty, is it? But we're striving for something so sublime that it takes a clear view. No man can love God who despises the least of his own. When we can learn to see that this pariah, or that beggar, is of our clay, and is better than many of us, then we've taken a long step forward in the conquering of pride . . ." He stirs on the cot and gets slowly to his feet. "But I've talked too much. It's easy to talk with you. Come, my feet are frozen. Let's go to dinner."

This, then, is the man who Marie-Ornoux called one of the great living Christians. Only now do I begin to understand . . .

Long talks with Marie-Ornoux. The Dominican tells the American of his past life; he had been a man possessed with overwhelming sensual desires until he was finally converted. He tells him of his forthcoming mission of going into the desert countries to live among non-Christians, to follow in the footsteps of the martyred Father Charles de Foucauld.

Dr. Castelar later informs him that Marie-Ornoux suffers from tuberculosis of the bone, a condition that causes him to limp. ("It's a terribly painful secondary form of the disease — and very dangerous. Yet he wants to leave the relative safety of his monastery for a hazardous life in the desert. But they feel they can't clip his wings by making him stay.") The doctor says that Marie-Ornoux is certain to die of the disease within a few years.

The American profits much from the conferences with Marie-Ornoux and Dr. Castelar, realizing that he must learn to accept those things which can be accepted, and discard the rest. He seeks to find peace in these new thoughts, in these new understandings. But his mind returns to Paris and to the memory of Lucette.

He tells Dr. Castelar of his current thoughts. He attempts to explain that he would rather be in the Monastery at this time than in Paris in bed with Lucette. That he believes he is finally gaining ground. Dr. Castelar accuses him of hypocrisy and a heated argument ensues. Engulfed with rage and humiliation, he tries to pray during morning Mass. ("For the first time in my life I really need to pray.")

Both the American and Dr. Castelar attempt to bring about a friendly reconciliation after Mass. A level of comradeship is reached again, but the original rapport between them has been strained.

Marie-Ornoux and Dr. Castelar leave for Paris, the first leg of a journey that will take the Dominican to Jerusalem and the desert countries.

24 december

Yesterday work was resumed as usual. After dressing me for the last time, Dr. Castelar left with Father Marie-Ornoux. Tonight they will celebrate Christmas in Paris.

Many visitors have made the pilgrimage to the Village for Christmas Eve services at our Monastery. Throughout the Valley there's a lightness, a hurrying of movement, as last-minute preparations are made. In the Monastery, monks move about sweeping floors, polishing woodwork, pouring new wax for candles. I am impressed by the restraint of Christmas here, a Christmas without the carols and the lighted trees. A Christmas of heavy clothing, of good food long hoarded, of overcast skies, of calm. Isolated in this Valley, far from other Christmases, the spirit of the season is no less contagious. Men become good — all men become good this day — and there's a greater nobility of heartbeat.

Alone in the paleography room, I lose myself in work. My feet are wet and frozen in my shoes. There are no presents, no cards, no decorations, no smells of pies and cakes and cooked meats. Outside, the world moves in its greenery, in its shaking of hands, in the happy redness of its cheeks. In this room only my pen moves, scratching against damp paper. I recall other Christmases spent alone, when I walked aimlessly in search of exhaustion that would let me sleep. When I wept at the sound of a Christmas carol. When the day was an unbearable separation from those I love. Here it's not like that. I am alone, but alone among solitaries; and there is a deep, serene joy in looking on while others prepare. In hearing cries in the street. In knowing that below, the chapel is being swept and dusted and polished. In the certainty that all men carry a charity and a generosity in their hearts these last hours before Christmas, having somehow cast aside meanness and cynicism and hatred.

. . . My Christmas present is in my cell. They have changed my bed, putting on freshly laundered linens that have been turned back from the pillow ready for sleep. In this maelstrom of activity someone has changed my bedclothes, and it's a finer gift than I ever got.

On the night table is a new card containing the schedule of Christmas services. Dinner is earlier tonight, it informs me, so that the dishes may be washed in time for all to attend Christmas Eve High Mass at nine o'clock. "At 8:45 you should go to the kitchen for a hot drink": this is scribbled on the schedule in Father Clément's hand. Mass will last from nine P.M. till three A.M., after which we may sleep until the bell at five-thirty. At six a morning High Mass will be celebrated, and another at ten. The card also suggests that since we'll get no more than a maximum of two and a half hours' sleep, we nap for an hour after the noon meal.

I try to sleep, but in mid-afternoon it's impossible. Though there's no noise, no sign of activity, the activity is there and it is felt. Finding the Father Prior, I ask him if I can't help by carrying water. He reminds me of my injured shoulder, but I insist I can make twice as many trips. All afternoon I carry bucketfuls from the well into the kitchen, and, when they have been heated, upstairs to the cells so that the monks may wash and shave before tonight's celebration.

Supper, eaten hurriedly, is solid and satisfying — soup, extra bread, and a thick mush of potatoes, beans and meat broth. We swallow great mouthfuls, anxious to eat as much as possible before Father Abbot's mallet calls us to a halt.

At eight-forty-five I return to the kitchen for the hot drink. I find several other laymen there who have been invited to share in this little festivity. The drink, served in large cups, is the same as we have for breakfast. We stand about sipping the warming liquid, until one by one we put down the cups and go to take our places in the already crowded chapel.

Darkness outside, and rough-frozen snows. But the chapel is well lighted. Two monks serve as ushers. They place me far to the front, near the altar rail.

Noises of waiting for Mass to begin: whisperings, the blowing of noses into handkerchiefs, deep coughings reverberating like wind in the trees. Low, level sounds of waiting. A crowd of overcoats and

gloves and scarves and galoshes. We sit leafing through the order
of service, overcoated shoulder pressed against overcoated shoulder. Eyes are different, resting clear and calm. In the eyes of those
who believe, is a mixture of tenderness and excitement that erases
nineteen hundred and more years. They're not celebrating an anni-
versary but participating in the original.

From far to the back comes a first pedal tone of the organ, and
movements die to the stillness of expectancy. Other tones sound in
quiet beginnings, with a warmth of harmony closely knit. It is the
calm and radiant *Magnificat* of Frescobaldi. No trumpetlike an-
nouncements, no blasting of Christ's birth, no loud choruses of jubilation; but a serene, infinitely tender organ prelude telling emotions
to hush, to accept, to know a joy of humility more akin to tears
than to shouting. A fine little rhythm moves tones into the treble
flute register. Joy becomes an inner intoxication, breaking through
to lift the spirit high within the body, creating an adoration from
mood; and the emotion of adoration is prepared for its concrete
fulfillment in the beginnings of a chanted Introit. The emotion was
created in a vacuum by pure sound combinations. Now it is given
spirit and meaning with the opening words rising slowly, almost
whispered, carrying upward to tenderness for the Child; words
chanted in exquisite inner ravishment by black-robed monks swaying with the unisonal rhythm: *"Dominus dixit ad me: Filius meus
es tu . . ."* Soaring bodiless sound permeating the chapel, filling
our beings: "The Lord said to me: Thou art my Son . . ."

Candles and smoke, and incense floating up like smoke, gently
and inevitably lift man to worship, lift him above worship to a
plane beyond and within: a plane of intimacy and inner movements
of the soul ascending high inside the throat. Unbearable poignancy
of restrained joy, for in such restraint there is no horizon. Its dimensions begin and end in the vastness of silence, and its light is the
Source of all light.

Madame Renée, kneeling across the aisle, gives me a warm smile
of fine-looking teeth. Madame Vincent is lost behind closed eyelids. Nearby, Madame la Marquise de la Roche kneels with head
deeply bowed. Salesky, whose knees are not so ardent as his capil-
laries, rises to sit hunched forward beside his wife. The Chevissiers,
more humble, are placed far to the back. The beautiful Mexican

girl leans forward, her black shawl falling across her face. They are all here, the people who tomorrow will tear at one another again.

A delicate *"Alleluia, alleluia"* floats through the chapel. More candles are lighted. Seated in a fringed and canopied chair at the side, Father Abbot asperses his monks. And Mass goes on and on, unchanging in texture, slow in movement. Vestments of white and black mingle with robes in celebrating with infinite grace the loveliness of Christmas.

It moves timeless until the end. The chanted *"Ite, missa est"* empties the chapel — too soon. It is almost three A.M. on Christmas Day. We leave the chapel. We walk in the snow outside, not speaking, not shaking hands, not wishing to destroy our inner tendernesses. The night is black and still and frosted, with clean, unmoving air. I walk past the chapel, where lights from stained-glass windows reflect across the snow in long, inverted Gothic patterns, broken here and there by a frozen bush. There are no stars.

Without undressing I crawl into bed. I am gripped by a momentary violence of trembling as the covers warm. We sleep like angels this night. The chants, the cold, the incense, the reverberant night of Christ's birth — calm, filled with adoration — become sleep's dimension. We sleep alone, surrounded by walls, trembling in our beds. The sleep is pure and the night holy and the world better than before. We sleep heavily sprawling, faces buried in pillows. We sleep well, for our sleep is its own Christmas Night.

2 5 december

But in a moment, when night breathing becomes its heaviest and rest the sweetest-smelling before dawn, walls and floor and bed vibrate with the great bells calling us back, beating in our ears, surrounding and overwhelming us. We wake, staggering from sleep, and we go to early Mass.

Masses throughout the morning. Masses and emotions and growing fatigue. And a good meal at noon: oysters, lentils, a dry cake.

Christmas Day is its anticlimax. Following the celebration there is a Sunday quietness of afternoon, of great weariness and of welcome rest, when too much food finds its digestion in sleep. I sleep all afternoon. And tonight, at Vespers and Compline, we become as we were — simple, skeletal, clear.

Tomorrow will be yesterday. The fete is over.

We feel the loss. We seek to prolong the heights of hours gone until another year. But we sleep again as always, surrounded by the Great Silence. And we are glad, in a way, to be back — to be back in our lives.

BOOK 2 — THE DEVIL WITHOUT

⟶

The first of January. The American moves into his rented villa in the Village. But his fears of falling into the old evils again haunt him.

Father Clément assures him that nothing will be changed — except that he will have the comforts of a warm house. He accepts this explanation, and the Father's repeated cautions that he must be especially careful to guard himself against the petty local affairs in the Village, with abundant self-doubts. Father Clément promises that he can return, his health permitting, whenever he feels the need.

It is arranged that the Village postman will help the American dress until his health permits him to do it himself. He becomes friends with the postman (they share some wine together), only to be admonished later by Madame Renée about the social laws of the Village. ("I know you don't realize it, but everything you do in the Valley is known. You're a foreigner and the center of much talk . . . But, Monsieur, people of your station never appear in public with their postman . . . You see, you're more or less on trial here, as it were. The better people are certainly on your side,

*but this sort of thing is an indelicacy which can give you trouble
. . . They can make it impossible for you to live in the Village.")*

*He makes it clear to Madame Renée that he doesn't give a damn
about dictated modes of behavior. But, after it becomes apparent
that he will have to halfheartedly conform to these local prejudices
or relinquish Madame Renée's friendship and table, he promises to
conduct his affairs more discreetly.*

*Madame Renée, living up to her own assertions, is indeed a fine
cook, and her table is abundant with foods he had almost forgotten
existed. He feels a closeness to the enigmatic lady. ("I feel sorry
for this woman so helpful, and in a way so pathetic. She who has
known plenty is reduced to a cheap black dress and a black beret.
She smiles easily and laughs often, as if she were as delighted as I
with the arrangement. I feel that we shall be good friends, good
comrades.")*

*To conserve wood, she arranges for a wood stove to be installed
in his fireplace. Saying that her house is small, she seeks and receives permission from him to store potatoes and other staples in his
cellar. ("I can come and go without disturbing you.") Her attitude tends toward the maternal. ("Don't thank me, Monsieur. Both
my sons are gone from me. Caring for you will give an old woman
a new interest in life.") He wonders how she manages to obtain
such fine foods — and asks if she buys it on the black market. Her
answer is elusive.*

*Later, walking to the Monastery, he encounters Madame Vin-
cent. He tells her about the villa and asks her to come to him late
at night. She refuses. ("It's hard for me to live in this* pension.
*They don't approve of me in the Valley, you know . . . They all
agree that we did what we did in Town . . . I am sorry. You're
very sympathetic, and as you say, they're all cold to us. Your
Madame Renée would have me chased from the Valley. And besides, I don't want such a thing to happen to me again.")*

*At dinner that night, Madame Renée again counsels him. (". . .
you were seen with Madame Vincent in the street this afternoon.
She's not very well thought of here. She's considered a woman of*

rather easy morals. It does you no good to be seen with her. She's little more than a strumpet, and we know what to do with strumpets in our Valley . . . But please don't see her again. I can't receive you in my house if you continue to show such open indiscretion.")

He tells Madame Renée that he has been the cause of the whole affair — that Madame Vincent is in no way to blame. He admits that he propositioned Madame Vincent earlier that day. Madame Renée refuses to listen, all the while continuing to lambast Madame Vincent and women of easy virtue.

The conversation turns to the Monastery. Madame Renée refers to the Father Abbot as an uncouth brute, going on to explain that he had refused to accept her son, Michel, into the Monastery. He wonders about Madame Renée as she rages on and on. ("Something about this good woman irritates me. Is it her superiority of manner? Her lordly derision of local people? Her tendency to find meanness in everyone we discuss? Only toward me does she appear genuinely kind and tolerant.")

Madame Renée arranges for a young girl named Germaine to do his housework and laundry. She tells him that he reminds her a great deal of her dead son, about whom she talks incessantly. She insists he read Jean-Julien's war diary — which had been sent to her after his plane crashed. The diary is disappointing, the furtive attempts of a confused and troubled person to explain and justify his existence.

A few days later, Father Sauvac informs him that Madame Renée is lying to the Villagers. ("Madame Renée has put herself in the position of a protectress and made out your relationship to be something it's not. And I know once the lie is started, she'll do anything to make certain the truth's never revealed. It's not a healthy thing, and it will lead to disaster unless you stop it right now . . . Madame Renée is holding you up as something you have no desire to be, and when the time comes she'll show you off like a performing animal. Yet basically she's a good woman. You were simply her chance to lord it over the others, and she's taken it. But I do hope you'll be kind to her.")

Father Sauvac also tells him that Madame Renée is ripe for a sexual misadventure, and instructs him to be on guard against this.

The priest asks his permission to allow the elderly Villagers to warm themselves at his fire during the day when he is working at the Monastery. Knowing that Madame Renée would be opposed to such an arrangement, they telephone the Countess for full authorization and receive it.

As a guest for dinner that night, Madame Renée has invited one of her friends, Mademoiselle Marthe, an octogenarian spinster who at one time had held a chair in literature in the University of Nantes. A great humanist, Mademoiselle Marthe helps to dissolve the crusts of disgusts that the American has been struggling under since his conversation with Father Sauvac. He tells the two women of his decision to let the Villagers enjoy his fire. Mademoiselle Marthe is overjoyed with his spirit of generosity; Madame Renée explodes with derision.

Throughout the evening, he has exchanged meaningful glances with a beautiful young girl, whom he supposes is Madame Renée's maid. He looks again at the blond girl named Christianne in an attempt to momentarily remove himself from the tension that has settled over the dinner table. After a prolonged time, Madame Renée, in a conniving effort to be the gracious hostess, admits that the idea might work, that some good might be accomplished by letting the poor huddle at the heat.

The moment that Mademoiselle Marthe leaves, Madame Renée pounces again. She tells him that she has purposely lied to the Villagers about having enjoyed a long association with his family in America — and that his family had requested that he take his meals with her. She said she did this to insulate him against a growing hostility from the Villagers, a resentment based on two things: the stories that he had let the Petite Chevissier die, and his affair with Madame Vincent.

He partly understands her reasoning and actions, but tells her that he must be allowed to make his own decisions, choose his own friends, and direct his own course. He tells her he is not her son and that any ideas bordering toward that end must be halted.

She insists repeatedly that her actions have all been for his welfare, that everything has been carefully planned with him in mind. Back and forth, a verbal seesaw. He believes her; he doubts and disbelieves. He feels sorry for her; loathes her.

He learns to gear his conversations to placate her moods. ("We do have our understandings, our small debilitating heats; for I know that if she's angry or hurt I have only to share another confidence, or make another suggestive remark, and she'll laugh with sweetly indulgent disapproval.")

He attempts to pray more, but prayer remains tentative. Madame Renée carries wood and provides soap and helps the Villagers with their baths in the villa. The temperature stays around zero outside, and the Villagers have enthusiastically accepted his hospitality.

Madame Renée starts another argument. This time she tells him that Father Clément had been guilty of immorality with a nun who formerly was stationed in the Valley. When he defends the priest, she tries to wing her way out of the stalemate by telling him that he is nervous because he has been too long without a girl. ("And that's what's wrong with you tonight — you need a girl, don't you? . . . I wish I could help you . . . If it's so bad, why don't you send for Lucette? . . . I'll make sure no one knows. You see, I'm willing to debase myself to make you happy. I'm a terrible woman.")

Changing the subject, she tells him of the news she has heard about Salesky's mistress — supposedly she is pregnant. Madame Rouen, so Madame Renée relates, had become involved with Salesky and bore him two children while her husband was a prisoner of war. When her husband returned and learned what had happened, he deserted her. Madame Renée seemingly enjoys the woman's misfortune. The American accuses her and the other ladies of the Village of being obsessed with such matters.

Madame Renée confesses that her late husband had been married when she met him. When she became pregnant, he divorced his wife and married her. Madame Renée's family never forgave her for having to marry below her social class. Her mother had disinherited her.

Madame Renée receives word that Michel is leaving his monastery, despite the fact he has taken his final vows. The banks are closed when the message arrives, so she borrows money from the American for the trip to see her son. If she can't convince him to return to the monastery, she laments, she will have to help him find a place to live in Paris; certainly he can't return home and shroud her with this disgrace. She swears the American to secrecy about the matter. They decide she will leave at once, agreeing that he will take his meals at the Monastery for a week until she returns.

Mother Nourrie arrives to sit at the fire. She relates that her daughter, Germaine, has been fired by Madame Renée. ("Despite her grief Madame Renée hasn't overlooked a chance to dominate my life. But it was a ridiculous childish attempt made in apparent desperation. Otherwise she must have known I'd discover it immediately.") He tells Mother Nourrie that he knew nothing of this and that he wants Germaine to continue in his employ.

Later, after services at the Monastery, he encounters Madame Vincent. She tells him the Village ladies are forcing her and Mademoiselle de Castro to leave, by denying them quarters and food. She says she doubly regrets this because she feels she is making progress in her spiritual sessions with Father Clément.

The next day, Jacques de la Roche tells the American that the Chevissier family, who were making a good profit from their farm a few months back, are penniless and in debt. After a meeting with the Chevissiers the American understands what is happening. Madame Renée has been blackmailing them, taking all the food she wanted — even to the point of selling some of it to her friends — and they have been afraid to stand up to her for fear she will tell the truth about their child's baptism. They decide her bluff will be called the next time she demands free goods — after all it was she who illegally baptized the dead girl. If there is shame and disgrace to be meted out, Madame Renée will surely get her fair share of it.

Father Sauvac asks the American to help drive Madame Rouen out of the Village. Everyone should boycott her store, the priest insists. He says that the Village has tolerated her two illegitimate children — mainly out of pity for the poor wench — but that this time she has gone entirely too far. The American listens with unbelieving ears.

15 january

The remarkable goodness of Christians!

The targets of their virtuousness: Madame Vincent because she seduced me, and Mademoiselle de Castro because she is Madame Vincent's friend. They whitewash me and despise Madame Vincent because they are Christians with a profound sense of decency. And this morning they applaud justice and feel relieved, for their targets walk to Town to take a train somewhere.

You must pass the test here; you must elevate yourself to their high moral plane or they force you to seek your own level elsewhere. "If they can't respect our ways we know what to do," they say, and smile.

Two women walk in the snow-covered road, carrying heavy suitcases. And the air of our Village becomes perceptibly less tainted. The leaders of society and the humbler women of equal spotlessness feel deep satisfaction that, in seeing justice done, they have returned the rightful atmosphere of halcyon peace into the Valley.

Two women walk in the snow-covered road, carrying heavy suitcases. And I remain behind by my comfortable fire.

The American begins a new course in natural, ecclesiastical, Christian, and canon law. The studies are interrupted when he develops a new fever. Days of sickness and dreams of carnality. His strength gradually returns and he resumes his work, his happiness reduced only by the thought of Madame Renée's impending return.

21 january

I slept little last night; thoughts danced until dawn. Now at the Monastery I wait in Father Clément's cell, wait for Mass to begin. From the maze of our conversation comes my admission of the emotions which occupy me at night. Father Clément listens attentively, nodding for me to continue.

"The strange thing about it," I say slowly, "is that this desire seems almost — well, almost detached. It's sort of disembodied. I was wondering if maybe it couldn't be something important? If it couldn't be — ?"

"Yes, go on," he urges.

"Well, if it couldn't be God's way of drawing me to Him?"

Father Clément looks at me quizzically, half-frowning. "I do not know, my son," he says finally. "How can you arrive at such a conclusion as that? It does not look to me as if you were being drawn to God at all, but rather to something much more immediate in your mind — to sensuality. You must not let yourself become confused: nothing can be further from God than the feelings you describe to me. If you could love God with this same passion you would know it. You would want only to do His bidding. You would thrust such carnal thoughts away from you by force. And yet you embrace them, seeming to take health from them."

After a moment's hesitation I say, "Perhaps I don't make myself clear, Father — but for the first time since I've known you I think you misunderstand what I'm trying to tell you. Is it fair to disagree with your spiritual father?"

He smiles at me. "By all means. You disobey my orders, you do not rest properly, you are in a state of the most detestable sin, you do not study with any discipline — disagreeing with me should be the next logical step."

"I'm sorry, Father — I guess these feelings I have destroy discipline. They're diabolic, but I'm sure they're not the devil. There's something clean about them."

"Perhaps, my child," he says patiently. "But you may be deluding yourself. You present a most difficult case. What am I to do with you?"

"Tell me once more," I murmur contritely, "what you want me to do. I'll do it this time — I promise."

"You must try to live on a smaller scale until you learn more, until you can channel this passion into something a little less dangerous."

First bells sound for Mass. Father Clément stirs himself, and I rise to my feet.

"Now listen, my child," he says harshly, "you will — and this is an order to be obeyed — you will eat properly, you will sleep from midnight till eight in the morning, and most important of all, you will accept Madame Renée as a lesson in humility. You can help this poor unsympathetic woman. And one thing more — you will say a simple prayer every day. And you will try to keep these physical outbursts at a minimum."

. . . As I find a pew in the chapel I think of how balanced his life is, how clear in every conception. And a change in my feelings for Madame Renée, promised. My prayer, which will have little meaning, must be for her.

I leap with surprise at the first brilliant organ tunes above, ringing clear throughout the chapel: the *Prelude in E flat* of Bach. I forget everything, inundated to the edge of tears by the introspective tenderness of the opening measures.

It's hard to pray. I pray resentfully for Madame Renée, forcing myself till that part of my prayer is ended and the Mass takes me with it, praying for me easily. And this time every cell of my being echoes the texts.

Time stops. Then for a moment I'm aware that from somewhere within me I am giving words volition, words that find voice in the mouths of these monks. But they come from me: *"Sanctus, Sanctus, Sanctus . . ."* And later, with how much more affection, how much more warmth, the words to the Blessed Virgin from the dregs of this same inner darkness — the light of one phrase: *"Dei Genitrix, intercede pro nobis."* And with this melody, fearfully written by some poor one better than I, in the anguish of his love — humble notes on paper pleading from the soul's profoundest recesses — the Virgin Mary becomes startling reality for the time of a breath. We suddenly feel it all about, this warmth, this permeating presence. She has this instant heard something spoken to her centuries ago. Voices chanting tendernesses repeat, *"Dei Genitrix, intercede pro nobis."* And somehow, by some inner chemistry, by some brief changing of matter into the nothingness of delight, physiologically, imperceptibly, inexplicably, this phrase has been touched. The caress offered to closed eyelids of concentration has been touched by something ethereal. In the intense darkness of prayer I seek her whose name is on my lips . . . we become slowly united.

Squares mist milkily, and from the stillness and the dark the curve mounts immutably rhythmic, in ever-mounting intensity. A new gathering of momentum. And through the darkness an occasional glimpse of concentrated white. Now it begins to grow, this strangeness, turning over and over. Slowly, slowly, turning steadily, and the rhythm follows ever growing. And now from the very bottom of a faraway numbness is the quivering beginning of trembling. It's unbearable. The numbness is punctured. Momentum gathers. And the long sigh, unheard, pouring forth from the edges of consummation. From a distance, far within, curving swiftly now, a fast sighing swaying motion curling over and above and around. Beating, beating against the drum of the being, pounding louder and louder till there can be no more loudness, but increasing steadily into the very pulse of the blood. And now before the eyes, the before-hinted, now-brilliant flashing white, growing and expanding to break spattering against eyelids. And from without, a fog of ever-thickening intensity, sparkling and harsh to imagined sight. Simultaneous welling-up of the heaving exploding brilliance, and the beating, now-pounding rhythm piling sound and muffled obscenity, ever expanding above and around, turning faster and faster above the moaned "No! No!" Tightening of the heartbeat, drawing-up of the ribbon. Ecstatic point between life and death when all becomes hermetic and rigid. The pause in space without pausing in movement. The waiting without breathing. The muffled upward surge of the entire being to the crest of the wave, to the very top. Up and up, soaring high onto the peak of noise and heat. The whirling gyrating splash of warning to the mind. Louder now into the head and the brain. Upheaved violence of the belly. This is the flashing of the stars, the cleansing burning of the insides into fervent ash. And the taste of blood grows stronger on the rigid tongue. Finally the broad expansiveness of union, of man's warmness without pain. Sounds descend thinner, slower, draining away to sighing quiet. And the felt pulse of the rhythm faints away to enveloping blackness. The slow easy downhill slide with a final unheard catching of the breath, leading onward and downward until the curve slows to stop against the dark. And down, down again slantingly, quietly to a depth beneath the seas. Beyond movement to stillness —

Startled. Startled into a hard convulsive contraction of muscles. A hand on my shoulder and a raucous imperious voice: "Well, Monsieur, are you sufficiently frozen?"

Trembling, without rising, I mutter, "Yes, Madame."

It's Madame Marceaux, great, sacred lady oblate. She talks

loudly for a moment then leaves me still kneeling, miserable and bewildered. She hasn't felt what the rest of us have felt. Disappointment is on the faces of those about me. All of us sense that she's had the greatest possible presumption, that in reality she has, with her hideous loud voice and merciless calling-to-mind of the cold, chased the intangible whisper away from us. Now there's nothing to do but leave.

Standing in the door of the gatehouse, Father Dutfoy sees us walk out. He motions me to him, smiling questioningly. I explain what has happened.

His red face becomes serious, clouded. "It is a disgusting shame, my son. To be visited by a sensitive grace may occur only once in a lifetime, and to have it interrupted in such a vicious manner — it is a great shock to you, is it not?"

"Yes, it is. I don't know what happened exactly, Father," I tell him hesitantly, "but I feel —"

"I know. It is indeed a shock. Come, we will go back into the chapel and you must stay there till it has returned you to peace. That is the only way to undo the harm."

He enters first, dipping his fingers in holy water and touching my outstretched fingers with his. We kneel side by side for a long time. He prays silently. I say and think nothing . . . Father Dutfoy leaves without speaking, without looking at me. The chapel is dark now, heavily shadowed and obscure before noon, and I know that snow must again be falling outside. I kneel here watching the flickering altar lamp until the silence, the emptiness of spaces replace trembling with calm. And when I leave it's because the bells call us to lunch. I'm sorry to leave, finding it difficult to rise to my feet, to force myself away from this magical quiet. The breath, cooling in the dark air of the chapel, remains . . . I'm no longer alone, and the chapel isn't empty.

In the refectory a burdening exhaustion possesses me. Now I want only sleep — but many hours remain before sleep may be had. Lessons all afternoon.

At last, rapturously chanted Vespers — and soon there'll be rest. It remains, the spell. Past insomnias dissolve, become hushed. Pressures are removed. Only sleep — only the magic of sleep after such feelings, after such profound breathings . . .

The American walks through the Village on his way home. Stopping at a store, he learns that Madame Renée has returned. He remembers Father Clément's order. ("You will accept Madame Renée as a lesson in humility . . . You can help this poor unsympathetic woman.") But the experience he has just undergone at the Monastery makes the admonition unneeded at this time. He is happy that she is home and tells her so. She informs him that Michel is lost, but that he has hopes of a job.

Some small quarrels arise, but are quickly put down. He tells her that Madame Vincent has been driven from the Village. Madame Renée's answer of regret seems almost genuine. (". . . I'm very sorry. I know how fond you are of her, and I've grown to think of her rather sympathetically myself. I can understand such a woman, Monsieur. I can understand how she might fall with a man like you.")

She turns her tempers to Michel, declaring that he is a weakling who forsook God, who brought shame on her and their name and position in the Village. She tries to thrust Michel from her life, only to fail each time. She worries that the monks at the Monastery will find out. The American assures her that it is of little importance, for they would be certain to learn of it sooner or later. He tells her that her son has done the right thing under the circumstances — that he realized his religious vocation was false and corrected it by the drastic change of returning to the outside world.

A few days later Madame Renée invites Mademoiselle Marthe and a young woman from the City, Marguerite Désormière, an old family friend, to dinner. To the discomfort of the two older women (although Mademoiselle Marthe is secretly amused by it) the American and Marguerite flirt blatantly with each other. Madame Renée, realizing her error in inviting the young woman, attempts to dominate the conversation. She vies with Marguerite for his attention.

After the agonizing evening Marguerite, who had been invited to stay overnight, decides to return to the City. Against Madame Renée's protests, the American insists on walking her to the train. On the way they encounter Salesky. He tells Salesky to drive

slowly through the dark roads of the Valley until time for Mar-
guerite's train to leave. He seduces her on the back seat of the
taxicab.

28 january

A sudden feeling of great relief that it's Sunday. There'll be no
classes at the Monastery, no townspeople to come in for the fire,
and above all, no necessity of facing Father Clément today. Turning off my alarm I go back to sleep. I sleep until a timid knocking
at my door recalls me from this dreamless rest.

"Yes, who is it?"

"Monsieur, are you all right?"

"Yes, Madame Renée. Did you want something?"

"Did you intend not having lunch today? It's one o'clock."

"My Lord, I've slept the clock around. I'll be there in fifteen minutes."

Hurrying into my clothes, I splash water on my face, straighten
the bed, and walk across the deep, hard-topped snow to Madame
Renée's little cottage. It is clean and warm, with the impersonal
feeling of Sunday. The table is set with the whitest of linen cloths.
Savory smells arouse sleep-laden senses — a touch of garlic, meat
being cooked in a buttered skillet, dampened by the more delicate
perfume of red wine in our glasses.

We feel comfortable together. Madame Renée gives me a holi-
day from nagging. She carefully steers our conversation from dangerous fields. She is charming, and the day is charming and bright.

"There's something happy about a day like this," observes Madame Renée as we relax with our demitasses.

"Yes, there is. It's really perfect."

"And I fixed an extra pot of coffee for you. You can take it back
with you and enjoy something good and warming. Do you have
much work to do this afternoon?"

"So much I can't stand to think of it. And the day's so beautiful
it seems a shame to stay indoors. What are you going to do?"

"Think I'll walk to the farm for butter and eggs. Like to come
along?"

"I'd better not. After sleeping all morning I've got to prepare my lessons this afternoon."

"I know how tiresome it must be," Madame Renée sympathizes, "to stay cooped up all day. Why don't you run on now and do whatever you feel you must, and then come back for tea and the concert about four?"

"Sounds like a fine idea, Madame — believe I'll do that. I feel more like working now than I will later, anyway."

"Good, I'll fix you a wonderful tea — lots of tasty things — and we'll spend a nice afternoon. Run along now . . . Oh, and will you take this letter from Michel? It came this morning. It concerns you more than it does me. Whatever you decide will be agreeable with me. Personally I think he rather has a nerve. But you must remember he knows nothing of the ways of the world — he asks you to do for him only what he'd do for you if the situation were reversed."

In my room I light the fire and open the blinds to early Sunday afternoon . . . Desk and work forbid, and I take Michel's letter near the window.

Dearest Mama,

You see, my luck is good, and God still has a soft spot in his heart for me, for I have, just yesterday, worked the first day in my new job. No one knows that I have been a monk.

But, to tell you the details, I shall be paid 17,000 francs a month, and my work is designing advertising for an airplane company. I know you will be disappointed, as I am, for we had both hoped that I might find something, where my artistic talents could be used a little more seriously, but, this is a beginning, dear Mama, and the pay is very good for a beginner.

My evenings are spent visiting our old friends here, with more invitations than there are nights in the week, but I do not often accept, for I intend to make my own way in this new life. I must confess, I took a puff from a cigarette the other night, and almost choked to death, and I suppose if I smoked a whole one, it would kill me!!! But, don't worry about me, Mother, my eight years as a monk were not for nothing, and, although I get along wonderfully with the friends I have made here, I lead a life far above theirs. They seem to realize it, too, for they are beginning to come to me, with all sorts of personal problems, and I believe I will be able to carry on God's work, in a very special way, in this outside world.

And the interior life? Why, Mother, I go to Mass every morning, and I pray better than I ever did before. This very morning, I took two of my friends, who live here in the same pension, two young fellows who are pretty wild, to St. Thomas Aquinas Church for Mass, and they both remarked afterward, how much I seemed to know about the Mass, and how beautifully I prayed. They respect me, and the things I stand for, and they turn to me, and instead of going out with girls, as they have always done, they will soon be content to stay here with me, in the evening, and let me make portraits of them, and perhaps even teach them to draw.

The other night, I walked about the streets with the younger of these two boys, arguing with him, for he wanted to find a girl. I talked with him as we walked, like an older brother, but it did not seem to change his wishes, so finally, when we got in front of one of those houses, I decided to put it to him squarely, and I said: "If you want to go in there, if you want to commit this sin, then, you will have to knock me down first." As you can imagine, he returned here, to the house, with me. You see, Mama, nothing has changed, really, for I still bring all of my problems to you, and you still share in all of my life.

Now, then, I will not cash my pay check, until the end of the month. I know how little money you have, Mama, but I do need better clothes, than this old flying suit of Jean-Julien's, to wear to my work, for my position is fairly important, and I must, of course, dress the part. I wish you could be here, to help me pick out a cloth, and to give the tailor your ideas, for you always had such wonderful taste, when you used to choose Jean-Julien's and Papa's clothes. I am really lost without you, but if you could spare me 5,000 francs, until the first of the month, then I could outfit myself, keeping you always in mind, and trying to select clothes you would like. If you do not have the cash on hand, perhaps you could borrow it from the American boy, whom you write so much about, for, from what you say, I must have an adopted brother in him, and I am so glad. But I cannot understand, why he refuses to come to Paris to see me, for I would be tempted to come there, if only I could spare the 1,000 francs for a ticket, but these things will have to wait. From what you say about him, I feel that I could do a lot for him, for we are about the same age.

And you, Mother darling, I know the torment that you must be suffering, but have faith in me, and know that I have done what is right, for the indult should be here from Rome, within the next few days, and then I will be, officially, in good grace with my Church. Permission from Rome is absolutely certain, and you need not feel ashamed any longer, for I am, in the eyes of God, as good as any of those people there.

You are my dear little Mama, all I have left in the world, and you must be happy, in my choice of this new life. As yet, I have not even looked at a girl who interests me, for, despite my youth, my life in the monastery has made me much more adult, and serious. We will find me a fine girl, one day, a girl who is interested in artistic and moral questions, and, with your approval, you will have a daughter, and I will have a wife. Instead of being a Father, with a capital F, I shall be a father, with a small f!

The laboriously written letter goes on and on. It's incredible that eight years in a monastery could leave so little imprint . . .

Other things become clear. Only now do I understand why Dr. Castelar wished to take me to the worst whore he could find, for I should like to do the same thing with this Michel — to kill the rottenness of his goodness with the health, the humiliation of disgust. But he'd probably try to convert the whore . . .

Tortured by the memory of Marguerite and a growing religious awareness, the American confesses the seduction to Father Clément. The priest tells him that he must do one of two things to preserve his health and sanity. ("Either marry as soon as you can, or accept the fact that you can no longer practice licentiousness with impunity.")

At supper, Madame Renée asks him to go to Paris and see Michel. Refusing to do this, he loans her the money for Michel to come home for a visit.

Later that night, after hours of work and mounting fever, he falls asleep at his desk. Awakening, he knows he is too sick to reach the bed . . . that he must wait until someone sees his light and comes to help.

29 january

And the fever burns . . . I sleep again with my head on my hands, leaning over the desk, breathing with great difficulty.

. . . Bells from the parish church, announcing six o'clock Mass, arouse me from desultory sleep. It's still dark outside as the Villagers begin to stir about. My desk lamp seems tawdry with its diluted rays flickering into dark corners of the room. I haven't moved. I wait — wait for someone to find me and put me to bed. May she be young and beautiful, and have sweetness of voice and breasts . . .

Sometime later, a whispering voice above house slippers and lace nightgown and gray wool dressing gown. They move in the range of my vision, detached from the voice, framed by the rungs of my table as I gaze at the tiled floor. They belong to Madame Renée. And I laugh; I laugh and cry, for she's not young and beautiful with sweetness of voice and breasts.

Her voice whispers, "Aren't you well, Monsieur?"

"I'm sick, Madame Renée, really sick. Go find help."

I must have talked, for I remember words; and in the half-dream of my delirium I lie here and wonder how a woman could have put me to bed and taken off my clothes.

In the hall, a sound of something falling heavily to the floor. A moaning voice forces me to fight my way back through layers of coma and fever to reality — to a single hawklike image of Madame Renée, still dressed in night clothes, limping back into the room. She falls on a chair, clutching her leg, spitting and complaining about broken teeth in a high falsetto scream.

"Look, look, my teeth! The one beautiful thing left about me! I've always had beautiful teeth. Now they're ruined."

With two fingers she opens her bleeding lips to show me the damaged teeth. Clearly, the two front teeth have small pieces chipped out. I look, I gaze drunkenly, and I'm delighted.

"Be glad — you — didn't — bust — your —" I struggle to get out something, some word so magnificent . . .

"It's the Lord's doing. I shouldn't have been so proud of my teeth."

I try again to tell her that wonderful sentence: "Be glad — you — didn't — bust — your —"

Darkness. A shimmering chill and fevers running, racking, sinking out of consciousness, struggling to get words out. "B' glad y' di'n' bust y' ASS."

That was it. "ASS," laughing, yelling, screaming before the darkness, before the sinking out of sight. "ASS . . ."

Later, my screaming brings me back. From somewhere on the outside I hear the word repeated incessantly — "ASS, ASS, ASS, ASS" — shouted, moaned; and eyes open, wondering who says such beautiful words. Circle of black, beshawled, faceless women knitting, watching me, hearing my splendid obscenity . . .

The sickness lingers. Mother Nourrie and the other old ladies care for the American. They tell him that Madame Renée has gone to the City to see a doctor about her leg that was injured when she fell.

The fevers rise once more and the American is taken in Salesky's taxicab to the hospital in the City.

Almost a week later, he returns by bus to the Valley. Arriving after dark, he is able to walk unobserved from the bridge to his house.

The next morning he visits Madame Renée; she is still convalescing, her left leg heavily bandaged. Her doctor, she relates, told her she had the body of a woman of thirty and that she should remarry. When he encourages her to remarry, she begins another diatribe. ("The only reason I'd do it would be to spite Michel. Why shouldn't I pay him back?")

To her irritation, the American accepts an invitation to have lunch with Mademoiselle Marthe. After a pleasant meal, the old woman turns their conversation to Michel's impending arrival. ("As difficult as this will be for you, you must resist the desire to wash your hands of the whole affair. Madame Renée's bitterness may lead her to do anything, and you must be there to stop it. You must do all you can to cushion the selfish anger she will direct

*against Michel . . . I think they may break with each other, com-
pletely and irreparably. And you are the only one who can possibly prevent it.") After promising to try and reconcile the two, he
engages Mademoiselle Marthe to help him with his studies each day
after Vespers.*

*Papa Chevissier is waiting for him when he arrives at the Monas-
tery after lunch. The farmer tells him that Madame Renée had
come when she got back from her trip and paid for all the food
she'd taken. The American is both happy and perplexed at this
unexpected news.*

*That evening, walking home, he again tries to make some sense
of the situation. An overwhelming fatigue begins as he reaches
Madame Renée's house. She is waiting in the darkened salon, her
anger recharged. She accuses Mademoiselle Marthe of trying to
steal his friendship from her; she threatens to commit suicide, insisting that she no longer has any will or reason to live; she claims
Michel has ruined her life.*

*She gets the American to change the bandage on her leg and
reacts in a sensual manner while he is doing so. ("I become suddenly aware that she imagines a caress each time I touch her; that
she responds to it by contracting the muscles beneath my hand.
After a moment of this obscene exchange of touches, she stops
me and again takes my hand, this time placing it very lightly on her
knee. Still holding it, she rubs it gently over a slightly swollen spot
until I tremble with the sickness of my disgust. Her face is flushed.
She is magnificent in her piggish affection, smiling inwardly to herself, her lips half-open.")*

*More arguments follow. Finally, the American goes wearily to
meet Michel's train.*

15 february

. . . Beside the next car a young man, dressed elegantly in an overcoat and black homburg hat, bends over his suitcase to check the
tag. He straightens up, catches sight of me, and runs to shake my
hand. "I'm Michel Renée," he eagerly introduces himself. "Aren't

you Mother's friend? Recognized you from her description."

He has a long, thin face, and when he takes off his hat I notice that his hair hasn't yet grown out from his tonsure. He grins openly, and his eyes are wonderfully vital. As we prepare to leave the station he acts and speaks with the verve of a sixteen-year-old.

Hoping to avoid being seen, we walk quickly out of Town. We keep to the side of the road. I say little, listening to Michel's small talk. The distance to the Village is soon covered, and presently the Monastery looms in the starlit night.

"What a beautiful sight!" whispers my companion.

"Yes, isn't it?" I reply.

"You know, Monsieur," he says after a silence, "I was waiting for this. Up to now I couldn't be sure I was right in leaving my monastery; I couldn't be certain I didn't have a real monastic vocation after all. I was terribly anxious to see what my reaction would be when I came back here, where I spent so much of my childhood. But you know, I don't feel a thing — not the slightest desire to go in and say Compline, or to return to my habit." He shakes his head. "No, I'm a civilian and my past life was a mistake."

"Michel," I caution him, "I must tell you before we get to your house that you should be very attentive to your mother. This is a great shock for her. She feels she's losing you. Above all, don't say anything about girls — whether you have any or not. She seems especially sensitive about that."

We turn onto the bridge. "All right, Monsieur, I trust your judgment and your friendship for me." He lays a hand on my arm and we pause in the middle of the bridge. "Speaking of girls, there's something I may as well tell you right now: I'm planning to get married."

"Already?" I say. "A little soon for that, isn't it?"

"Well, I don't know — hadn't even thought about it. She's really —"

"How long have you known her, Michel? Your hair hasn't even grown out enough to cover your tonsure."

"I've known her for quite a while," he answers vaguely. "I want to tell you all about it."

"Not now, we don't have time. But you're sleeping at my place, so we can talk later if you like."

"Wish I could tell Mother about it," he remarks thoughtfully. "I hate lying."

"But you must realize how peculiar it looks, Michel: here you've been out of the monastery only a few weeks and already you're engaged. We can discuss it later — but remember, no hint of it to your mother. I'll tell you frankly, she's bitter over what she thinks you've done to her. You've got to give her time to get used to it before announcing any such plan as marriage."

He laughs. "I guess from what you say, Mama must be pretty ferocious. I'm awfully sorry to cause all this trouble. But don't worry, my friend, I know Mama — I've got around her before. She'll get over it when she sees I'm firm in my decision." We step from the bridge, and our pace becomes even slower.

"I've more or less prepared the way for you," I say to him. "But your mother's a spoiled child. Forgive me for saying this — but I don't want us to see her without explaining to you my part in the whole thing. Apparently her letters have given you a false picture of our relationship, for I don't have any special affection for her — what I'm doing for her I'd do for anybody."

"My poor friend," he says sympathetically. "She's been that bad, eh? She can be a hellion when she tries. But we must be patient with her . . ."

As we approach the house Michel's voice loses its mellifluous assurance. "Ah, here we are. Wish me luck. Bless her heart, I'll try not to tell her about Madeleine, but I won't lie."

"You'd better lie if you want any more help from me."

A momentary pause outside the door, followed by a drunken emotion of quick light in our faces as the door is thrown open. Swirls of overcoat and black skirt in a sudden embrace, and a confusion of kisses and hugs and words of endearment between sobs.

"Ah, Mama, my dear little Mama," he cries weeping, burying his face in his hands, then kissing her again.

"My child," she croons, "my Michel. There, don't cry."

We finally calm Michel's heartfelt sobbings, and sit down to dinner. I eat in silence while they chat happily about Paris. Madame Renée's conversation is excited and full of love.

"Ah, you do look well, son," she murmurs after a while. "Are you happy to be back here with your mother?"

"You know I am," he says, swallowing.

"All I want," she says warmly and sincerely, "is your happiness" — and I stare at her open-mouthed.

After the coffee is served, Madame Renée leans forward across the table and pats Michel's hand. "And tell me, my son, how is the spiritual life?"

"Wonderful, Mother. I pray better than I ever have in my life . . ."

"And your love life?" She asks this jokingly, cajolingly, as if she didn't really care.

Michel hesitates, and I shoot him a warning glance. "I have no time for that, Mama," he lies openly.

But he hesitated and his mother saw my glance. She draws back; her face muddies with suspicion. "You're keeping something from me, aren't you? I'm honest with you, why can't you be with me? Tell me the truth," she demands — "have you slept with a woman?"

"There's no woman, Mother," he replies nervously, "and there never has been — and there won't be until I'm married."

Fatal word. She stares haggardly, knowing nothing, detesting the unnerving suggestion. "Surely you're not thinking of marriage, Michel? Not this soon?"

"Well . . ." he mumbles awkwardly, looking at his plate.

"So you are!" she exclaims hoarsely. "You are thinking of marriage!"

"But, Mama —"

"Look at yourself," she goes on, her voice rising. "Did some woman pick out those clothes you're wearing? Look at that" — pointing to his coat. "Who picked it out for you?"

"Madame," I interject feebly, "his jacket is the same material as mine. I think it suits him well."

"But it isn't the same cut," turning to me with unexpected warmth. "You're always dressed in perfect taste, Monsieur. My son is best suited to a monk's habit. He only looks like a gigolo in that outfit."

"But, Mother," pleads Michel, "things are different in Paris. Everyone dresses like this."

"What do you know about it?" She rises, impatient, and begins stacking the dishes, shaking her head. "You've been in a monastery for eight years. People of good taste dress the same the world over. You're like a child, trying to follow the herd . . . And that red tie — have you become a communist in addition to your other idiocies? Did she pick that out too?"

Michel protests, "But there isn't any girl yet."

"That's right, Madame," I come to his aid. "We talked about it on the way here. Naturally Michel's thinking about marriage, but he hasn't had time to think about finding the girl yet."

She looks at both of us for a moment, then gathers up the dishes. "Well, I still don't like the tie," she says in a softer voice. "I'll find you one of your father's old ties. We'll burn that thing," she adds, carrying the dishes into the kitchen.

Michel looks at me worried, and his lips form the word "Madeleine."

In a loud voice that his mother can hear, I tell him, "Give it to me if you don't want it, Michel."

Madame Renée returns with a fresh pot of coffee. "Very well, you can look any way you please, Monsieur. Give it to him, Michel."

He appears relieved. I laugh at Madame Renée, who grudgingly smiles in return. She resumes her seat and pours coffee, asking Michel, "Have you been approached by any street women?" — but the anger has vanished, she says this lightly.

"No, Mother, not a single time. I suppose they can tell by looking at me that I'm not the kind who'd do such a thing."

"You look pretty common to me. Out of your monk's habit you're common."

I stir my coffee. "Please, Madame Renée, let's not start in on that song tonight."

There is a muffled gasp in her throat, and suddenly she staggers from her chair in a storm of weeping. Now it's her turn to wage an offensive of tears. Falling on the couch she sobs violently, shaking off Michel's frantic caresses, twisting her face away from him, hiding it in her hands. After a few moments she leans forward, sitting up, with Michel on his knees trying to comfort her.

With a gesture she thrusts Michel to his feet, turning half away and staring dazedly at the fireplace. "My poor Michel," she murmurs, "you see how I suffer, how miserable I am with you. You'd better go back to your life in Paris — perhaps that way we'll both be happier." Her voice becomes quiet, pensive, resonantly sweet. "This thing's too much for me, Michel. I can't bear to think of it any longer, so — so we must consider our relationship at an end." He looks at her in pained surprise. "I shall always do what I can for you," she continues in the same tone, "just as I have in the past — and you'll be welcome here whenever you care to return. But you must live your own life — a life I detest."

He falls again to his knees, buries his head in her lap, and begs her, weeping like a child, not to say such things, never to give him up.

Calmly she strokes his head, cradling it in her lap. "No, my son," she coos, "you've made your choice. Both of us will suffer this way, but it's the only way."

She lifts her eyes, full of love and compassion, to me as if to say, "I've done it. I've given him his freedom at the cost of God only knows how much suffering. Poor child, he'll get over it. But I — I shall live only to die."

But instead of bursting into tears I grin broadly, leaning far back in my chair, and pantomime applause with both hands. As she swells with rage, I whisper, above the uncontrolled sobbing of Michel, "It could have stood another rehearsal."

But the scene has suffered irreparable damage. Madame Renée no longer caresses her son, no longer listens to his words; for I have touched tendernesses, and she can't go on.

"She won't give you up, Michel," I answer him, my voice calm. "Your mother has proved herself in the past, and she's still the same fine person she was then. She'll see you through all this, even to marriage. And she'll make your children the best grandmother in France. I'm sure of that. You're two of a kind, you and your mother. You're both selfish, and you both insist on turning every emotion into a cheap and tawdry act. Now kiss each other good night — simply, I beg you, and not as if one of you were going to the guillotine in the morning — and let's all go to bed."

I light a cigarette while the celebration of the night's affection is consummated. Multiple, open-mouthed kissing, saliva wetting cheeks, despite my plea.

"You run along, son," Madame Renée dismisses Michel. "I want to speak to Monsieur here a moment." When he has gone she turns on me furiously. "How dare you make me appear so foolish in front of my son!"

"And how dare you," I retort angrily, "appear so foolish in front of me! Now forget all this and try to act like a human being tomorrow. Good night."

"Wait," she entreats repentantly. "Will you and Michel sit up and talk tonight?"

"I've no idea. I have nothing to talk about, but if Michel wants to, I don't mind. I explained your feelings to him on the way from Town. You can be sure everything I say is in your favor."

"Tell him how much he's hurt me. Beg him to go back to the monastery, won't you? And try to find out if there's been a girl."

"All right. Shall I make a list?"

"Don't forget you and I are friends," she smiles — a smile tinged with guilt. "What's my son to you, anyway?"

"I'll do as you ask. And now, good night." At the door I turn. "And please, for the love of God, won't you leave off these exhausting emotional antics tomorrow? Stop acting."

. . . Outside, the street, the freshness of night air make me realize how sick I am of obvious emotions. I pause before entering my house, before going in to comfort the broken Michel.

He is in the salon searching in his suitcase. Taking out a large envelope, he places it on the table, glances up at me with a whistling smile of relief, and closes the bag. His resilience is apparent: young, boyish, untouched by the scene.

"My poor old man!" he laughs. "How can I apologize for her? She usually doesn't go quite that far."

"I'm used to it," I tell him. "She acts like that nearly all the time now. It's a sad thing to see, when really she has so many fine qualities. She's completely alienated herself from her friends."

". . . Here, I brought along some snapshots of my fiancée, Madeleine." He sits beside me, holding the photographs in his lap, and begins passing them to me one by one.

"Why, Michel, she's beautiful," I tell him after a moment. "But how did you find a girl like this so soon? Tell me all about it."

"Last year Mother got permission from my Father Abbot for me to make the pilgrimage with her to England, to visit the grave of my brother, Jean-Julien. When I left the monastery one of my close friends, a young Brother, asked me if I'd take a packet of letters to his sister in Paris. He told me only that she was a Madame Defourque, the mother of two children — there, that's a snapshot of one of her daughters, she's the younger. Well, Mother had no objections, so I left the hotel and carried the letters to Madeleine's apartment. Both her daughters were there, and since that was my first time to be out in the world as a grown man — to be in a private home, and see what family life could be — well, I stayed on most of the afternoon. We talked about her brother, and my life in the monastery, and her life there in Paris. Her husband has been dead for eight years. I thought nothing of it except that I hadn't talked with a woman like that in a long time, and I went on to England with Mother. When we returned I decided to visit Madeleine once more, to get the latest news to take back to her brother . . . She was lovely. We spent the afternoon together and she sent me off with a package of food for the monks. I dreamed only of getting back to my cell, to my life as a monk. But, when I came in sight of the monastery — well, something changed in me. And gradually, the prospect of a lifetime devoted only to God became almost unbearable. I made a tremendous effort for an entire year. I prayed to God to give me peace, and make me satisfied with the only life I'd ever known. But finally I became obsessed with the idea of a home and a wife and children; and I knew I'd put a bullet through my head if I stayed on. They released me from the monastery and gave me a little money. When I got to Paris, Madeleine found me my job. She's helped me in every possible way — it was she who picked out my clothes. And now she's returned my love and we spend every spare moment together. Can you understand why I want to bring her here and break the news to Mama, and marry her as soon as possible?" He fingers the envelope nervously. I offer him a cigarette, which he takes, which he lights and smokes without choking.

"Well, Michel, you saw how your mother was tonight. I'll do my best for you, but you must realize it would be unforgivable to break the news to her now."

"I know," he answers, exhaling smoke from nose and mouth. "And of course the fact that Madeleine has two children makes it seem even more impossible. Mother'll think I'm saddling myself with a big family to begin with. But when you're in love like this it makes waiting awfully hard. I'll tell you one thing — if there must be a choice I'll choose Madeleine, even if I have to break with Mother."

"Of course you will, Michel." I walk into the kitchen for a glass of water, calling back, "That's only right. But by waiting a few months you may be able to have your marriage and your mother too."

I return yawning, closing the door behind me.

"You say to wait a few months. But that's not possible. I'm willing to go along with you for a few weeks . . ."

"You're willing to go along with me?" I stare at him angrily. "Why, do you know I wouldn't give a damn if you and your mother went straight to hell this instant? Make up your mind right now. I'm here on the scene, and I know your mother much better than you do. But if you're going to marry immediately, then don't ask for my help any more. Tell your mother now; go face her — alone. I'm sick of this mess anyway."

For a long moment we find no words. Restlessly I sit again on the bed . . . Then, grinning, he reaches over and pats me on the knee.

"Don't be angry with me, huh?" he says. "You must know how it feels to be in love and want someone so badly you can hardly control yourself. Why, a doctor friend of mine even suggested that if there's any further delay, we go ahead and have physical contact before marriage. What do you think?"

"I think," I say slowly, "the doctor is a damned fool. Do as you like — I don't care one way or the other. But I must tell you frankly, Michel, your mother has a lot on her side despite her childish actions. Do you realize how it would look for her, as your mother, if you were to marry almost as soon as you'd grown enough hair to cover your tonsure? And what disrespect for the monks here!"

"Disrespect for the monks?" repeats Michel, surprised. "Why, they're my brothers; they'd be the first to advise a quick marriage. As a matter of fact, my Father Abbot told me I must marry as soon as possible to guard against falling into sin."

"Yes, I understand that. But how will it look here? Here, you're known; your mother must live in this community. The only thing outsiders can think is that a monk leaves his monastery and gets married almost immediately afterward. You and I know this happens very seldom, so seldom as to be nonexistent — and in your case we know it happened because you were put in the monastery too young to make the decision of your own free will. But those on the outside won't know that. They'll say, 'Ah, those monks! What do you suppose really goes on behind the walls? They're a queer bunch. Just show 'em a pretty girl and they go chasing after her.' . . . They'll take your case — an isolated case — and make it a generality. You won't be hurt by it; it's the monks and your mother who'll bear the shame. As for me, I don't care — but explain the situation to Madeleine. Such things take time; they must be done with a certain discretion."

Michel laughs, "You are a good friend. Very well, we'll wait till you give the signal, all right? But make it as soon as possible. And tell me, do you think maybe I should try to keep her satisfied in the meantime? I've never had any sexual experience, I'm just asking you."

I sigh disgustedly. "If you've gotten no more than that out of your years in the monastery, go ahead. I probably should, but it's disappointing to see a man of your background who'd even consider it. You see, I've grown to know a great love and respect for monks since I've been here. I expect them to be above people like me, and I'm a little sickened when they aren't."

"But," he protests, "I'm not a monk any more. I'm a man like yourself now, with the same problems."

"You threw off the mantle too quickly, Michel," I say bitterly and quietly. "I'm beginning to doubt if you ever really were a monk."

He winces, a flush of anger; then immediate control as the eyes become calm. "You're very frank, Monsieur."

"We're not playing games. I learned that sort of frankness from your own monks."

"But it seems to me you use it as a coward's weapon." His smile is gone. "When frankness turns to insult it loses its value."

"I suspect you're right," I tell him evenly. "You see, you and I, who should be the best of friends, who rushed into a quick friendship, appear to have made a mistake. I'll do everything I can for you, and for your mother — but on the whole I find you most unsympathetic."

"Please" — turning to me — "you mustn't feel that way about me, I'm not a bad sort. Say we'll be friends — all right?"

"All right, Michel," I agree wearily. "It's late. Let's get to bed." . . .

Madame Renée and Michel argue for several days. At last she has convinced herself that his purity is still intact and, just prior to his leaving, they embrace in reconciliation. Madame Renée's leg is still heavily bandaged and the American must change it daily; her ritual of touching and flirting during the process continues.

The days pass easier after Michel's departure. Madame Renée — hampered by moral suffering and an inability to move about — demands more and more of the American's time. ("She does everything to make my life pleasant, and in so doing she takes me from my work. She has assumed a gentle sweetness — but it's too late; I've seen in her too much ugliness to believe that this is more than transitory.")

A month goes by without any news from Michel, except short notes which serve only to irritate Madame Renée. Believing that she has lost Michel and his affections, she persuades the American to write to him. In the letter he tells Michel of Madame Renée's degeneration. ("She will either lose her mind or continue in her foolish attempt to starve herself. Her worry has now become a real sickness for which there is only one cure — your paying her more attention . . .")

Madame Renée begs him not to tell Michel of the anguish and heartbreak that she is undergoing. (". . . Don't tell him . . . that his mother's dying. I — I prefer him to be notified after I'm gone.") The American insists that she is a healthy woman, not yet fifty-five, with a long life ahead of her.

Again, she accuses him of withholding information about Michel's personal life from her. When he answers that she must accept the fact that one day Michel, as well as himself, will marry, she becomes more petty and vicious. She urges him to take up the monas-

tic life and forget about marriage, and swears that she will break all ties with Michel forever if he marries. She tells the American she hates both him and Michel.

He tells her that she is wrong in making Michel choose between her and a wife. The American threatens to move back to the Monastery if their relationship doesn't become more pleasant; retaliating, Madame Renée declares that if he does she will drive him out of the Valley by renewing the rumor that he let the Chevissier child die. He counterbalances the charge by threatening to expose her baptism of the girl. Surprised that he knows anything about this, Madame Renée succumbs to weeping. He promises never to bring the subject up again, but is firm in his position against her threat of blackmail.

He encounters Father Clément after Vespers and confesses his recurring pornographic images. The priest tells him that they are the result of fatigue. When he responds that Madame Renée is increasingly monopolizing his time away from the Monastery, Father Clément advises him to go to bed by midnight every night and to tell Madame Renée that he has ordered him to do so.

The American goes to Mademoiselle Marthe's for his lessons, but is too exhausted to work. Instead, they talk. He explains to her in detail everything — except the threats and the story of the baptism — that has happened between him and Madame Renée since the beginning. Mademoiselle Marthe says that she believes Madame Renée has fallen in love with him. They agree that Madame Renée must be convinced that she's wrong for feeling as she does.

He returns home and sits in the dark, relieved after his meeting with Mademoiselle Marthe. The solitude is soon shattered by Madame Renée's knocking at his door. She tells him that she stayed in the chapel and prayed for a long time after Vespers, and then made her confession to Father Clément. The priest, she relates, agreed with her that Michel's life would be difficult on the outside; also he told her that she must see that the American got more sleep and rest. She promises to obey the priest's directive.

To his amazement, Madame Renée further states that after Vespers she stopped to seek Mademoiselle Marthe's opinion about their relationship. ("She suggested — and I think this is true — that there's nothing wrong in my actions but that I'm a terrible tease;

*that I sometimes do and say things to annoy you without meaning
any real offense. She suggested I stop joking with you so much
. . . and start taking you more seriously. I assure you I really
will change. A friendship like ours must be based on mutual respect . . ."*)

Madame Renée then invites him to come to her house and visit
while she prepares supper. Wanting only to run and discuss the
incredible change with Mademoiselle Marthe, he declines; he tells
Madame Renée he will come over as soon as he picks up some work
he left at the Monastery.

He hurries to Mademoiselle Marthe's house and enthusiastically
thanks her for producing the miracle. He asks her what she said
that caused Madame Renée to change so quickly. The old woman
stares at him and says she hasn't had a visit from Madame Renée
since Christmas. ("*Why, she no longer even speaks to me when
she passes me on the street. Certainly she'd never lower herself to
seek advice concerning her precious American from someone like
me.*")

They decide that it will be best not to let Madame Renée know
they have discovered her lie. Mademoiselle Marthe plots their strategy. ("*If she has any brains left, my child, I imagine she'll come
to see me tonight. Then she'll know that if you happen to mention
her visit, I won't deny having seen her . . . Since she thinks you're
at the Monastery she may be on her way here this very minute.
Return the back way so your paths won't cross — or better still,
go on to the Monastery as you'd planned.*")

After borrowing a book at the Monastery, he walks back to
Madame Renée's house. They talk quietly and happily through
supper. She tells him of the happy times she had enjoyed with her
husband. ("*Honestly, you'd have loved my Julien. As you know,
he was twenty-nine years my senior . . . and he could never get
enough of me . . . I never once betrayed my husband . . . Julien
only suspected me once, and that was the time Father Sauvac asked
me to discourage his love-making. Julien was too old to give me
healthy children, so I turned cold to his advances.*")

The next day is Saturday; classes at the Monastery only until
noon. On his way home, he stops to chat briefly with Mademoiselle
Marthe; she tells him that Madame Renée had come as they antici-

pated. ("And do you know she mentioned you only as being such a lucky person to have her?")

Later that day, Madame Renée tells him that Madame Vincent has returned and has rented a room in Town. ("In order to get the room she told the proprietor that she's just come from a doctor in Paris. She's sick. She says she needs an operation which she refuses to have.") Madame Renée says she's pregnant and threatens to run her out of the Valley.

The American walks to Town to talk with Madame Vincent. She can't be located when he reaches her room. People in Town tell him that she is sick — that she was sick that morning after breakfast.

The American stops at a small café to rest. There he encounters his postman and they begin drinking.

The two drink all afternoon. The American gets steadily drunker and eventually sick. The postman, aided by Salesky, gets him home and to bed. Before they leave, he asks them to take Madame Renée some money he owes her for provisions, and to tell her that he is drunk and to stay away.

Alone now, sick and weaker, he drifts toward sleep. Suddenly the lights in the room switch on; he struggles out of his semi-stupor to find Madame Renée bending over the bed. She has come, she says, to check on him and to see if he wants anything to eat. He tells her that he's drunk, that he needs nothing but to sleep; she remains, speaking in nuances, bending down to look at him more closely, casually patting her hand on his stomach. She increases her sensual caressing and his body begins to respond. He pulls her down and kisses her, his hands joining hers in a growing excitement of fumblings.

Abruptly, Madame Renée draws away and slaps him hard against the face. As she stands scowling at him, he breaks into uncontrollable laughter. He accuses her of being a tease, of leading him on; she darts from the house into the darkness.

Sounds from an orchestra reach him, loud in the spring air. He remembers that a dance is being held in front of Madame Rouen's store.

Still feeling weak, he dresses and walks to the dance. He sees Christianne among the dancers and mentions her to Mother Nour-

*rie. The old woman cackles, tells him that the girl is her cousin,
and arranges for Christianne to join them.*

*At Mother Nourrie's encouragement, he and Christianne dance
together away from the crowd and off down the street without
speaking. They dance further into the darkness, ultimately stopping in a concealed doorway. Rain begins to fall lightly. They
kiss and, pressing her against the locked door, he begins to un-
button her clothing.*

*Christianne notices that a car has stopped in front of the Amer-
ican's house. Through the rain they recognize the woman who
gets out of the car. It is Madame Vincent. She walks rapidly to
the house and returns to the waiting car which pulls away. Promising to be gone only a few minutes, he leaves Christianne in the
doorway and runs after the car, calling for it to stop. But the roar
of the motor prevents Salesky — for it's his taxi — from hearing.*

*On his hall table the American finds an unsigned note, its mes-
sage scribbled in pencil: "Meet me on the bridge at 7:30 tomorrow
night. I would like to talk." He reads and burns the note. He
remembers the waiting Christianne, but his desire has gone.*

*He walks reluctantly back to where he left her. She isn't there.
Relieved, he goes on to the dance and seeks out Mother Nourrie.
She tells him that Christianne has just danced off down the street
with another youth.*

*Monastery bells awaken him the following morning. By the
time Madame Renée returns from Mass, he has determined to pretend that he remembers nothing that happened during his drunkenness. But she takes the initiative and says she has decided to forgive
him for his unseemly behavior if he will apologize. Some time
later, Madame Marceaux, one of the Valley's leading gossips, calls
on Madame Renée. She asks the American if he enjoyed the dance;
he tells her "yes" and leaves the house hurriedly, fearing that she
will tell Madame Renée of his escapade with Christianne.*

*He wonders if he should tell Father Clément what has happened.
He attempts to persuade himself that nothing really happened. But
something inside him rebels and tortures. He walks to the Monastery and confesses his acts to Father Clément.*

*The priest says that an evolution is taking place within him.
("Do you remember a few months ago when you fell with Madame*

Vincent? Do you remember your reactions then? . . . a mixture of pride and regret and fear . . . You were not afraid of God — you did not give God a thought . . . No, your reactions were directed toward your fellow men. You were afraid of the judgment of men — of my judgment . . . Your concept of morality was purely social . . . But after you had committed another indiscretion, with the girl in Salesky's taxicab, I began to see the change in your reaction. On that occasion there was no reason for you to fear discovery, there was no reason to tell anyone of your misdeed. And yet you felt compelled to come to me. Your fear had changed because, somehow, you felt that you had offended not man, but God. That was the first sign of a true Christian remorse.")

23 march

. . . Father Clément's words fill me with a longing to leave the world outside and return to the safety of these walls. I tell him of my conviction that Madame Renée is in love with me. "I was wondering if perhaps I could return to my old cell?"

Father Clément gazes at the water a long moment before answering. "Well, you must know my affection for you — I am tempted to bring you back here. But my logic as a priest forces me to pause." We walk toward the grove of fruit trees. "What makes you think that Madame Renée is in love with you?"

"Well, Mademoiselle Marthe told me several days ago that she thought Madame Renée was in love with me — but I didn't have proof of it till last night. I got drunk in Town yesterday, and she came over to see me in my room. You may not believe this, but — well, she put her hands all over me, and did everything imaginable to excite me. And then when I did get excited and started making advances, she slapped me. Now I'm glad it didn't happen, of course; but it's made her more repulsive to me than ever."

"But if you leave Madame Renée now," he reasons, "what intolerable heartache it will cause her — especially if she is in love with you, as she apparently is. You have no affection left for her — but can you allow yourself to heighten her grief at this time of unhappiness? She is a human being, no matter how terrible her actions have seemed to be. We must stop this, but as painlessly as possible and not with such abruptness."

"But, Father, I'm no good for her. Something's wrong with me. I lose my temper and become something I can't stand. Here with you, there might be some hope of progress. I could finish my work more rapidly and hope that much sooner to make a decent life for myself."

"I shall be happy to think of you well married, my son, but that is in the future." He shakes his head. "No, the fact that you occupy this poor woman's time and thoughts, is the important thing. It is her salvation; she told me so herself. We know all about Michel here . . . that he is going to be married soon. That will come as a great shock to Madame Renée, and you must not desert her. The two things could combine to drive her to distraction. As a friend I am truly sorry; but as a priest, how can I counsel you differently? Pray for her, my child. The very act of your prayer will soften the hardness of your feelings toward her."

. . . He walks slowly down the path to pass out of sight . . . Tonight I must meet Madame Vincent. I trust her; whatever it is, I trust her. And my only prayer, alone in this garden, is that she not suffer because of me or my past deeds.

Leaving the Monastery, I begin walking in the country . . . When I come in sight of the bridge, a lone figure is standing at the railing, the vague figure of a woman. She doesn't look up as I walk toward her. I stop at her side and lean on the railing, waiting for her to speak.

"You came. I'm so glad you found my note."

"Of course I came — I've tried to find you ever since I heard you were back."

She lifts her hands to her forehead and draws her fingertips slowly back across her temples. I peer at her through the darkness. She breathes a long sigh, as though she were searching for words with which to tell me something.

"What is it? What's happened? Why didn't you let them operate?"

"The doctors have told me I'm incurably ill."

"What?" I mutter dully, not understanding.

"They say it's hopeless."

"Hopeless? But — surely, Madame Vincent, you don't mean —?"
On the railing my hand instinctively seeks hers.

"Yes." Her hand in mine is cool and moist, absolutely still. "If
they operated I might die on the table. If I lived what would it
mean? — only a year or two more. I couldn't stand to die like that
— on an operating table, under bright lights."

"I had no idea, Madame. I thought it was —" My hand tightens
about her fingers with such force as to make tendons ache deep
inside my arm. "Maybe," I say without expression, "maybe the
doctors are wrong."

"No, I'm afraid not. With cancer they know pretty well."

"I can't believe it."

"No, no," she says softly, "you mustn't feel that way."

"Do you know —? Did they tell you —?" The words hang in
my throat, and I force them out: "How long do you have?"

"They give me about two months."

"Two months! But — there must be something, some way —"

"No . . . there's nothing." For the first time she turns her head
to look me full in the face. "Can you understand why I refused the
operation? Surely you must. You know what this place means to
me. It's so much better to die here where I can hear the Monastery
bells. It gives me a feeling of peace. I can accept here."

I find nothing to say. Numb, I gaze at the unchanging Monastery. I release her hand and cross my arms, leaning on the railing.

"I pray well here," she goes on slowly. "Life's an enchantment
now. How fortunate I am," she whispers fervently, "to know in
time! You must know what it means to me. I'll have these last
weeks of complete happiness, for I live now only to die well prepared, and with the certainty of God's love for me. I've always
been afraid I might go suddenly, you know, without being able
to . . ."

I glance at her. The way in which she speaks of her death is as
calm as the night about us. There is no fear, no uncertainty in her
voice; mine is the only fear.

"Look," she says, pointing, "isn't that the most beautiful sight on
God's earth? That's why I had to come back. Knowing what all
that means, it's not possible to be afraid."

Something unspoken passes between us. I look with new eyes.

Beneath us, the swirling torrents of the River; to the right, the lights of a neighboring village; and to the left, in an alcove of still waters, the reflection of our Monastery topped by its high silhouette. I see through her eyes, seeing as she must be seeing. The stagnant putrescence is muted in favor of the delicate sweetness of cooking fires, of spring, of the intangibly hinted moisture of night on the River. Living sounds from the water's edge: the stippled background of crickets and insects accompanying the deep-throated croaking of frogs, no longer lonely. In a moment of watching, of waiting, this vast scattered night becomes intimate, living with us here and now. A new focus has changed the swift vision of the eyes and the heart. Through her senses, enlivened by death, this woman beside me has lifted a muffling haze from my own senses, deadened by life. Tonight all this becomes a part of us in a bloodless union of infinite completeness, as completely shared as our flesh was once shared. I think of that other night long ago, and of our walk back from Town through the snow. But now, tonight, we stand under a magically transfigured sky; and for an instant it destroys the need of man to huddle against man, of man to protect man.

I whisper, "I suspect you're more fortunate than I realized, Madame Vincent."

"I know, my friend," she answers simply. "It's good to live. You realize that, when you know death. I ask nothing. I've lived, and now I'll die — and both will be . . ."

"Yes," I say gently, and then, "Is there much pain?"

"No, not yet."

"There's something I must tell you," I say quietly. "When I came here tonight I was afraid you might be pregnant. I came with that one thought. Now I wish —"

"I'm so sorry," she whispers. "I should've written you. It never occurred to me that you'd think that, but of course you would. I'm glad it's not that; I'm glad it's this."

"You know," I say slowly, "I believe I understand you. I believe I understand how you feel. I don't pity you — nor envy you either, for that matter — but I'm thankful that things have worked out the way you wanted them to. Is there anything I can do? May I call on you?"

She doesn't answer.

"I understand," I say after a time.

"Yes," comes softly from the darkness, "I'd like to be alone. I think it will be better that way. Completely alone. This is between God and me now."

Dew has started to form on the bridge railing. The dampness begins to chill. I step close to her, turn to face her. "Of course — it'd ruin it to have all the old ladies in to change your bedclothes and clean your room and feel sorry for you. No reason for them to find out. As for myself, I won't try to see you again."

"Thank you."

"Tell me one thing before we separate, though — I must know — are you very sorry about what we did?"

"I'm — really not sure," she replies thoughtfully. "Perhaps I'm sorry, but that part of it's been paid for and seems unimportant now. At any rate I'm glad it made us friends."

"Thank God you feel that way," I tell her. "I'd never forgive myself if I had hurt you . . . I'll leave you now. If you want me — if you find things changed and need me for anything — you know where I live. God bless you. Good night, Madame."

She has turned her back and is gazing again at the Monastery. I walk swiftly away . . .

The American returns home, filled with jubilation for having known Madame Vincent. ("I think of Madame Renée, of the good ladies who will hound Madame Vincent to the grave never knowing the splendor of her; never knowing how great must be her worth in the eyes of God.")

Later, he goes to Madame Renée's for supper. He finds her lying on the sofa, her eyes swollen from weeping. He tells her that she can stop her remorse — that Madame Vincent isn't pregnant. But she is mourning another matter: Madame Marceaux has told her of his encounter with Christianne.

They wrangle again after supper. Madame Renée denounces Madame Vincent, calling her a prostitute. The American reminds her of her own indiscretion with Julien before they were married. The argument is abated only after he tells her of Madame Vincent's

incurable illness. Madame Renée then expresses a reserved interest.
("If she really is ill I can help her. You don't understand our cus-
toms, but don't expect me to feel sorry about it.")

The next morning the American receives a letter from Michel.
It tells of his decision to marry Madeleine Defourque on the tenth
of April. Michel explains that he has also written a full account of
this to his mother. He asks the American to stand by Madame
Renée and to help her understand and accept the marriage. At the
end of the letter, he announces that he is bringing Madeleine to the
Village on Thursday to meet his mother.

24 march

. . . Crumpling the letter, I drop it in the cold stove. With a letter
of her own, Madame Renée should be here any minute. I decide
not to dress. Instead I climb back into bed to wait.

Then, from the courtyard, the imperious clang of the gate bell.
Quickly I face the wall and close my eyes, pretending to sleep.
The front door opens noisily.

"He's got a woman! The idiot thinks he'll be married next
month. Wake up! We must do something to stop him." The door
slams loudly and I hear her fall into a chair.

I turn heavily in bed to glare at her.

"Were you asleep?" she asks.

"No, damn it," I admit. "Michel wrote me too. All right, so he's
an idiot and so he's getting married. Good riddance!"

She lifts her eyes to the ceiling. "God damn his soul for doing
this to me! I'll stop it! He can't do it!"

"Oh, yes he can."

"I tell you, I'll stop him if it's the last thing I do."

"You're hysterical. Now get yourself under control and read his
letter aloud. Let's see what we can make of it." I sit up in bed.

She reads to the end without stopping. After a silence she
glances up at me, then stares out the window.

"Very well," I say as normally as I can, "he's found himself a
nice girl and they're in love. Nothing bad about that. I'm happy for
him, aren't you?"

"A widow," she mumbles, "four years his senior, with two daughters. A woman of experience. He should have a virgin, a girl as pure as himself — a girl who's never been touched by a man. And they're coming here Thursday. Apparently she doesn't have the discretion of a maidservant — flaunting her love affair in the faces of these people who don't even know Michel's no longer a monk."

"That is bad, isn't it?" I agree. "But after all, it's not terribly important. They only want your consent."

"Sure, they want my consent. But I'll fix her with him," she announces bitterly. "I'll make her look like the cheap thing she is, grabbing at the first man who comes along."

"You've no right to say that," I answer. "The fact she's been a widow for eight years looks pretty decent to me."

"I'll explain a few things to them. Why, when Michel's forty-five — in his prime — she'll be used up. He'll probably go out looking for other women."

"Maybe she won't be used up," I seek to quiet her. "When she's your age she may still have the body of a thirty-year-old woman, like you have."

"Take his side!" She spits the words into my face.

"Listen, I take nobody's side. I think Michel's an ass — and you're a woman eaten up with selfishness. I think the girl's too good for him, but their wedding date's been set now. Accept it and you'll at least have their affection; reject it and you're alone — completely alone in the world."

"No one has the right to hurt his mother like this."

"He's a grown man, Madame Renée, doing what grown men have always done — you're the one causing the hurt. And why? Because you're too damned selfish to share your son with another woman. When the initial shock wears off you'll realize I'm right; you'll accept Michel's marriage and make a fine mother-in-law. It's a wonderful new beginning for you."

"Never! I can issue ultimatums too. If he marries this woman I'll never speak to him again. Write him," she commands harshly, "tell him to marry her. But above all, tell them both to stay away from here."

"Write your own letters."

Weeping, she lowers her head. "I'm in no condition to write."

"Any good news you have, you can dictate to me. But I'm through being your go-between, understand?"

"If you don't write them," she gasps, "they'll come Thursday and I won't receive them."

"I don't give a damn," I say coldly.

"So now that I'm in trouble, you wash your hands of me."

"I'm ashamed of you, Madame, that's all. . . . I can't get interested in either of you till you decide to do what's right."

. . . "Mothers have rights over their children. They bear them, they suffer and give up for them. They should be able to choose for them when the time comes for marriage."

"That's excellent logic, Madame. It holds true only for male children, I suppose?"

"What do you mean by that?" she asks innocently.

". . . For the love of God!" I roar, making her back away, "for the love of God put yourself in Michel's place! You went through exactly the same thing. You even lived with a man and got pregnant in order to force your parents' consent. Seems to me that Michel is treating you with much more consideration than you treated your parents. You married a man below your class . . . If ever a marriage should've failed, that one was it — but it didn't. Think how much better chance Michel's has of succeeding."

She bends over me and whispers, "Yes, but my mother disowned me . . ."

"And caused both of you intolerable misery. Do you want to make the same mistake with Michel? You want him to hate you like you hated your mother?"

Drawing herself up, she proclaims, "I am right, Michel is wrong — and he will pay."

"Fine! — vengeance, the same as your mother's. The world won't justify you; in the eyes of the world you'll be just another mother who couldn't accept the responsibilities of motherhood, who couldn't make the sacrifices. A mother selfish enough to kill her child's love rather than share it. The only one to suffer will be you — not Michel nor Madeleine nor me nor anyone else."

"Ah," she groans, "I can't even think any more. Providence is punishing me for my past sins."

"No, don't think of it that way. All you have to do is accept — and love — your new family." She sinks slowly to sit beside me on the bed; I go on, "Now, why not let them come ahead Thursday like they've planned? Let's not condemn this girl without knowing her. Then if things are worse than they seem, at least you'll have done what's decent."

"It's more than a woman can bear. At least I was in love with my husband."

"I know, but your parents didn't think so. Remember how you yourself felt, and look at Michel's affair from that point of view —"

"Then you must stay close to me. I don't promise anything, but I'll try. If you leave me alone, though, you know how my mind dwells on these things. And — you must promise not to worry me. Please. You won't see Christianne or Madame Vincent again, will you?"

"Very well," I assure her. "I promise."

. . . "I suppose you think Michel is absolutely right?"

"I don't know what I think. He's certainly going about all this in a crude way." I draw my legs from behind her and crawl from the bed. "Now go home and we'll let things take their natural course."

She looks up at me in alarm. "No — please. If I go home you must go with me."

"I have to get to my classes in a few moments, Madame."

"No," she mutters, "you can't leave me today. The classes aren't that important."

"I'm sorry but I'm here for the classes, and if I stay away from the Monastery I get too far behind." I stand before her in my pajamas, hoping she'll leave.

She whispers resentfully, "Easy enough to see how important I am to you."

"That's not true. But let's not waste time arguing. Unless you want to watch me dress, please go in the kitchen for a minute." . . .

Father Gardener and another monk are pruning fruit trees when I enter the courtyard of the Monastery. Branches fall and are gathered. Suddenly, the prospect of going into the paleography room — of bending over books and manuscripts — seems impossible. I ask Father Gardener if I can work outside with him today. More than anything else I feel the need of exercise, of flowing sweat, as though the sweat would carry off all spiritual poisons. He tells me to join him after lunch . . .

. . . At noon I hear monks pass in the corridor on their way downstairs to the refectory. I think of Madame Renée. Time for lunch. Time to go to her. My stomach trembles uneasily, rejecting the thought of more food cooked in vitriol and tears. I light a cigarette, toss the match out the window, and decide to miss lunch . . .

. . . I go down to the kitchen and ask for a piece of bread. Their noon meal is over. I wash the bread down with a glass of water, then go out to join Father Gardener and his trees.

He gives me the job of stacking fallen branches into a large pile; and when that is done, I shovel mulched manure around the bases of the trees. The work warms and freshens the blood. The earth is soft, spongy — it invites you to lie down and look at the sky. Muscles react as blood surges into robust activity.

Later in the afternoon, we set fire to the wood. . . . The fire has smoldered almost away by the time Vesper bells fill the courtyard. I enter the chapel and kneel on the back bench, puffing from the exercise. Music and prayers lull tired senses to a point near sleep. I rest, my head on the hard wood of the pew in front of me, listening. And the desire to return to this place overwhelms me.

. . . Thunder rumbles in the distance as I make my way to Madame Renée's house. The house is dark, forbidding — the shutters haven't been closed. I put my hand on the gate to open it . . .

I hesitate, then turn and cross the street rapidly, unable to make myself face her. Without turning on the lights, I sit on the side of the bed and smoke a cigarette. Nothing matters but sleep now. After a time I finish the cigarette, drop my clothes on the floor, and crawl into bed.

A faint knock on the door awakens me from profound sleep. Without answering I feel myself sinking back into the thick fog, when I hear the door open. Footsteps approach my bed. Through a drugged veil I'm vaguely aware of a presence hovering over me. The presence waits a long time until my awareness of it fades into returning sleep . . .

Then I hear a retreating step and breathe easier — until I feel a sagging weight at the foot of the bed. Her nearness sets nerves trembling, gathering force gradually. She is dead weight, unmoving, and I know she must be peering at me. I feel nerves quake with increasing violence, building in a long arc of ever-greater intensity. Occasionally a prolonged sigh escapes her. I hold myself tensely still, not moving a muscle; but the bed seems to rock with tremblings.

Time passes. Nerves reach the high point of the curved arc and for a long moment cut into the quick. I close my eyes and concentrate on the weariness that pains dully in all my muscles, and the tremblings begin to shudder away into the distance. But I have felt only the beginnings of warm relaxation when I'm shocked back into wakefulness by a shifting of her weight, as she stretches out along the foot of the bed and then turns on her side, facing me. I turn and face the wall. I am naked under the covers. Something not right about this. I decide to go sleep in one of the upstairs bedrooms, locking the door — but it's not right to get up and walk naked across the floor, even in the dark, while she is here. Again I feel the bed give as she inches into a more comfortable position . . . there is pressure against the bottoms of my feet. After a while it occurs to me that she has them cradled on her stomach. It's like standing on a soft floor.

I bury my head deeper in my pillow until I can hear the regular thumping of my heartbeat against my ear. Vaguely I feel pity for this softness beneath my feet. A loud snorting snore punctures the silence, and the soft floor begins to move evenly up and down beneath my toes. Gradually, the muffling haze of returning slumber causes all sounds to fade away . . .

25 march

. . . I shake my head and try to remember. Was she really here last night? No, I must have dreamt it.

Crawling out of bed, I turn back the covers to examine them. On the coarse woolen quilt I see a whitish circle. I bend down and smell the lingering odor of face powder. Close beneath my eyes a silver hair curls upward. Did I kick the covers off? Irritation of not knowing.

I reach for my cigarettes. A folded piece of paper flutters to the floor, and I pick it up. A note from Madame Renée: she has gone to Town for provisions and won't be back till late this afternoon. She hopes I'll condescend to have dinner with her tonight.

I crumple the paper and throw it in the direction of the stove. The damned peeping bitch!

. . . Hopelessly, I seek today again to recapture the warmth of prayers. I know that their warmth is somewhere close to me — that it can be mine — but it eludes my efforts. I remain in the chapel a long time after Vespers are over; but this evening I am uncomfortable, trespassing.

. . . Before I get to my house I see that the windows are lighted. The door to my salon is half open. Madame Renée is lying asleep across the bed.

I step inside and slam the door behind me. She sits up and begins massaging her eyes. "What's the matter?" I mutter. "Didn't you sleep well last night?"

She ignores my question and hoists herself from the bed, stifling a yawn. I look at her ravaged face.

"How're you feeling?" I ask more gently.

She directs a vague smile of affection at me, and I reject the insane thought that I should start undressing. "I'm all —" Her eyes roll far back in her head and she reaches quickly for a chair to keep from falling.

I almost knock over the table getting to her.

Releasing her grasp on the chair, she teeters into my arms.

"Here, here — sit on the bed."

"So tired," she whispers almost inaudibly.

"I know you're tired. Here — just lean back. I'll fix you some coffee."

"I'll be all right."

I hurry into the kitchen. Without bothering to heat it I pour her a cupful of the thick black coffee left over from this morning. She is too weak to hold it to her mouth. I support her head with one hand and carefully place the cup to her lips. Looking down at her as she swallows, I am shaken with pity. The hair at the crown of her head is disturbed. Absently, I put the coffee cup aside and, with the comb of my fingers, arrange the gray strands.

She raises her gaze to me with an expression of consuming tenderness, and gratefully pats my arm. Irritated, I'm about to move away when she asks for more coffee. As I hold the stained china cup to her lips, it seems to become a jeweled chalice filled with some medieval elixir; and we, two lardy adolescents in a forest exchanging desperately heroic glances.

"Thou art the spring," I whisper in mock passion.

"Hm?" she moans, relaxing against my arm.

"I'm sorry," I say, "but really now — you're too old to play the maiden-in-distress convincingly."

Her expression becomes apoplectic with loathing, until finally she abandons herself to face-in-hand weeping.

"I — I'll fix us some dinner, Madame," I say haltingly. "Look — I don't know what the hell made me say that. Please forget it."

She allows me to bring her a platter of bread and butter and preserves. She eats, her flushed cheeks drawn and wet with tears, her mouth twitching convulsively downward at the corners. A thin, simpering cry escapes her as she drops a preserved peach on the sleeve of her black wool sweater. Dazedly raising the sleeve to her mouth, she licks the peach off.

After she has eaten all the bread left on the plate, I sigh cautiously and suggest, "Won't you let me take you home now, so you can rest?"

"I can't sleep," she says dully. "Fine chance I have of resting. You realize they'll be here day after tomorrow?"

"Well, let's not think about it tonight. Try to get some rest and we'll both feel more like working things out tomorrow."

I rise and, reaching down, take her arm to help her up. She pulls away from me with surprising strength. My finger touches the sticky spot on her sleeve where the preserves were dropped.

"Please, Madame Renée, this isn't doing you a bit of good. Let me take you home."

"No . . ." she moans. "Couldn't I sleep here? I can't stand to be alone any more."

I hesitate, then, "Let's not do that again, Madame," I plead gently. "If you sleep here again tonight there's no telling what might —" My words wither into silence under her sudden glare. "I'm sorry," I say lamely.

"Just what did you mean?"

"Nothing. You know I'm happy to have your company, but I've got to keep my privacy. What if somebody had walked in here this morning and found us together — with me naked? . . ."

"What?" she asks expressionlessly.

"Well, how would it look? What would you think if —?"

"Why, you nasty-mouthed —"

"It's the truth, isn't it?" I blurt out. "At least I don't go around peeking at naked old women. I don't —"

"You don't?"

"Hell, no!"

"Of course not," she says sweetly, "you're an angel. You prefer tickling their stomachs with your toes, don't you?"

"Well, I'll be damned!" I stare at her. "I think you owe me an apology, Madame. I can't — Ah, the hell with it."

She snorts, "I don't apologize to kids."

"I think you'd better be going, Madame."

After a time she says in a flat, harsh voice, "I know all about you — you and Michel. You're just alike. Know what I think? I think you and he worked out his marriage together, behind my back."

"I've done everything I know to help you," I say sharply, "and you dare accuse me of conspiring against you!"

"Try and make me believe that."

"Frankly, I don't give a damn what you believe."

Madame Renée rises slowly, not taking her eyes off mine; hers are grave and clear. She opens the door and holds it open, standing in the hall. My shoes creak as I walk around the table to accompany her outside. She doesn't move.

"Well?" I say coldly.

Madame Renée looks curiously into my face. Her voice taunts, "Tell me something — what do you really think of me?"

"Well, if you must know, I think you're the most selfish, false, bad-mannered — Ah, it makes me sick to be with you."

"You're right," she whispers, smiling, "You're right. What else?"

"I'm sorry," I say with genuine regret, "I don't really mean that — but if you'd just act like a human being!"

Still smiling pleasantly she listens carefully, her head slightly averted.

"No," I go on, "it's mostly my fault. I fight you too much."

"Uh-huh?" she murmurs questioningly.

"What do you want, anyway? I never should —"

She doesn't let me finish; her face clots with rage and she flies at me, shaking her clenched fist under my nose; she screams, "You — you — God, how I hate you!"

"Good night, Madame," I say bluntly, my voice quaking in disgust.

She smiles again, uncertainly, and draws back a step. Angrily I reach for the doorknob to shut her out, but she won't move and the door strikes her left shoulder. As I walk away she steps back into the room; she is holding a handful of her left breast, the breast large and cupped in her hand as a lover might hold it.

"You closed the door on my breast," she whines. "You hurt my breast."

The sight of her standing there, grimacing from the imagined pain in her breast, pressing it, squeezing it, is more than I can bear. I burst into laughter. "Ah, what a brute I am! The door didn't touch your breast and you know it. Now, if you want to expose yourself, do it — but for God's sake stop playing with that thing and leave me alone."

"Good night, Monsieur."

"I'll see you out, Madame." And I add hastily, repentant, "I'm sorry. There — don't think of this any more. We'll forget it ever happened. Get some sleep, won't you?" I open the front door to cool night air and darkness.

"Pig!" she whispers in a hesitating voice . . .

At breakfast the next morning, Madame Renée is still complaining about her injured breast. The American halfheartedly consoles her. They apologize to each other, reiterate their feelings of friendship (the American forces his words out through layers of resentment), and then she switches the conversation to Michel and Madeleine's imminent arrival.

Hoping that by his efforts strife may be reduced during Michel's

*visit, the American placates Madame Renée. ("I can't stand all this
friction between us. I worry about Michel just as you do; but most
of all, I worry about you. I hurt your breast last night when that
was the last thing in the world I wanted to do. That's what I mean.
Michel's come between us. That's all. Is it bruised?") She takes
his hand and guides it to her breast. ("Isn't there a little knot —
there?") He feigns worry, struggling against a strong desire to pull
his hand away. ("Believe there is.") He asks her to be as pleasant
as possible to Michel and Madeleine.*

*Michel and Madeleine are waiting for him at his house when the
American comes from the Monastery at noon the next day. He
greets them, cautions them to be patient with Madame Renée, and
the three go across the street for lunch.*

*Madame Renée greets them with an expression of genuine charm,
but refers to Madeleine as "Mademoiselle," a subtle insult that no
one notices except the American.*

*As soon as Christianne has served apéritifs, Madame Renée begins
her inquisition. She states that she is a poor widow who had hoped
for her son's financial support in her growing age (Madeleine expresses assurance that they will see that she's provided for); she
questions whether Michel will break his marriage vows as he did
his final vows as a monk (the American tells Madame Renée that
she put Michel in a monastery school and that he took his final
vows before he had a chance to find out what he really wanted);
she accuses the widowed Madeleine of marrying Michel just to provide a father for her children; she asks Madeleine the cause of her
husband's death, hinting that he might have died of a contagious
venereal disease.*

*Madame Renée then counts on her fingers — contrasting the ages
of the children and the years of Madeleine's marriage — to suggest
that the children might be illegitimate. Finally, when Madame
Renée decries the fact that Michel is a few years younger and will
be at the prime of his masculinity when she is an already used
woman, the incensed Madeleine walks out of the house. Michel
looks desperately at his mother, then dashes after Madeleine. Later,
without returning to Madame Renée's, they catch a train back to
Paris.*

Once alone, Madame Renée brags of her accomplishments to the

American. ("Takes something better than a Parisian strumpet to outwit the old heads . . . He'll see her in a different light now, and be thankful for what I did.") She asks him if he is angry at her actions. ("No . . . All you've done is ruin two lives. And you're proud of it. I don't get angry at things that low.")

She walks across the room, puts a hand on his shoulder and asks him not to be cross with her; she pats his cheek, her fingers turning the gesture into a caress when they reach his lips. He recoils, lashing out at her cruelly, telling her to keep her hands off him. She asks him to leave and he immediately does so.

All afternoon he ponders the events. Unable to stand the gloom of his salon any longer, he walks through the Village streets. He returns home as twilight settles. Madame Renée comes across the street and asks him to supper. Most of the meal passes in silence. Her voice is emotionless when she finally speaks. ("I did what I thought was best. Poor Michel.") She promises to behave better toward the American.

After a while, she reaches across the table and takes his hand. (". . . you hurt me this morning . . . When you told me not to touch you . . . I know you didn't mean that, did you?") When he whispers a convictionless "no," her foot touches his under the table and her hand squeeze intensifies.

He tells her it is time to go. She accompanies him to the door, holding his arm affectionately. She gazes up at him as they say good night. For an instant he can feel her stomach pressing his.

1 april

. . . As I work I am aware of the pervading quietness all about me of Holy Week, serenely unobtrusive despite the influx of pilgrims coming to attend the miraculous services at the Monastery. The very atmosphere is transformed by the single purpose in the hearts of all. Aspects are purified in calmly waiting for the Passion and death of Good Friday, and for the Resurrection of Easter — not in remembrance, but in anticipation of these events which, seemingly, will happen again this week.

Even Madame Renée seems deeply affected. She attends all the offices and usually remains on her knees long after the others have gone. A generous tranquility marks her actions, and she appears content to let the old niggardly probings lie dormant.

In the salon, I find a stack of mail which the postman has left on my table. Idly I look through the letters — until I come to a square blue envelope with a Paris postmark. A sudden flash of nervous fear: Michel's scrawled handwriting. I lay aside the other letters and, filled with misgiving, tear open the envelope.

My dear friend,

After three days of anguish, in which Madeleine refused to see me, I have, finally, persuaded her to listen to my pleas, but it has been impossible for me to work, so will you, please, tell Mama that I cannot send her the money, that she asked for?

My feelings for Mama are very bitter, and I see now, that she was unforgivable in her conduct toward Madeleine, and completely unfair to me, but, I cannot bring myself to write to her, when I know that she makes a joke of every real emotion I have. Will you, therefore, tell her that Madeleine and I will be married, in the Church of St. Thomas Aquinas, on the 10th as planned?

Needless to say, we want both you and Mama, to be here for the great event (!), so, will you do all you can, to make her see reason?

Michel

I reread the letter slowly as all emotions combine into a vague, imponderable dread within me. I fold the letter resentfully, my happiness for Michel smothered under the realization that there will have to be more scenes, more caresses — her hands seeking marasmic comfort, her voice insinuating its demands for more gorging on my heart and blood.

I finish dressing. My mind puckers with the sour taste of mounting uneasiness. Stuffing the letter in my jacket pocket, I walk across the street, a hopeless fury stirring me.

Madame Renée, fresh, gay, opens the door. "Going to the Monastery this morning?" she asks, looking up into my face.

"Yes . . . I got a note from Michel this morning."

"You did?" she says unconcernedly. "I suppose he's still angry with his mama. Poor Michel. What did he have to say? May I read the letter? After all, he is my son."

"Yes, here it is. Now I must go," I tell her abruptly. "See you at noon."

Her hand finds mine and she whispers, "You know, you're like your old self these past few days. It does me good to see you so peaceful and happy."

"I am happy, Madame," I say bluntly. "See you in a few hours."

. . . When I arrive at the chapel, it is already crowded with pilgrims. I kneel far to the back and close my eyes against the stark black hangings. I concentrate away from thought, away from dread.

Silently the monks enter. During Holy Week there's no organ music and the chants are unaccompanied. The Mass is skeletal, austere in tone. Above frequent outbursts of reverberant coughing, chant follows chant, creating calm in all hearts.

. . . Reluctantly I get to my feet, filled with a sensation of loathing. I leave the darkness of polished, empty pews, of smells of dying incense and moldy prayer books. And I walk to her house with the fullness of the past, unable to bear more; unable to bear the inevitable degeneration of myself and of her and of the union of ourselves in anger and despair.

She is prostrate on the couch. Her unblinking eyes are dry and protruding. Fury bursts like obscenity from her lips: "You knew what was in that letter!" It's a dry, catlike sound. "Why'd you leave me?"

"Why should I stay?" I shout back.

"How could Michel —? Why, that —!"

"Don't start that again! I've heard every filthy thing you can say. This morning when you thought you'd won, it was 'poor Michel' — remember? Well, I'm glad he had the —"

"Shut up!" she screams uncontrollably.

"You'll never see clear!"

"You — you left me!"

"Listen to me!" I bellow. "If you promise not to mention this again and to accept Michel's marriage, I'll stay. Otherwise I'm moving out —"

"Get out! Get out!"

I step outside and slam the door with all my strength. Quaking with disgust I stump across the street, as Madame Renée screams her loss to the emptiness.

. . . I think coldly on another plane, a detached plane. I think of the past days of quietness, of healthful activity — destroyed abruptly, savagely. Her words, "You left me," sting with the realization that her grief, her madness are due not so much to losing Michel as to my own brutality. A tinge of remorse grows sickening. I think of possessing her — of going to her and possessing her deliberately, in hatred — giving nothing of myself. That's her obsession — why not?

The sudden ringing of the gate bell, ominous, makes me pause. I get up and go to the salon door.

Calm, sullen, looking as if she can hardly stand, Madame Renée announces quietly, "I have a plan. Want to hear it?"

"Not if it concerns Michel's marriage," I answer, turning away.

"No, it's about something else," she says, following me into the kitchen. "I want to go to England, to visit Jean-Julien's grave. But — there's only enough money for the trip. Can you help me clear up my debts here?"

I resume my seat at the table. "Why not wait till you return to clear them up? I'd let you have the money, but I'm down to my last few bills."

"What can I do then?"

"Why not," I suggest with more warmth, "take some sort of a job? Be good for you. After all, everyone works these days."

"What could I do?"

"Cook, take care of children. You can't imagine how the rest of us would admire you if —"

"You'd like to see me sink to the very bottom, wouldn't you?"

"If you're going to start that —" I glance at her warningly.

"Well, I plan to stay in England. I don't want to be near Michel when he loses his purity."

I grunt. "The answer to that's obvious — we won't discuss it. But I think England's a good solution for you. I'll give you all the money I can raise — but you owe me six thousand francs already and I expect to be paid in full for everything I lend you."

She nods, her lips turned down at the corners in a morose smile.

"When do you leave?"

"As soon as possible. But you haven't heard the rest of my plan." Her voice becomes soft. "You see, I plan to make sure Michel doesn't marry. I intend to kill myself on Jean-Julien's grave the day before the wedding."

"Good God!" I groan. "What'll you think of next? Now I suppose you think I'll get on my knees and beg you to change your mind . . ."

She purses her lips pleasantly. "Are you going to write to Michel?"

"Hell, no."

"No? Why not?"

"Might spoil your plan." Looking at the table, I say wearily, "Can't you understand? I've had all this I can take. What do you want with me, anyway?"

"I'm so sorry," she says in a cracked voice. "I know you. You've needed me and I've failed you. That's what makes you so nervous." Her hand touches the back of my neck, fondles around to my cheek. "Remember the night you got drunk? You wanted me then. If — if you'd just be nice to me . . ."

I feel her breath against my face. I sit stunned as her cheek brushes against mine. Unconsciously I arch my head away, but the tingling juncture creates in me a suppressed excitement as hinted animal tangents converge into focused desire. I recoil, but muscles and nerves become hypnotized. The taunting possibility — the offer of her body to my body, of her nerves to my nerves in brute slakings of inverse pleasure — is irresistibly compelling. I feel myself relax against her and at the same time stiffen with dread. I feel her hand prowling across my chest. A suffocated exhalation rasps loudly from her as her fingers grasp hungrily at my chest and, with a circular motion, caress a wide path to my belt . . . crawl stealthily searching . . . until clothing is no longer a wall and flesh touches living flesh to stimulate engulfing desire. A battery of sensuality is exploded into my belly. Her lips against my face. Through slitted eyes I look downward. The black wool sleeve, disappearing beneath cloth, weaves gently. For a drunken moment my sight is caught by the glistening stain of coagulated sugar where the preserves were dropped on her sleeve. Her lips trail a pattern of sensation across my cheek and I turn to meet them. A whimpering sob escapes her as our mouths join and move liquidly, hungrily against each other. Shock as her mouth exudes its warmth onto mine. I struggle to my feet, my legs shaking so that I can scarcely support my weight. I gasp as she withdraws her hand. Her arms snake their way beneath my armpits. We stand pressed together, hands and mouths and groins searching living tumescence.

But passion falters with a caught breath. A thought bolts through my consciousness — a faint protesting plea that warns me of the moment, begs me to break away. She rubs against me. She is like a bitch in heat dragging me into her, and tensions build hopelessly against the plea. The plea is a fleck, an irritation flecking mucous union, as groins and bellies become united in overwhelming thirst. Her arms, tentaclelike, tighten around me and we float in feverish embrace as the plea sends words tracing themselves in dreamy sequence, like a curl of smoke, through a faraway consciousness. *Mary, conceived without* . . . I lean back against the table, rejecting the flecked words, and pull her full against me, my hands . . . grasping the whale softness . . . *sin, pray for* . . . Suddenly I see a throbbing heartbeat in the hollow of her scarlet throat, then blackness as hands seek intimacy and lips suck lips in hyena laughter . . . *pray for us who have* . . . The plea begging me, pumping words against the diaphragm of my craving. Now or never. I feel her hands grasp my head and lower it inexorably to her throat. I taste the flesh and feel her swallowing muscles beneath my lips. *Mary, conceived without sin, pray* . . . Her belly twists with pleasure in a gigantic serpentine voluptuousness, tossing me into a full dream of carnality. But somewhere in the back of my mind, clogged with screaming desire for her, the resisting plea flickers, hesitates, blinks out, pulsates to the fore as bloods pound out visions of strong legs . . . I lift her higher over me as her hands force my head downward into the opening of her dress . . . *without sin* . . . The two images — nakedness full of rich odors struggling against the dim image of words, blotted and blinded. All things — the past, the hopes — combine into ambivalence attracting, opposing, striving as all futures and all times become the moment . . . The will like an inflexible pole, the will tall and phallic — and something beyond me seeking to bend the will, to change its course for the first time, for the very first time in my life. *Mary . . . con-*

ceived without sin . . . forcing the words against all desire . . . *pray for us who have recourse to thee.* Words die in suffocation as a slow undulation knots the entrails with her bitch cravings. I feel her knuckles hard against my chin as she opens her dress. With the other hand she pushes my mouth against the upward slant of her exposed breast, my lips clutching. Concentrating, not letting it die . . . *without sin, pray for us* . . . Insistent, refusing to escape into the fog of dreams. *Mary* . . . like the faded print of an old newspaper, yellowed, mixed with the reek of my saliva on her breast as my mouth is guided hopelessly toward the goal . . . Muscles in my neck resist. The dread of arriving at the prune nipple. Her hands lock my head, forcing. *Mary* . . . Great exhaustion from struggling against the faded print that now dominates my inner vision. Eyes glimpse blue veins beneath transparent white skin, saliva-streaked, saliva-stenched. *Mary* . . . pleading, begging as the nippled goal draws near. *Mary* . . . and the hard warm shriveled bulb against the corner of my mouth. Fighting back the choking rise of vomit, as muscles tense rigid and all concentration divides between the dreaded goal and the words pulsating clearer. *Mary, conceived without sin* . . . And the faded print is suffused slowly with luminous black, and the old newspaper, yellowed, becomes atmosphere shimmering behind words, destroying the other image as I feel the nipple bending to enter my mouth and my mouth rejecting it in a convulsive wrenching as the . . . rasping whiteness slithers away to sudden nothingness. I shove her away. The room swims wildly. I see her congested face, the exposed breast glistening. Without opening her eyes she flows toward me, arms outstretched. Slowly, dazedly, I lift my arm high in the air and bring my fist smashing down into her face. She crumples to the floor. Dimly I see tiles coming up to meet me as bloodmists float across my eyes.

   Madame Renée, wallowing on the floor, is wrenched with sobs. Slowly, I lower trembling hands to my belt, and stuffing in my shirt tail I buckle my pants. I lower myself into the chair and let my head fall forward on the table, inundated with gratitude for the insistent phrase *For the very first time* — abandoning myself to it — *For the very first time.* I am filled with the gentle, floating pain of unbearable relief.

A scuffing sound attracts my attention. I open my eyes and look downward. The table angle gives a triangular view of the floor. Absently I watch, seeing only her sturdy black shoes and the hem of her dress as she gets to her feet. I watch the shoes turn sideways, hesitate, then disappear beyond my range of vision. I don't move for a long time after the front door clicks shut . . .

The American goes to the Monastery for Vespers. Returning home, he finds a note from Madame Renée. She tells him that she has left for England and asks him not to follow her. (". . . my disappointment in losing . . . both you and my son is more than I can be expected to accept; and after your conduct today, I know that you have never been sincere in your feelings for me — and that you never will be . . . Someday you will realize that my every action was dictated by the unique thought of your welfare and his.")

She asks him to sell her belongings, pay her debts, and forward any remaining money to her. She ends by saying that she will live in England permanently, that she is breaking all ties with Michel, and that she forgives the American for his part in her remorse.

The American writes Michel, advising him to marry as planned, and encloses Madame Renée's note. He then goes and tells Father Clément what has happened and asks to be allowed to return to the Monastery. A few days later he moves back into his old cell.

6 april

Movements are slow. Eyes are leaden. Cigarette smoke curls about my face as I unpack the last of my clothes. I open the window of my old cell. The morning smell of distance enters fresh on cool sunlight.

And after the long darkness of Holy Week there is the lightness, the joy of Easter morning in this Monastery. Festive colors and candles and the resounding organs quiet these forty days. And through the texture of morning, the delicate radiance of many and often-chanted *Alleluias* sung by monks who seem to lift themselves above the earth with the miracle of the Resurrection. On this final day they breathe the chants — sounds made by the human heart, restrained overflowings of joy too profound for jubilation. The long vigil of Lent is past.

I press my forehead against the bench in front of me. The lingering obsession with Madame Renée splotches dissonant color on the soul's retina, destroying the hint, forever the hint. The gray hair, the beautiful face shrivel space and time into a knot that can't be swallowed — a knot of my own guilt, a knot of my own hatred.

Shut out the mystery of her without ever understanding. But words haunt me, whispering back from the mind's crypt, old words never meaningful until now. Pray for the hated. Sink first into chasms of destruction, and in totality of humiliation build again. Know depths first before black hate can find its light of compassion and pity.

Pray for her, for she gave you this — these walls, these ringing silences, these thirsts. As the seed must be bruised from its outer shell before it can grow fruit, so must the soul. Chasms of destruction turn roots to air. The plow kills before it gives life, doing quickly what earth's timeless erosion never accomplished. Her gift was the killing gift of life without which this might never have been . . .

I walk from the chapel stunned with the fantastic thirst for solitude on my lips. The morning passes, and afternoon grows into lengthening shadows. My fingers absently examine flowering greenery; and inside, the soul cringes and begs for rest.

And later, when Compline is over, I walk in the garden. Magical spring night. Infinite blackness of silent skies, alive with drifting stars. I sit in the orchard, and the night grows late. The air is perfumed with blossoming lime and pear trees . . .

And it turns, slowing, this thing within me turns and dissolves in night. Coolness against face. Careening night of hidden sounds rising from the water's edge to float low over the countryside, bringing new life.

I lean on the wall. Fingers idly explore rough seams of mortar where great stones have been joined. But it's dark — living darkness of skies and clouds of stars and earth's purity of resurrected night, of resurrected body.

Now they sleep. In many cells they sleep, and in houses across the way. Only I am awake at this hour. The air becomes rarefied and begins to chill. They sleep while I remain awake. It dissolves slowly. Lips taste wetness. Chords break loose and create freshness. Universality of desires, of loves, of climates of thought this deepening night.

Night of all nativities. Moisture of lateness. Bend low. Lean on the wall. Feel the beginnings of reeling vertigo and —

No. Turn. It can't be borne. Listen for sounds that bring you back. It's too soon, and the weakness too great. Listen. Sifted undertones of crickets' lonely raspings hanging like luminous mists in the Valley below. They live out there, outside the high walls; they breathe and sleep and are nourished. And there's no understanding now. It's the mystery of all things. Clutch something there in the dark. Hold to it. The grasses are wet. Hold. Look at the night and beyond to the Source of all nights and of all things, things coming alive in spring and reposing until the light of another day. It is late in our lives, forever late.

. . . Move away from the wall. Feel shrubs against your legs as you walk. And the change is deep and not a change to be seen. There must forever be bread and sleep and twisting in a bed of dreams. The change is in the greatest of all acceptances. Let it be in quietness, flowing out with its prayer, easily. For there can be no more loneliness.

Open the door of the cell. Step inside. Let the words flow no longer cramped and stingy, but outward in long undulating waves of easiness.

Pray for the hated. Somewhere in the green health of the English countryside a woman dreams distorted dreams. God be with her this night. God cleanse all things this night. God turn the wax embryo and puncture the transcendence of trembling viscera.

The window is opened wide. Pray for the hated. No, there is nothing hated. Greater than that, the night lifts words stratospheres above to all mankind sleeping outside these walls. They soar into tenderness for all the promised and unpromised; for all the sleepy-eyed and wakeful-eyed; for all the predawn coughers and chokers and turners-in-bed; for all the hands clutched soft and feelingless beside faces in sleep; for all the legs moving under covers seeking comfort. All that is mine tonight. And more: the sudden waking pierced with bolts of terror in black rooms; the bloated bellies in dark alleyways; the drunken half-mad horror of sleepless women who finger the ribbed edges of a coin while they become hunks of meat glued to other hunks of meat in a loveless embrace; the sacramental sleep of blessed, cursed, great and ungreat, all seeking, seeking, seeking . . . The world in Thy hands, the world turning in universal sameness forever. Calm the hearts, calm the sleeps and sleep again. Turn in beds and feel quakings die, feel quakings become a long sigh, and before the sigh is completed become slumber, slumber for all the soft midnight hours. All of that . . . always . . .

I crawl into my cot, crawl between clean sheets damp with morning freshness. I pull them close about me in a cell smelling of stone and dew-filled air from the deep lands alive.

Night of all nativities. Night of all nights with its waking morning. Quiet, rhapsodic joy this night of return.

PART III

Short Stories

Notes

⟶

THE SHORT STORIES and exercises ("Diversions") in this section have been chosen to illustrate the wide range of interests that encompasses the creative world of John Howard Griffin. They range in nature from serious to fanciful, from tragedy to comedy, and touch on many bases between these extremities.

They stretch from the taut horrors of a Southern lynching to the wandering thoughts of a professor in Scotland; from the antics of an old monk in mythical Dleifsnam to the disillusioned maneuvers of a young lady in San Diego to the multi-talents of one Mabel Bamberg.

There are few references to his short stories in Griffin's journals. The stories were completed usually at one writing and were written to exemplify an exact problem or need at the particular time. One of the stories included in this sampling, for example, was written expressly for one of Griffin's friends and never intended for publication.

Several years ago, when asked his opinion of contemporary short story writing, Griffin responded:

> I'm afraid I have none. Since I work very long hours, I have no time for anything except eating and sleeping. I would like very much to read short stories, but I also refrain from doing it on purpose, for I am so imitative and so afraid of learning trends that I avoid anything that will teach me. One of the great delusions that we have today is our idea that knowledge should be unlimited. For a writer, that seems to be true only of knowledge about the human heart and soul; knowledge of techniques, trends and rules becomes stultifying (at least to me), and it seems best to avoid any contact with them even though that may be a great personal sacrifice. I've seen too many potential talents destroyed through training and study in the creative fields. This does not imply that there

should not be a rigid personal standard of accomplishment, for there must be, but it is best for technique to evolve from basic knowledge rather than to be developed from refinements of knowledge. For that reason I avoid reading as much as possible.

*

"The Whole World in His Hands" is a poignant account of a woman's furtive efforts to keep her sister alive. The sister, whose physical ailments are negligible, has lost the will to live and has settled herself in bed, resigned to await death. The story analyzes the question of endurance, the ability of a person to rise above the sometimes cruel, or neglectful, restrictiveness of human attention. It asserts forcefully a theme that runs through much of Griffin's work — every human being's need for individual dignity. "The Whole World in His Hands" first appeared in *New Voices 2: American Writing Today* (Hendricks House, Inc., New York, 1955).

"The Cause" is a nightmare story, preoccupied with man's dehumanization — the blood lust of man, fully matured and implacable in its demands. It is tragic because it exists submerged in an illusion of human affection: the lyncher's affection for his victim. Almost tenderly he destroys his victim. This happens, one dredges into it, stumbles upon it everywhere in life, and is always shocked anew by it. Since it is unbearable when perceived, we cling to the "good things" and choose not to face the beast that has been formed within these "good things."

"Sauce for the Gander" has been an amazing story of success. Griffin wrote it in a few hours one afternoon to lift up the spirits of a close friend in New York who was very ill, and mailed it to him without even keeping a carbon. Victor Weybright of the New American Library was present when the story arrived and immediately telephoned Griffin for permission to publish it.

Griffin was horrified at the thought of the story being published, but Weybright assured him it was a nice little piece and nothing to be ashamed of. It first appeared in *New World Writing No. 3* (The New American Library, New York, 1953), and then quickly sold to Sweden, Denmark, France and England. It finally found its way into a textbook, *Communicative Reading* (The Macmillan Company, New York, 1956).

"Diversions." These five exercises or sketches came out of Griffin's correspondence with Maxwell Geismar. "During a particularly difficult period in my life," Griffin explains, "I felt that I needed to start over with writing, to become 'disciplined' and to develop techniques of characterization. The characterization involved in mere names fascinated me."

Geismar wrote Griffin about other of his writer friends — Nelson Algren, James Jones, William Styron, Truman Nelson and John Hersey, among others. They wondered what would happen if each were given the name of a character and asked to sit down and write a sketch with no other clue than the name. A time limit of no more than thirty minutes was allowed for each exercise.

"The idea reminded me of the manner in which different composers have treated musical themes, such as the *Dies Irae*," Griffin noted in his journal entries during 1961. "Our vague intention had been to send a list of names to a number of writers, each to do sketches. It never really materialized, except that the names and the technique of quick characterization around an incident intrigued me. I wrote many of these, at least one a day, over a period of many months."

The five that appear here are unchanged from the original efforts: *John Selfridge, Elise von Hofmannsthal, Polly Harlow, Mabel Bamberg* and *Professor MacIntosh.*

THE WHOLE WORLD IN HIS HANDS

Around four o'clock, the laughter and shouting of school children, as they walked past on the dirt lane in front of her shack, caused Sister Lissie to open her eyes. She sat up in her chair, pushed the quilts to one side, and nudging a pair of tin-rimmed glasses up on her forehead she rubbed her eyes with the heels of her hands. Gradually the room faded into focus. She glanced at the bed and saw that Sister Callie had not moved.

The fire had gone out. Lifeless November sunlight of the Texas sky stretched pale across the unpainted wooden floor. To Sister Lissie's waking senses the air smelled strong of snuff and apples and kerosene. Gathering strength, she hoisted her almost frozen body from the chair. Quietness had returned. The room seemed to shake with quietness. Sister Lissie rubbed her chunky hands together to warm them. The rasping sound was magnified so loud that she winced. She waddled across the room on tiptoe, her slippers thudding in emptiness. At the bed, she leaned forward, supporting herself by grasping one of the brass bedposts where a carved rose felt like ice beneath her fingers.

A large flake of gray ash had floated over and settled on her older sister's bony black temple. Sister Lissie flicked it off and watched it fall to pieces and sift to the floor.

Sister Callie lay on her side, motionless and thin in the sagging bed. Lissie hesitated, staring uneasily at her kinky white hair and at the wrinkled folds around her eyes. But the old woman's steady breathing continued and, reassured, Lissie turned away.

A few moments later, Sister Lissie stooped down to light the stove. A match sizzled into flame, loud on the silence, causing her nerves to tremble.

A soft knock on the door shattered silence and Lissie jerked her hand away from the stove.

"Who's there?" she whispered, quickly throwing the match back into a nest of kindling.

"It's Brother Vernon Satterwhite, Sister Lissie."

"Thank God," she murmured to herself. The silence would be broken and the noises would stop having loudness. She pulled her glasses back down to the bridge of her flat nose and opened the door to even colder air.

"I'm thankful you come, Brother Vernon," she said, looking up into the smiling face of the old preacher towering above her. "Something about your prayers seems to uplift poor Callie and give her the determination to go on a while longer."

"How is she this afternoon?" the preacher asked, closing the door behind him and taking off his black fedora hat.

"She's low. Awful low," Sister Lissie said. She pulled a second chair close to the stove. The old man shook his head regretfully and sat down, placing his hat on the floor beside him.

Sister Lissie twisted the top from her snuff can. "Would you care for a pinch, Brother Vernon?" He dipped his thumb and forefinger into the powder and deposited it in his lower lip.

"Here, you can spit in this," Lissie said, bending forward to place an empty coffee can on the floor between his feet. "Heard your radio program last week," she went on, straightening up. "It was just grand, just the grandest ever."

"Well thank you, thank you," he nodded vigorously, smiling into the reddening stove window. Suction in the flue roared pleasantly and the metal band around the potbellied stove began to glow. After a moment, the preacher turned to her. "You look tired, Sister Lissie. It's a hardship on you taking care of Sister Callie all by yourself."

"Oh, she's not no trouble," Lissie said. "If she'd just talk to me once in a while. Can you say a prayer for her, Brother Vernon . . . — soon's she wakes up?"

"That's what I'm here for." The old man's voice was gentle. "I'm going to pray a special blessing on her. And don't you worry — the Lord'll take care of her. If she'll just look up to Him, God'll heal her body." He settled back in his chair, folding his generous hands under his chin. His lower lip protruded and worked the snuff as he frowned off into space.

Sister Lissie looked at him for a long time before deciding to break the silence. "How's things at the barber shop?" she asked finally.

"Very well, Sister Lissie," he said in a livelier voice. "It seems my radio program helps my business. Did I tell you about the young man that was in my shop the other day? He heard me on the radio, so he decided to come to me for his haircuts. When he got into the chair, he says, 'You're not the Brother Vernon, the one that prays and sounds as though you're busting a blood vessel, are you?' So, I says, 'Yes, I'm he, Young Man, and I'm always glad to look up to heaven and shout — and if I bust a blood vessel for the Lord, let 'er go!' "

Lissie leaned back in her chair and grinned. "You just love Him too much not to holler for Him, don't you, Brother Vernon?"

In the gathering dusk, Lissie saw a mouthful of shining teeth, flecked with gold.

"Yeah," he whispered expansively, "He put shoes on my feet, Sister Lissie." Then, in a louder voice, "Say, how long's Sister Callie going to sleep? It's getting close to supper time at my house and I catch it if I come in after the food gets cold."

"Oh, she'll wake up before long," Lissie said quickly.

He shook his head in the gloom. "What'n the world come over her to make her like this?"

"I don't know." The chair creaked under Lissie's shifting weight. "She's poor and old and . . ." She wrinkled her forehead, trying to find words. "So she's just dying."

Firelight glistened yellow from the preacher's wedding band. "I can't understand it," he said. "She's always been such a important woman. Why, she and Brother Furgeson were —"

"That's just it," Lissie interrupted. "But she lost all that when he passed on. I been trying to make her feel big and important — you know — like she used to be. 'Cause she ain't ready to die yet. I figure if she could just feel big and important enough to want to live . . . But she won't even hardly talk to me at all."

Burning wood popped in the stove. Lissie's head seemed to fill up with dead weight when she tried to think too hard.

"I just don't know," Brother Vernon muttered.

"Well, something's got to change," Lissie said. "I can't leave the poor thing while she's like this, and I ain't been able to take in any washing in more'n a month. We're just about out of money." Her voice trailed off into silence. Frosty air seeped up through the floor. She stomped her feet to warm them.

"Tell me," Preacher Vernon said. "How come a woman like you never got herself a husband?"

"Me?" Lissie laughed quietly. "I don't know. Of course, Callie was always the pretty one, and the smart one, too." Pride lightened her voice. "She was the smartest thing. She and Brother Furgeson used to go a lot — clear to St. Louis once. But she didn't have much gift for sewing or running a house — things like that. I used to make all her nice dresses. I guess I just didn't have time for marrying. Poor old thing, I never thought it'd be her living in my house like this. They had such nice places all their life . . ."

"Seems like. Well," he said after a long moment, "if she don't wake up in a minute, I'll just have to be going."

The alarm clock ticked loudly as they waited. In the deepening gloom, light from the stove window flickered red on the wallpaper above Callie's sleeping form. Lissie's footsteps shuffled across the room. She hovered over the bed and strained her eyes. A glistening ball of sweat dribbled across Sister Callie's forehead.

"Well, she ain't near waking up, Brother Vernon," she said disappointedly.

The preacher lingered long enough to kneel beside the bed and mumble a prayer. Then, bracing himself against the cold, he left, clicking the door quietly shut behind him.

II

Sister Lissie returned to her long wait, and tried to think of something big, really big and glorious to bring Sister Callie out of her sickness and make her want to go on living. But something like that was sure to cost a lot. She lighted the kerosene lamp and reached across the table for her purse. When she counted her money, there were only six dollars. She sat for a long time and stared helplessly at the bills clutched in her hand. From the bed, a rattling snore punctured the silence.

Six dollars. "Lord, help me think of something, something," she prayed, in the sudden terror of realizing how little was left. She would have to put more water in the soup from now on. The clock ticked off the endless time. Sister Lissie prayed until calm returned.

She opened her eyes wearily. Maybe if she brightened up the room a little. Sister Callie always loved bright things, even if she did pretend never to notice them. From the corner, rasping sounds cleared into good breathing, and Lissie relaxed a little. She took down the faded cheesecloth curtain from the back window and began lacing a long strip of red wool yarn into it to make a border at the bottom. That way, when Sister Callie turned her face away from the wall and looked about the room, she'd be sure to see it.

Gradually, Lissie became absorbed in her task, holding the curtain close to her glasses: a woman alone in the night, alive and awake in the flickering circle of lamplight. Slowly, from the depths of some mystery beyond her consciousness, her lips opened, and the silence of the small room echoed back to her old-woman's throaty voice as she talked to herself, sang to herself, searching an answer too great for her mind. The words of a spiritual found voice as she forgot the world and the time in her careful work. *"He's got the little babies, in His hands,"* she crooned. *"He's got the little bitsy babies, in His hands. He's . . . got . . . the . . . whole . . . world . . . in . . . His . . . hands."*

A car horn blasted outside, and drunken laughter faded away with skidding tires. The whole world in His hands. The whole world out there living and dying and praying and sinning and laughing and crying. Lissie got to her feet and ambled to the back window to hang the curtain. "The whole world — that's something sure enough big," she said to herself, arranging the folds. The whole world and something exciting to make Sister Callie want to live. She tilted her head from side to side and studied her handwork through weak glasses, a faint smile on her face. The wind ground away outside. She stepped back and admired the curtain with the red border. Something bright and exciting. Maybe if she made a real nice dress, the kind that Sister Callie used to wear, something she'd be proud to get out in. Maybe if she fixed up the other curtains. Sister Lissie returned to her chair grinning. The night, full of gusts and loneliness, with its own strangeness, made

Lissie decide to spend every penny, if necessary, to get Sister Callie out of her sickness. Sister Lissie sat down and pulled the quilts around her. In her mind, she'd found a way. She nudged her glasses up on her forehead and settled back to admire the new curtain. Tomorrow was Sunday. First thing Monday, then, she'd go down and get about four yards of percale for the dress, and maybe some scrim for new curtains for the other windows. Something she could dye green.

After a time, she blew out the lamp and dropped off to sleep.

Late in the night, Sister Callie's choking caused Lissie to sit bolt upright in her chair. She threw the quilts to one side and ran to the bed. Numb with exhaustion and chill, Lissie gathered up her sister in her arms and cradled her skeletal body until it relaxed again into quietness. The fragment of sleep had destroyed the night's strangeness. Percale was forty-nine, maybe fifty-nine cents a yard. The new dress wasn't the solution it had seemed earlier. Lissie's body was wracked with paroxysms of chill. She started to turn the frail body loose for long enough to get her shoes on, but a whimpering protest stopped her. Dully, she wondered how she could feed the older woman in the days to come. She felt the cover's edge with her feet and slipped them beneath, but Sister Callie's body was unyielding and there was no room at the side.

At the point where discomfort and chill were becoming unbearable, she heard quiet slumber. She lowered Sister Callie's head to the pillow. Sitting in the dark, she put her face into her hands and began sobbing gently. Far in the distance it seemed to her that she heard rain dripping from the eaves.

Next day a deadly Sunday calm settled over the room. Rain poured against the windows, and early in the afternoon it was as dark as twilight. Lissie huddled in her chair and prayed for God to show her a way. Her glance fell on the new curtain which Callie had not noticed.

Sister Callie had not moved for hours when suddenly she rolled over on her back to an accompaniment of loud bedsprings and began babbling to the shadows. Lissie rushed to the bed. The older woman seemed gray and lifeless against the white pillows.

Rain blew in sprays, staining a widening circle of wallpaper above the bed. Daylight faded and Sister Callie got lower in herself.

Dampness crept in, cold and numbing. The day was made for dying.

"She's trying to die," Lissie cried. "Lord, she don't want to live. Help me think of something to bring the poor thing out of this."

Above the steadily falling rain, the loud clacking of the clock attracted her attention. Five-thirty, almost time for Brother Vernon's broadcast. He was a great man to get to talk to all those people.

Bedsprings rasped as Sister Callie flopped over on her side, mumbling with her nose against the wall. Lissie stood in the middle of the room and listened until the older woman's babbling drifted off into even breathing.

A flash of lightning flooded the room with greenish glare. Lissie gasped. Another followed, and then it was all blackness in the room, and a frozen, rumbling silence.

"Lord! Show me a way!" Lissie cried in terror. She moved in darkness to the bed and put her hand on Sister Callie's thin shoulder. "Honey, Honey. Talk to me, talk to me, talk to me! If you don't talk to me, if you don't say something . . . Honey, please —" The shoulder did not move, did not wince under the tightness of Lissie's grasp. She turned. Her footsteps padded heavily and rapidly across the room. Parting the curtains, she peered out for some sign of help, some human soul to call to. Puddles, gray and muddy in the rainfilled dusk, formed in the lane as far as she could see. Here and there a light glistened through sheets of rain. Thunder rattled bottles on the shelves.

Lissie dropped the curtain and turned back into the room. She picked up the clock and held it close to her face. Twenty minutes to six. Thank God, Brother Vernon would be on in a few more minutes. He would talk through the little speaker on her battery radio, and his words would find a way to stop her trembling. Brother Vernon . . . Lissie stood motionless for a moment, half cringing. Then, grabbing her headscarf, she ran out into the rain as fast as her heavy legs could move.

She was soaked and her glasses were fogged so that she could hardly see, when she climbed Brother Vernon's porch steps. The old man, covered with raincoats and carrying an umbrella, was closing the door behind him, stepping out on the porch. They talked together for a moment. Through the frozen cloth of her dress,

Lissie felt his huge hand touch her shoulder. "God bless you, Sister Lissie. It might work. We'll try, anyhow." Lightning turned his face green and pinpointed a sudden background of door and mailbox behind him.

Breathing heavily, Sister Lissie sloshed back to her house, too tired to hurry anymore.

She stood in front of the stove and dried herself with a towel and put on dry clothes. She lighted the lamp and put the pot of vegetable soup on to boil, noticing with surprise that almost half of it was gone. "Shouldn't have let it boil down like that," she said vaguely. "Little as we got. The stove must've been hotter'n I thought."

At six o'clock she turned up the lamp wick to its highest brightness and bent over and put her hand on Sister Callie's shoulder.

"Wake up, Honey. I got some hot soup for you. Wake up now." She felt Callie's shoulder shrug.

"All right, Honey, but you ought to eat a little something," she said, relieved that Callie was conscious. "It's about time for Brother Vernon's program. You want to hear it?"

Again Sister Callie's shoulders shrugged beneath the quilts.

The small radio clicked and hummed. Lissie put more wood on the fire and the room began to smell dry again. Static crackled from the speaker as she turned the dial until she came to the sounds of clapping and singing. The smell of simmering soup filled the room. The rain, the storm seemed further away somewhere out in the night, as jubilant voices of singing people brightened the atmosphere within. The spiritual came in clearer through static. Sitting in her chair, Lissie quietly joined her voice to the music, humming at first, then singing the words. Slowly it took control of her and she began snapping her fingers and weaving her square body in time. Brother Vernon's voice broke through as the singing faded abruptly into the background.

"Jesus is truly the light of the land," he began softly. "I'm glad to say that I've come into your homes — byways or wherever you are — in your automobiles maybe." Lissie turned up the volume as a piano accompanied the preacher's words and the singing and clapping died out. "I just want to say tonight that I'm praying a special blessing on Sister Callie Furgeson, who is ill-sick tonight."

"Callie!" Lissie cried. "Listen to that. Your name's on the

radio!" A shock of pride almost paralyzed Sister Lissie, even though she was expecting the words.

"I'm dedicating this program tonight to that dear lady, and saying that if you just look up to Him, God'll always heal your body. I'm *glad* to say that He's a doctor that never lost a patient! And so tonight, dear brothers and sisters, I want Sister Callie Furgeson to know that all the thousands of radio listeners is remembering her in their prayers. May God ever bless her and ever keep her!" A chorus of fervent amens sounded through the speaker. Lissie's gaze was fixed on Sister Callie's back.

"Oh, Callie," she whispered breathlessly. "Listen to that. Your name is on the radio. Why, you're famous! I didn't know that!" She watched in anguish as the old woman began trembling under the quilts.

"Sister Callie Furgeson, I'm preaching for *you* tonight. For the Lord's made a way for you!" The preacher's voice climbed in pitch. "When your way was dark, and you seemed not to find a way, He *made* a way for you. Yeah! He touched you early this morning! And He told you to get up and blow a little harder for Him! Yeah!" Lissie's voice echoed the "yeah!" and she watched the spellbound figure of Sister Callie as the preacher went on with his sermon.

In a trance of slow motion, Sister Callie was, seemingly without moving a muscle, turning over to face the radio, her eyes wide open in disbelief, her hollow jaws puffed out smooth. A thousand expressions streaked across her bewildered face.

"Folks," Preacher Vernon was saying, "our little time is almost up, and in closing I just want to say that when Sister Callie gets back on her feet, I'm sure she's going to come down here and take charge of our adult class. We all know how much she traveled, how much she know. Now, let's have some music!"

The piano banged to the fore and voices were raised. Lissie's gaze did not leave Sister Callie's shrunken face. "You're *famous*, Honey," she whispered uncertainly. "I didn't know that. Why, there's thousands of people hearing your name!"

Rain tore at the windows, but the room seemed warm and light. Sister Callie worked herself up in her bed and leaned back against her pillows. She stared into the space of daydreams, a vague smile gumming its way across her face. Sister Lissie noticed, and her grin became fixed as though it were aching, and her eyes were shining too bright. She watched red highlights from the fire glisten on Sister Callie's wrinkled cheekbones.

"Let's have some soup now, Honey," Sister Lissie suggested cautiously. Sister Callie nodded without looking at her.

Standing above the stove, stirring the last dregs of soup, Sister Lissie felt the great pain of tiredness mingled with happiness. She nudged her tin-rimmed glasses up on her forehead with the back of her hand and then went on stirring. She wondered if the Lord had done a miracle or if it was just hearing her name on the radio that had brought Sister Callie back. "Maybe both," she suggested to herself. She stirred the soup more rapidly and the words of the spiritual returned to haunt her lips. *"He's got the little bitsy babies, in His hands,"* she crooned, and then skipping part of it: *"He's got you and me, Sister, in His hands. He's . . . got . . . the . . . whole . . . world . . . in . . . His . . . hands . . ."* She cast an almost awed glance back over her shoulder, and saw Sister Callie, who was sitting up in bed, lift a thin hand and frizz up her gray hair.

THE CAUSE

───────────────────────────────────────➤

"Why Lily, what's the matter?" Myrtle asked, allowing the kitchen screen to close on its springs.

"They's going to kill one of the boys," Lily said in a voice that rasped deep in her throat.

"What?" Myrtle drew the word out and stepped quickly to the table where the aging Negro was depositing two sacks of groceries.

"Yes'm, they is," Lily mumbled without looking up. "It's all over town. Mister Dan can tell you."

"What on earth are you talking about?" Myrtle asked. She bent her stout body forward in an attempt to gaze into the Negro's face. "My Lord, has something —?"

"Nome, not yet," Lily said quickly. "But you can sure see it's coming, Miss Myrtle." She nodded her head of kinky white hair and began unloading the sacks. "Them men sitting around in front of the stores with their whittling sticks, staring at every nigger that goes by. They got a funny look on their faces —"

"Oh, Lily — you're imagining."

"It's the truth, Miss Myrtle. They got the idea of seeing a black boy hang. It's in them like a lust now. And can't a thing turn it away. What're you cooking there? — gingerbread?" Lily asked, sniffing loudly and rubbing a large bony hand over her eyes.

"Yes, doesn't it smell good?" Myrtle said. Her head scarcely came to the tall Negro's shoulder as the two women stood together and unpacked the canned goods in silence for a moment.

"Listen, Lily," Myrtle said gently. "Just because somebody hung a dummy on Main Street last night — that don't mean . . ."

"Yes'm, it do. That's what put the idea in their heads. Now they won't rest till they really see a hanging. I seen it before, Miss Myrtle. It's something around their eyes."

"It makes you sick to think about it," Myrtle sighed.

"Yes'm. They're just going to wait and then, when that lust gets right, they'll pick theirselves up a nigger boy and go hang him. Lord . . . Well, I better get on down and fix a bite to eat for Junie and Malvie. Anything else I can help you with up here?"

"No, I don't think so. I wonder what's keeping Dan?"

"He's unloading the chicken feed, Miss Myrtle." Lily stooped and hoisted a sack of her own groceries from the floor of the back porch. "Thank him for giving me a lift into the store, won't you?" she called over her shoulder.

"Lily?"

"Yes'm," the Negro said, turning back. She wrinkled her forehead and stared questioningly.

"Why don't you talk Junie and Malvie into going away somewhere till this blows over?"

"You worried, too, ain't you?" Lily asked.

"They keep talking this 'mongrelization.' And since the cross-burning up on the hill last week. I just don't know, Lily. Why not send them to their grandmother's for a while?"

"I'm sure going to do that," Lily nodded. "Yes sir, that's just what I'm going to do."

Geese grazing the sun-parched grass of the back yard honked and ran hissing after her as she walked away. Myrtle Ferguson listened to her mumblings and watched until she disappeared around the corner of the barn. Beyond the pea patch, she saw the front porch of Lily's shanty with two dogs lying in the dust beside its plank steps.

"Ed, you've got to quit. I can't stand any more of this," Elsie Buchanan finally burst out. "Those men mean business."

The town constable sat in a cane-bottomed chair beside his kitchen table, looking blankly at the scrawled note in his hand.

"If I just knew who they was," he said. "It's like quicksilver. You can't put your finger on anybody. They're hanging these damned effigies and burning crosses right under my nose. But you don't know who —"

"I don't care who it is. You've got a wife and two children to think about. Please, Honey. When they write you a letter and threaten to dynamite you if you make one false move — then I want you to quit."

"Everybody'd think I was a coward. Hell, I'm on their side, but I'm supposed to keep order around here."

"They had two sticks of dynamite laid in the ground around that cross!" Elsie said too loudly. "They'd've blown you up. If you'd made one wrong move, they'd've blown you up."

"They're going to hang somebody, I know that," he sighed.

Elsie threw a handful of potatoes in deep fat and a hissing filled the room.

The constable turned, put both elbows on the table and studied the newspaper account once more. He stared at the photograph of the tarpaper dummy dressed in men's clothes, and read again the signs, crudely painted in red, attached to each of its legs: THIS NEGRO TRIED TO GO TO A WHITE SCHOOL, one of them said, and the other: WOULDN'T THIS BE A HORRIBLE WAY TO DIE.

"Promise me you won't get in on it?" Elsie pleaded.

"What the hell can I do?"

"If they do anything, it'll be after dark. Soon's it gets dark, take off down the highway. If anybody calls, I'll tell them you're down there investigating gambling in some of the taverns. Please, Honey . . ."

"OK . . . OK."

The last light of August dusk fell over the countryside. A hot breeze, fragrant with odors from the earth and the parched fields sifted through the curtained window above Myrtle Ferguson's sink.

Dan Ferguson sat quietly at the kitchen table with his hand resting on the newspaper and watched it grow night outside.

Myrtle was peeling carrots for supper, absently watching how the paring knife cut away bright orange ribbons that curled into the white sink. Far across the west meadow, vague forms of haystacks rose on the horizon. Myrtle shook her head at the view. Instead of looking peaceful, as it usually did, the whole countryside was murky to her eyes, like when someone in a farmhouse is terribly sick or gone mad, she thought. The strong sweet odor of gingerbread struck her as being out of place.

The chair squeaked behind her as her husband shifted his great bulk. She heard him sigh.

"Is anything wrong?" she asked.

"No."

"There's lynch talk, ain't there?"

"Well, they shouldn't have made Leesville the guinea pig. All the other towns around here got integration postponed a year. Hmph. But they order us to go ahead and take the niggers. It's not right."

"Don't you get mixed up in any of it," Myrtle said.

"I'm not," he answered disgustedly.

Myrtle watched him sitting there with his mind a mile away while she set the table for supper. Sometimes he'd dream that way, with his face puckered up and squinting at something invisible right there in front of his eyes. She'd seen him do it on many a Sunday when there was work to be done and he wouldn't break the Sabbath to go out and do it; and she'd know early Monday morning he'd strike out and come back at noon looking relaxed and normal again. But it was something else he was dreaming about this evening. There was something violent and cruel in it. She could sense it, something gloating and obscene in his heavy paunch. And in the man she loved, it turned Myrtle sick inside of herself.

If they'd just hold off till the preacher got there to hold his yearly revival, she thought hopefully. Dan was devoted to the young man, who always stayed at their house. She was sure that if they'd wait till he got there, Dan wouldn't join in with them. Otherwise, she knew right now he was dreaming of it, seeing it in his mind, seeing a nigger boy dying.

"It's about ready," she said.

Dan roused himself and glanced idly about him while she brought the meat to the table. Crock jars of warm milk stood in the corner of the linoleum floor next to jars of yesterday's milk which was thickly coated with yellow cream. His boots and work shoes were neatly arranged on a newspaper by the door.

"That sure smells good," he said, shaking his head as though to clear it and forcing a smile on his face.

*

Lily turned away from the screen door of her little two room shack.

"Junie's never been this late before," she moaned. "I just know it. Something's happened to him, Malvie."

"I tell you, he's down on the creekbank partying with Iris," Malvie chuckled. "He told me he was going to meet up with her this evening." The older boy sat at the table and cut into a pork chop. "Come on away from that door. He's all right."

Lily opened the screen wide enough to spit snuff juice into the night.

"Did he say when he'd be coming home?"

"He said around sundown."

"It's after sundown now."

"Bless this food and forgive us our sins," Dan Ferguson mumbled hastily.

"Amen," Myrtle whispered.

She lifted her head and looked at his heavy but gentle face above the apron of his blue striped overalls, saw it preoccupied and flushed to an unnatural expression, as though the flesh were puffed; and his pale blue eyes under thick gray eyebrows were clouded.

Without speaking, she passed a bowl of yellow buttered corn to her husband.

Dan waited until he had finished cutting off a portion of browned shortribs before taking the corn from her hand.

"Dear God," Lily whispered as she scraped the congealed pork chop bones from Malvie's plate into the darkness beside the door-stoop. Dogs scrambling below stirred a billow of dust in the out-streaking light. "I'm going to walk up and see if Mister Dan won't tell me what to do."

"No, I'll head on down around the creekbank," Malvie said from the darkness out by the shed, his voice hushed and uneasy, carrying clearly in the night's stillness. "I'll find him and bring him back. Don't you worry."

"Let me come along too, Malvie. I know something's happened."

"You stay right there. I'll find him," she heard the boy's voice fading away.

She stepped down from the stoop and walked to the side where she could have a view of the Fergusons' kitchen. She saw their light, but restrained herself from going toward it. Malvie didn't want her to for some reason. She'd go back in and wash up the dishes, and then if Junie wasn't back . . .

She sniffed the distant odor of cattle and dried grasses, a faint odor of manure and sweetness, a gathering odor of night rising up from the countryside. In her ears, she noticed the loudness of the silence — not even a cricket, not even a frog or a leaf stirring.

Myrtle Ferguson watched Dan hoist himself up from the table and stroll out through the screen door. Geese honked drowsily at the noise of the creaking springs. She listened to her husband's footsteps on the porch, down the wooden steps, and heard him clear his throat and spit. The kitchen light made the dust-covered screen a thin red wall and she could see nothing of her husband's movements.

As abruptly as though starting from some secret cue, the silence was filled with undernoises of crickets and frogs.

"I'm going to run into town for a while," she heard Dan's voice through the screen.

"Don't you want your gingerbread?"

"I'll eat it when I get back."

"Honey, please don't go."

"I've got to see about that vetch seed," he said impatiently.

"All right, Dan," she answered. And then, pressing her nose against the screen: "Dan . . . ?"

"What?" she heard his voice full of irritation.

"You won't be gone long, will you? Please."

"I won't," he snapped.

"Reckon we ought to call Dan's house?"

"Nah, he'll be along in a minute. Probably had to hear a lecture from Myrtle before he could get away."

"Did anybody call the constable's?"

"Yeah, I did. He'd just left somewhere up the highway. Elsie sounded half scared to death. Said she didn't know where he was or when he'd be coming back. Probably late."

"He's playing it smart for once."

"You all pass that bottle over this way, for Christ's sakes."

"There comes a car up from Dan's cattle-guard now. Jim, some of you fellows get up there on the road and wave him off into the clearing. Now, I think we ought to split up and just go in two cars. We can leave the rest of them here and pick them up after it's over."

Myrtle stood with her mouth close to the telephone and tried to disguise her voice when it finally clicked on the other end.

"Is Ed Buchanan at home?"

"No, he's out for the evening."

"I can't tell you who this is, Elsie, but I'm just sure there's going to be a lynching tonight."

"Oh, God no . . ." Myrtle heard as she hung up.

"Don't drive too fast," Dan said.

"We ain't going to lose the other car on this road," the driver said.

"Yeah, I can see their lights coming around the curve back there," Snooty Cox said from the back seat.

"Dark as it is, though," Dan said, "we might miss somebody walking along the road. And we said we'd take the first one we run across."

"OK. How about you passing that bottle up here, for Christ's sakes," the driver called over his shoulder.

"Here you go, Dan old boy."

"Hell, you know Dan don't drink. Give it to me," the driver said.

"Looks like we're going to have to go in and drag one out," Snooty said. "Ain't no niggers on the road tonight."

"We'll run across somebody 'fore long."

"They say a nigger can feel it in his bones when a lynching's in the air. They're all sticking close. We ain't going to find —"

"Slow down," Dan warned.

"See somebody, Dan old boy," Snooty said. He leaned forward and looked out the front window, with his face so close to Dan's that Dan could feel its warmth and smell the whiskey fumes.

"Just ahead there to the left."

"Dan's got eyes like a hawk," Snooty chuckled.

Headlights picked out the heavyset figure of a young Negro standing against a background of thorn thickets at the side of the road.

The driver cut the motor. On the silence, the distant yowling of a dog carried to their ears.

"Ain't that Junie-boy?" one of the men from the back seat asked.

"Can't tell with his hand up shading his eyes like that," Snooty whispered.

"Yeah, that's Junie-boy," Dan said somberly.

"Don't forget, Dan, we said we'd take the first one."

"Hell, he's got a gal with him," the driver said as the boy stepped to one side and continued to peer into the headlights.

"That's Iris, Sister Callie's gal," Dan muttered.

Dust from the road drifted forward and began to settle slowly across the headlights, turning them into orange-colored cones crosscutting the two figures beside the thorn thicket.

"Let's take the gal, too," Snooty laughed.

"Hell no — just one," the driver whispered. Then he stuck his head out the door and shouted: "You get on home, gal. Beat it."

The girl plunged into the thicket and they could hear her footsteps crashing through underbrush. The fat young boy turned to follow her.

"Hold it, Junie!" the driver called. The boy hesitated. "Come on, Junie, hop in."

"I ain't going to get in that car."

"Mister Dan's in here. Come on, Junie," the driver said cordially. "You can sit up here next to Mister Dan." He opened the car door and stepped out.

The boy stooped and gazed into the front seat.

"That you, Mister Dan?"

"Yeah, Junie," Dan said thickly.

"You want me to get in there, Mister Dan?"

"Yeah . . ."

The driver climbed in behind him and closed the door. The second car pulled to a halt behind them, casting a lurid, reddish dust-glow from its headlights through the back window.

"What's going on, Mister Dan?" the boy asked.

"Who'd you get?" the driver from the other car asked, sticking his head in the door window while others crowded about behind him.

"Junie," Dan said.

"That's tough, Dan. Know you hate that."

"Didn't we see a gal there, too?"

"Yeah," Snooty laughed. "I tried to get them to take her too."

"What was you doing there, Junie-boy?" the driver of the second car asked gently, " — having yourself a little party with that gal?"

"Yes sir," the boy sniggered.

"I guess before long, you'd be having little parties with some of our white gals, eh?"

"Oh, God no — if you're thinking that. I wouldn't never do that. Would I, Mister Dan? Tell them that, Mister Dan," the boy pleaded. "If that's what you all's think —"

"Let's get going," Dan said harshly.

"Sure, Dan. Sure. I know this ain't easy for you," the driver of the second car said.

"We'll meet over at the barn behind the old Turner place, eh?" he called from the other car.

"Right," the driver of the first car said.

A rustle in the bushes attracted their attention.

"What the hell?"

"Probably that gal. She'd have to come back this way to get home," Dan said. "We'd better hurry it up."

"Reckon she heard?" Snooty asked.

"You know damn well she did," the driver said uneasily.

"You want me to go in after her?" Snooty suggested.

"No, you'd never catch her. These niggers know the thicket backwards."

"What you all going to do to me?" Junie asked quietly.

"Man, I'd sure like to give it a try," Snooty laughed.

"Yeah, you'd like to get stuck up in some thorn bush with that gal, wouldn't you, you old dog?"

"What you all going to do to me?" Junie asked again.

"Ah, that crazy Snooty," one of the men in the back snorted.

"We're going to fix it so you don't never have a chance to mongrelize our white girls," the driver explained seriously as he shifted the car into motion. "I'm sorry it has to be you, Junie. I know you're a good boy. But we agreed to take the first one we runned across. We got to make an example, show the other boys we mean business. We warned you all we wasn't going to fool around with you and we ain't. We figure that when the other black boys hears what happened to you, they're going to stay in their place and not try to mix with the whites."

"What you going to do to me?" the boy exhaled.

"They got Junie-boy!" Lily screamed over and over again as she ran toward the Ferguson's house.

"God in heav —" Myrtle gasped.

"They got my Junie!" Lily wailed. Her footsteps clubbed across the back porch. "Please, Miss Myrtle," she said, jerking at the hooked screen. "Where's Mister Dan? He's got to do something!"

"Lily . . . Lily . . ." Myrtle cried, unhooking the screen.

"He'll help the boy, won't he? He knows Junie's a good boy."

"Lily. What're you saying? They got Junie."

"Iris just come up. She's with him on the road. The men chased her away and took the boy."

"Dan's gone, Lily," Myrtle said dully. "He had to go see a man clear over in Junction about some vetch seed," she heard herself lying.

The aged Negro sank into a chair as though her spine had suddenly dissolved.

"I'll call the police," Myrtle said helplessly. "Not Junie-boy, dear God. Not him," she whimpered while she reached for the telephone.

Lily gazed blankly at the dish of buttered gingerbread on the table before her. She listened with a strange calmness to the other woman's gurglings and sobbings, aware within herself that she was unable to move, unable to lift her arms from her lap, unable to smell even the strong fragrance of the gingerbread.

"Hello. Hello. Sheriff's office. Listen. You've got to do something. A bunch of white men. They've got our colored boy. They're going to lynch him. What? This is Mrs. Dan Ferguson. I called the constable, but he's gone! Who? His name is Junie.

His mother's worked for us for years. Listen. He growed up here. Listen. We don't have time to talk. No, I don't know where. Just a minute. Lily, Honey — you got any idea where they taken him?"

"The old Turner place," Lily whined, staring wide-eyed at the plate.

"The old Turner place — a deserted farm. Yes. Hurry — you'll be too late."

"Mister Dan. Mister Dan."

"I'm sorry, Junie."

"You want a drink, black boy?"

"He don't drink," Dan said disgustedly.

"You just going to hang me — like that?"

"You bastards got to be shown," Snooty said.

"Watch it," Dan said. "Junie's a good boy."

"Well, the other bastards got to be shown. They had plenty of warning. But they wouldn't listen to it," Snooty said.

"We all got young girls to think about, except you, Dan," the driver said as though he hated the whole thing as much as Junie did. "They get into our schools, they'll sure not stop there. You know that. Well, we ain't none of us willing to stand by and risk having half-nigger grandkids, I don't care what the law says. Maybe this'll teach other black boys we mean business."

"Mister Dan. I'd never've believed it of you."

"You remember how I learned you to pray, Junie?"

"Yes sir."

"If I'se you, I'd be praying, son."

Dan's arm rested on the car door. Warm wind rushed up his shirtsleeve. Beside him, he smelled the earth odors of the boy's recently scrubbed body, odors of soap and freshly ironed denim, and above it all, some neutral odor of terror detaching from the folds of his black flesh. It smelled more like dew than sweat, Dan thought. He felt the boy's thick shoulders slowly slumping forward and knew that all of the life had already gone out of him.

"God — it's too late already. I feel like it's too late already, Miss Myrtle."

Myrtle poured coffee shakily into a white mug and carried it to the table.

"Try and drink this, Lily. Please. Where is everybody?" she shouted in sudden exasperation. "I'll try to call somebody else."

She walked distractedly back to the telephone and picked up the receiver to dial.

The white-headed Negro sat limp in the chair with her head stretched back on her scrawny neck, staring blare-eyed at the light globe above the table. Her black lips were moving in voiceless speech.

"Hurry it up, Dan," Junie heard one of the men shout. "The moon'll be full up in a minute."

Junie glanced dully toward brooding masses of trees that were silhouetted against a scarlet disk of rising moon down over the dried-up pond.

"Mister Dan, I can't hardly stand it," Junie heard himself saying, though he wondered at the words, because he hadn't meant to say anything, and it was like somebody else talking from inside of him. He peered down on the men grouped below him around the car on top of which he and Mister Dan were standing.

"Pray like I taught you to," Mr. Dan told him hoarsely.

Junie felt the car rock as the older man jumped to the ground, leaving him standing there alone. A breeze turned moisture to ice on his body.

The car door slammed beneath him.

"OK?" someone asked.

"Yeah, take her away," someone answered.

Dimly, Junie was aware that somewhere down there behind him the car's headlights had been switched on.

He closed his eyes, hearing a faraway motor and a shifting of gears, and in dizziness concentrated on the words Mister Dan had taught him: *"Our Father who art in heaven . . . hallowed be Thy name, Thy kingdom come, Thy will be done on earth as it —"*

The dry sweet perfume of clover blossoms mingled with exhaust fumes in Dan's nose. The distant purity of a whippoorwill's song rose above the incessant underthrumming of frogs and crickets; and from somewhere beyond the woods, that dog kept yowling, after a skunk or a possum, likely enough, Dan thought. He didn't look up.

He let his mind dwell on the other things, on the drouth and the dried-up cornfields and the terrible peace in his belly that was spreading throughout his body, and leaving him weak and wanting to fall to the ground and never bother to get up again. He wanted to give in to its downward drag, to lie there face down on the earth and never think of anything. He held himself erect, telling himself that he had to get home, get to bed, sleep for a long, long time.

"I can feel it. He's gone," Lily announced in a low voice become calm. "It's all over now."

"Try to drink some coffee."

The aged Negro looked up into the pain-distorted face of Myrtle Ferguson. "I'm all right now. God's willed it," she said gently. "If Mister Dan'd just been here, he wouldn't've let it happen. But God willed it for him to be gone."

The rattle of gravel in the driveway brought Lily to her feet. She strode to the screen door and cupped her bony hands beside her face to peer out.

Heavy footsteps mounted the stoop.

"Mister Dan? . . ." Lily whined, her voice spiraling up to a final high tone.

"What're you doing up so late, Lily?" Dan Ferguson's voice boomed pleasantly.

"Oh, Mister Dan — they got our boy," Lily said, backing to one side in a clumsy, shuffling step to let him enter. "They got Junie . . ."

"What the hell are you talking about?"

"Mister Dan — they done hung my boy," she whimpered and her body crumpled slowly forward against him.

"Lily . . . Lily . . ." Dan murmured. He patted her skeletal shoulder. "Who got —" His words died in his throat. Over the weeping woman's head he saw his wife eyeing him with the devastating bluntness of a stranger. There was nothing left in his eyes, nothing — no strength to hide the truth from her.

He looked wearily at her until her expression faded to one of terrible grief and pity for him.

"You all sit down," she sighed, and walked toward the coffee pot.

SAUCE FOR THE GANDER

———————————————————→

News of the aged friar's request spread throughout the cloister in no time. An early sun had already begun to distill October frost when the Father Prior of the Abbey of Dleifsnam puffed his way up the narrow stone stairs to the Father Abbot's study.

"Come, look out your window, Father Abbot," he said. The two monks gazed down into the sunlit courtyard which was surrounded by high stone walls, and beyond which the Flemish valley stretched serene to its hazy horizons.

"But what is happening?" Father Abbot asked. "Why is there such agitation among my monks? They run about the courtyard as though . . ."

"I don't really know," the prior replied soberly. Under his black robe, his chest still heaved from the long climb. Waiting a moment to catch his breath, he turned away from the window and looked about the Father Abbot's study, so peaceful with its scrubbed flagstone floor, its crisscross leaded windows ajar to let the sunlight pour in, and its sturdy oak table covered with rolls of parchment. "I don't really know, Father Abbot," he went on finally, "but I think it's because our decrepit old St. Clud begs to have audience with the Father Abbot and all the other Fathers in Chapter — on an urgent matter of morals."

"What?" Father Abbot's white head turned slowly, and his gentle blue eyes blinked in disbelief. "Now what could he possibly have on his mind?" Robes rustled in silence as the abbot inched feebly to his table, brushed some of the parchments to one side, and seated himself on the edge of it. He stared at the floor, his thin eyebrows lifted in puzzlement. "An urgent matter of morals? What can it mean? He's too dim to be tempted in the spirit, and surely he's too old to be tempted in the flesh. Why the poor old friar's done nothing but care for the hogs and waddle around babying those geese for the past twenty or more years."

It was true that St. Clud, as he was affectionately called by the other monks, was the menial of the monastery. It was he who performed, with seeming relish, those duties generally considered unpleasant and bothersome. He never tired, for example, of caring for his sick brothers, of tending the small herd of skeletal sows, or of driving the geese out into the open countryside for pasturage.

The other monks were occasionally disconcerted by his personal habits, for he had arrived at the monastery already a man of advanced age, too old to adopt that quality of discreet refinement usually associated with a religious vocation. He was completely unhampered by physical modesty, but in such an open, honest way, and with such childlike simplicity that indeed he made modesty seem almost a questionable virtue. But he was clumsy and noisy. He would blow his nose, even in chapel, with great honking sounds, and he had never learned to control the rich grossness of his language. However, all knew him to be a man of immense generosity and charity and they loved him for tending his menial tasks with such simple fervor.

While the Father Abbot and the Father Prior were discussing him, Friar Clud was in his cell, located in an old grange far to the end of the monastery properties, where he had been moved when the other monks had found it impossible to sleep because of his grotesque snoring. At this moment, he was sitting astride a squat three-legged stool, staring into space and cudgeling his poor brain to know what to do. He had long since forgotten about the world, and gradually, as his age had become very advanced, his entire manner of thinking had become centered around God and geese. Now, he was trying to remember how it was in the world. He sat with his elbows on his knees, his chunky hands holding each side of his head. He closed his eyes in prayer, mumbling his paternoster in provincial dialect. He prayed fervently for a moment, ruffling stubbed fingers through his sparse white hair.

Then a screeching honk outside made him open his eyes and wince with sympathy. He got wearily to his feet and shuffled across the doorstoop into a small enclosure that was surrounded on all sides by the monastery vegetable gardens. He bent down over a slat cage in which a giant blue goose was squatting. He reached in and fingered her bandaged leg, and noticed that she had not touched her food.

"You must eat," he coaxed gruffly. "You must try to forget. In about five days now, that thing'll be as pretty as it ever was and you can use it once more."

Moments later, the finest gander in all Flanders marched past, his plumage brilliant in the sun, his scarlet beak held high in the air. Beside him, a goose hen strutted, a very young hen. And the wounded goose once more raised her head to the sky and honked her heartbreak. Clud's watery eyes were stricken with an expression of pity. He looked helplessly from the caged hen to the gander and then back to the caged hen.

"It's all right," he soothed in a cracked voice. "It's all right. Here, eat a little. You know you'd best not get excited. You tear the wound open every time." But she honked her grief again, and the strangled cry pierced the aged friar's heart. He raised himself painfully into an upright position and turned on the gander, brandishing his stick with exaggerated gestures. "Go away. Get out. You old fool," he muttered. "All right, I can understand. You need a little friend maybe. That's understandable, but who ever heard of a gander changing his mate? She gets her little self hurt. Is that her fault? Is that any reason to pick up with the first loose wench that comes along? And then to strut in front of her like this, rubbing it in. Go on. Get out of here. You old fool!" Friar Clud's ruddy face turned scarlet above his beard.

The aged friar did not drive his geese out to pasture that day. He went to Mass and prayed for guidance, after which he returned and sat with the injured hen until the late afternoon skies were filled with clanging vesper bells from the tower. Then he got to his feet and absently dusted off his bottom. After a last worried look at his charge, he headed through the cloister gardens, trudging between rows of gigantic purple cabbages, toward the chapel.

The others watched him, knowing only that the poor friar was struggling with a problem of morals, and their faces wore expressions of great concern and pity.

As soon as vespers were completed, all of the monks were called together in the Chapter Room to hear Friar Clud's distressing problem. Father Abbot was uneasy about some of the younger monks' hearing what might come from the old friar's untutored and indelicate lips. In his mind, he prepared a little lecture that would serve the occasion if necessary. He would explain to them how in advanced age, certain long-forgotten spiritual and physical phenomena might resurge with diabolic insistency. His meditation was interrupted by a slight wave of laughter. He looked up to see Friar Clud ambling across the room bowing to right and left, his uncertain grin revealing his three good teeth. Father Abbot studied that good-natured face with its goatlike eyebrows and its watery blue eyes, and felt a stirring of immense and compassionate affection. No matter what St. Clud had got himself into, he could not have done it viciously and he must not be judged too harshly. "After all," the Father Abbot told himself, "After all —" Usually, if he said "After all" a couple of times, some fine thought would come to follow it up, but this time no thought came to the abbot and he shrugged his shoulders in intimate irritation with himself.

When all the rustling sounds of monks settling themselves in place had died down, the prior, speaking in a voice of great gentleness, told Friar Clud that he might address the Fathers. The old friar rose from his bench, adjusted a pair of wobbly lenses to his snout, and with loud clearings of his throat he genuflected to all sides as though he were about to be knighted. Father Abbot's gavel rapped on the table and the tittering stopped abruptly.

"Reverend Fathers," St. Clud began, "as all of you know, I have been the menial of this monastery for a long time, with nothing to do but care for the hogs and drive the geese, so that in twenty and more years my poor brain has become as empty as an unused churn. That is why I begged this audience, for I am faced with a problem I do not know how to solve." The uneasy smile once again gummed itself across his face, and he wrinkled his forehead and concentrated on words with which to express himself. A blush seeped upward into his cheeks.

"Tell us simply what troubles you," the prior urged after a long time. "Do not be embarrassed."

"Well . . ." the old monk hesitated, cocking his eyes prayerfully in the abbot's direction. "This week something happened that never should happen."

A hush claimed the room instantly. Father Abbot's gaze softened with understanding and deep pity. "After all," he said to himself. "After all —" He was just opening his mouth to explain about natural phenomena resurging in senility, when Friar Clud went on in his unleavened voice.

"The goose, as you know, is the most moral of all animals. The goose mates for life and does not change mates."

Father Abbot's expression became sad and a little mystified. The poor old friar was rambling.

"Three days ago," Clud continued, "our finest goose caught the shameful portion of her leg in the garden fence, and now she cannot walk. Only three days, and now her gander has left her to go prowling after a much younger animal. This is unheard of. Now," Clud's voice became hoarse with emotion, "the betrayed hen will not eat. She is grieving herself to death and soon she will die. Her screams are heart-rending, Fathers. I'm sure you heard them at vespers. Unless some solution to this terrible situation can be found, I'm afraid I'll . . ." His voice trailed off into confused silence. He squinted his simple blue eyes about him, seeking some expression of help from the surrounding Fathers. Most of them had their heads buried in their hands in concentration, their shoulders quaking.

Father Abbot tapped his mallet on the table once again. "What would you suggest we do, Friar Clud?" he asked patiently. "Couldn't you just find the bereaved goose another gander?"

The aged friar's face clenched into an expression of shock and disappointment. He shook his white head gravely.

"I see," the Father Abbot said with apology in his voice. "Well, it's up to you, but it seems to me that if the poor hen is going to starve to death, it would be better for you to kill her so that she can be cooked into a hash for one of our meals. Now, let's get back to this disturbing problem of morals, my son. You started to tell us about it a while ago. Don't be humiliated. You say this misfortune has already occurred?" The abbot fell silent as he saw Clud's shoulders sag. The old monk stood there in his brown patched robe, thunderstruck.

"But it was that," he protested, his blush deepening, "the gander going off. What must I do? In the world what do they do when a lecherous man leaves his wife for another wench?"

The prior's hand flew up and slapped his forehead with a loud smack. Father Abbot's face congested. Other monks stared dolefully at the ceiling and their mouths dropped open. Friar Clud was almost abject in his expression of bewildered misery. He allowed his hands to drop to his side in a forlorn gesture and tried to smile, but he looked more as though he were chewing.

Clearing his throat, the prior broke the silence. "I have told you before, Friar Clud, that you cannot judge animals from a human standard of morality. You have made this same error a —"

Father Abbot interrupted. "My son, if the goose is to die, persuade yourself to kill her so the cook can prepare her for our dinner. If there is some way to save her, you will know best. Now, go in peace, and do not let this torment you further."

The gumming movements of Friar Clud's mouth became more agitated, and his eyes half-blinked with great slowness. He seemed rooted to the spot. It was inconceivable to think of killing the hen he had so tenderly cared for. Kill her and let the other two go free? Some deeply ingrained sense of justice made the solution seem monstrous to him, and he was stunned that such a fine man as the Father Abbot could make such a suggestion.

He stared about him helplessly for a long moment. Then he turned and walked slowly from the Chapter Room, his whiskered chin buried in his chest. Outside, late dusk enveloped the countryside in the soft blues and grays of twilight. First stars glistened pale. Friar Clud walked with great heaviness, swallowing back the forgotten nostalgias of all the years when dusk had been a time of quietness, of gentle acceptance — a time when he could sit on his stool in the door of his cell, surrounded by his animals, and rest after a long day's work. Tonight there was not that peace. Tonight he felt lonely and incomplete, and his loneliness was made more poignant by the placid countryside that rose on all sides from the valley, half-veiled in mists, chilled by hidden night breezes, lighted by brass chips of stars. All of those things that had made for peace in the past, seemed now to destroy the peace of the night.

He stooped and entered his cell. By the last vague light that filtered through his open door, he wetted some mashed grain for the injured hen. He fixed a new bandage on her leg and tried to force a handful of feed down her throat. But she pulled her head away and placed it under her wing, issuing sobbing sounds that wrenched his heart.

Later, after the last prayers of night had been chanted, Friar Clud remained alone in the darkened chapel and repeated endless paternosters in his childish patois. Again and again he prayed for guidance, abandoning himself into God's hands. Long after the last bells had reverberated throughout the cloister and the other monks were asleep, he stayed on his knees. He knew there must be a solution, and he wracked his poor brain to think of it. His heart turned cold at the thought of putting the hatchet to her. It was unthinkable. She was so pitiable, so completely blameless. The giant cacao-seed beads of his rosary dribbled through his fingers, one by one, as he concentrated on his prayers and tried to remember about justice and about how the heart works when romance is involved. Then, late in the night, he returned to his cell, burdened with the sadness of not having solved a thing.

All through the night monks rolled in their sleep and heard the grief-stricken honking. All during the prayers of matins and lauds, in the pre-dawn chill, they heard the pathetic sound. And then it stopped.

And there was more than one sigh of pity. More than one heart became a little heavier for St. Clud, for despite his roughness, the monks loved him, and many of them felt that he had recesses of goodness and generosity that none of them could match.

During the morning, bits of fine down floated about the cloister courtyard, wafted here and there by a faint breeze. Under the bright sunlight, they looked like snowflakes.

At noon monks filed into the dimly lighted refectory and stood before tables of steaming goose hash. During the long *benedicite* attentions were divided. Glances were stolen in Clud's direction. Dampness made the stone room seem as somber as a cave, and spirits were heavy. Father Abbot made a mental note to have the cook prepare a pie for St. Clud. The friar would surely be unable to eat any of the goose. In fact, none of them felt much like eating it. A final "amen" echoed in hollowness throughout the long room, and benches scraped against the floor as monks took their seats.

The Father Abbot was waving to the cook when he noticed with astonishment that Friar Clud was gulping down hash with great

hunger, making fantastic noises chewing with his three teeth, spill-
ing it on his front with a trembling hand. Others watched and felt
sure that the poor friar had taken leave of his senses from grief and
worry.

And when lunch was over, and the short prayers were finished,
some of them followed him back to his grange. They saw him
enter the tiny courtyard and bend down over a slat cage. And inside the cage they saw a bandaged goose serenely eating her mash.
Imprisoned with her, they saw a giant blue gander, his long neck
stretched through the slats, flapping his wings and struggling to get
out. They saw the gander reach over and bite savagely at the hem
of Friar Clud's robe. But the old monk merely rubbed his hands
together and beamed toothlessly.

During the night, by dint of much prayer and meditation, St.
Clud of Dleifsnam had found his solution. The young wench was
nowhere in sight.

DIVERSIONS

———————————————————————————→

JOHN SELFRIDGE

It wasn't always a hobby for John Selfridge. In fact, he's only learned to make it so after a series of thirty-seven sessions with Baytown's leading psychotherapist. John has been fourteen years widowed from a woman who left him a comfortable income from her vast sulphur holdings. It is to his credit that he never took a dime of Lucy's money during the many years of their marriage, and to hers that she never used it in a way that would discredit John as a provider. She was far too wonderful a woman for that.

Yes, things are fine now. John can once again bear to live with himself; he understands himself since the treatments, and no longer feels that paralyzing sense of guilt in being glad Lucy's gone to her reward. He's learned that it's all right for him to rejoice in his widowhood.

It wasn't easy. John had been a model husband and Lucy a perfect wife to whom he had been utterly devoted. He had therefore considered his feelings of lightness and release at her death absolutely unspeakable — to such a point that he had refused to admit them to his consciousness. He had buried them, so the doctor said, deep in his unconscious, suppressed them and repressed them until they had finally boiled up and made him a neurotic, filled with guilt-feelings and uncertainty. This is all very complicated but very real, of course.

John is going fishing now, for the first time since Lucy's passing fourteen years ago. He looks at his old gear and there is a constriction in his chest, almost unbearable, because Lucy, God love her, was the last one to pack these lines and leaders and sinkers and fishhooks and bait boxes away, and no hands have since touched them. It is a poignant moment. Will he really be able to bear going fish-

ing alone after all the times they went together? Can he enjoy it
without the return of those guilt-feelings?

John is out in the middle of the lake in a boat. The sun flashes on
the water. Sweat rolls down the small of his back and the odor of
shrimp is strong from his bait can. His heart expands with gentle
enthusiasm. It is so good to be in the boat alone, surrounded by the
lapping quietness of waters and sunlight, to sweat alone and hum to
himself. Yes, he sighs with relief — there's not a twinge of the old
guilts. He thoroughly enjoys it — more than he ever did with
Lucy.

ELISE VON HOFMANNSTHAL

Elise von Hofmannsthal is one of twenty-seven thousand workers
at the aircraft factory in San Diego. She speaks no German, but she
scarcely speaks English either — although until recently she talked
rather like anyone else brought up in this country.

Her linguistic transformation began some weeks ago when
Strauss's opera, *Der Rosenkavalier*, was given a gala production by
the San Francisco Opera Association. Elise happened to be glancing through the fine arts section of the *Chronicle* in search of the
local movie schedule, when the name "Von Hofmannsthal" vividly
attracted her attention to the music column. She forgot everything
else and pored over the article containing her family name. She
read that *Der Rosenkavalier* was a masterpiece not only because of
Strauss's music, but also because of the incomparable libretto provided by Hugo von Hofmannsthal. Yes, there it was — her name
in an association with greatness — in black and white for all to see.
Sharing a name so unusual, Elise was almost certain they were related. And hadn't her mother spoken of a cousin Hugo?

The following morning, rereading the article for the twentieth
time, Elise felt the Viennese blood of her forefathers pulsing
stronger in her, and a slight guttural accent crept into her speech.
She carried the newspaper to the plant and showed it to some of
her fellow workers, admitting that she and the playwright were
second cousins and observing: "At least *somebody* in the family
made good."

Such news spreads quickly, so it was not long before she was

interviewed on one of the local TV programs as the great von Hofmannsthal's only living American relative. There, with the cameras
turned on her, and with the studio organist playing an arrangement
of the *Rosenkavalier Waltzes* in the background, her accent became perceptibly more pronounced.

Since then it is difficult to make out a word she says, but we
cannot fail to be captivated by the gaiety of her Continental manners, and particularly by the way she has learned to pronounce her
name; for it is sheer music when she murmurs "Elise von Hofmannsthal" with that true Viennese inflection.

Elise spends all of her evenings alone now in that tiny apartment,
listening to the latest LP's of *Der Rosenkavalier*, imagining herself
as the lovely Marschallin or the sparkling Sophie. With the music
turned up to deafening volume, she loses herself in gentle dreams of
her Danube heritage, sips instant coffee Viennese-style and tells
herself that life in San Diego is a sonofabitch.

POLLY HARLOW

Polly Harlow glanced up from her latest issue of *The Adult Mind
Quarterly* toward George, who sat opposite her dozing through the
final movement of a Beethoven quartet. It was another moment of
rare fulfillment for Polly and she smiled. Here was the reality of
it — the dream of the good evening at home, the close marital kinship that would allow them to remain silent together before the fire.
She gazed at his dinner-jacketed figure, at his chubby cheek in his
fist. Bless his heart. Psychic space — that's what she'd allowed
George; psychic space and a certain respect for that mind of his —
respecting his mind even though it was full of crudities, limitations
and had a downward tendency.

It was a perfect time for making some of those private tests in
which Polly occasionally indulged in her seeking of the Socratic
route to wisdom through self-knowledge. And tonight she felt safe
enough to make some of the more daring ones, to be completely
objective about George, to see him as he really was. First, it was
possible, of course, to see him simply as a big fat cherubic slob loung-
ing in his chair with a silly expression on his sleeping face. This was
the way an immature person might be seeing him. And she could

go even further. She could envisage him beneath his dinner jacket, all fleshed and puffy like some immodest ape, or again like a pink sow slumbering on its digestion.

The music entered the lovely descending melody of the second theme.

She could, in detachment, see him as a sloth walking about on all fours with his belly dragging beneath him, or as a hippo, and wonder how she ever tolerated being united to such a thing, being kissed by it or even driving in the car beside it.

There was the tricky little rhythmic passage, almost like a gavotte.

It was the same with Beethoven, though, Polly mused. He was deaf as a post when he wrote this, and a hippo and a sloth with an intestinal inflammation — and yet, what a talent, what a God-given talent.

George had no talent, or even much taste. With him it was business, business, business, damn it — and thank God, after all. He was there before her in slumber, brute dead to this magnificent downsweeping theme, a man to whom the highest emotions and reactions were unknown.

Yes, she could see him as all these things, see that although she might well elevate him, and certainly did if you looked back over the subtle changes of the years; still on his side, he most certainly dragged her down a bit, too.

But, she could see, too, her triumph. She knew that another woman just slightly *immature* could be sitting there glaring at that hunk of flesh, hating it, feeling sullied by its presence. Not Polly. It was possible for her not to hate him at all, but to have real compassion and affection for him — yes, even reverence. Dear old George. It was what one of the psychology articles called the mature woman's ability "cheerfully to accept her lot."

The music came to a thrilling halt with a flourish of tonic chords, and then the needle scratched into the groove.

George stirred, sniffed and listened groggily to the noise. He lumbered to his feet and lifted the record from the turntable. It slipped from his hands and rolled under the table.

"Mmm. God . . ." he muttered and got down on his hands and knees to retrieve it. His epithet caused Polly to look up again from her quarterly with an affectionate smile. She saw against the background of gray carpeting not George, but the rear end of a sloth crawling about on all fours with his belly dragging beneath him; and she understood vividly for an instant how a person of immature mind could loathe being tied down to such a thing.

MABEL BAMBERG

All of us at the Corsicana Conservatory of Fine Arts loved Mabel. She was the sort that you refer to as "Good old Mabel," although she was not old at all, but in her early twenties.

Who can ever forget the horror of her in the practice room with that big, generous and innocent smile on her face, frankly reveling in her loose-jointed playing of the Liszt *Hungarian Fantaisie?* Did she ever play anything else?

There was no question in Mabel's mind but that she would be the great woman pianist of her age. Her scale passages, which utterly entranced her, sounded altogether as though she were playing them on a xylophone. This is not meant to be uncharitable, but it was always one of those really embarrassing situations. Who could tell her the truth, except her own teacher, whom she dismissed as being merely jealous and thwarted. Mabel favored the Matthay system of the loose-fling, the energy-shot followed by muscular relaxation. Her teacher, of course, was a Letchitisky disciple, so you can imagine how little influence she had on the girl, who had, after all, studied all of her life.

History, languages, harmony, theory, counterpoint — they played no part in Mabel's life. If the music itself couldn't teach you all you needed to know, you weren't a real artist and Mabel contended that all of those subsidiary studies were merely cover-ups for some basic lack of musicality.

Mabel married a good-natured, enormously virtuous young baritone, whose accompaniments she played and whose rendition of the *Prologue* to *Pagliacci* was so dramatic that Mabel would sometimes go to pieces and be unable to continue, except with tears in her eyes. The rest of us merely blushed, but we encouraged the romance, since they were obviously made for each other.

They are in Hollywood now, making their way. Mabel writes letters back to the music editor of the local paper and we all read them and talk about "Good old Mabel." They say that she's dyed her hair blond, that her husband has dyed his jettest black and grown a moustache, and that they are practicing a skating act in case their present musical plans don't entirely pan out with M.G.M.

PROFESSOR MACINTOSH

Professor MacIntosh, the distinguished former archivist of the University of Glasgow, is a pink old cob of a man now returned to his family country home in retirement at the age of eighty. He sits in the family pew with his seven sons and their families in the little village Presbyterian Church this Sunday morning, gently daydreaming as service drags to a close. A rustling brings him back to the moment as a young lad no more than fourteen rises from his seat directly in front of the Professor and stoops over to pick up his hat from the floor between his feet. The movement hoists his blue velveteen jacket up over his hips and the Professor catches himself staring squarely at a pair of rounded buttocks, outlined in every curve and muscle beneath taut gray flannel, stitched down the center with crisscrossings of matching thread.

And then the youth stands up, solid and ruddy cheeked, shakes hands politely with his neighbor and prepares to leave.

Professor MacIntosh has never met the boy, never even seen him, but he goes home to lunch harboring both irritation and a peculiar softness in his heart. He appears detached throughout the Sunday dinner for he cannot put his finger on the speck of irritation that spoils an otherwise mellow emotion. And then it comes to him and his watery blue eyes sparkle amused indignation. "Damn that Freud," he says to himself. He admits the private desire he had in church, chuckling that such things must remain buried in a man's private heart — the desire to plant a benevolent kiss on the lad's sturdy bottom — a desire that used to be natural, he muses, one that befitted a good healthy man with the strong blood of humanity in his veins until Freud came along and taught us that there might be something buried and filthy about it and made us cautious. The old man lights his pipe, looks out the window to the gnarled Scottish countryside, sun-slanted and softened with greenish hints of spring, and tells himself that civilization didn't profit much by finding out how nasty it is . . .

PART IV

Nuni

Notes

⟶

At the outset of World War II, John Griffin was studying medicine and conducting special research in the use of sound — most notably the Gregorian chant — as therapy for the insane at an asylum in Tours, France. During this period, he became an active member of the French Defense Passive, acting as liaison agent for the evacuation of Jewish refugees from Tours to the port of Saint-Nazaire.

In 1942, after being forced to leave France or risk almost certain capture by the Gestapo, he joined the United States Army Air Force.

His second novel, *Nuni*, published in 1956, and like *The Devil Rides Outside*, written while he was blind, grew out of an idea born during service in the South Pacific. As a language specialist, he volunteered for a classified assignment which placed him among primitive savages. His task was to conduct a complete survey of their culture, to study their language, customs, fetishes, mental attitudes — virtually to become one of them through research and duplicated living patterns.

What would be the result, he pondered, if an American, any average American citizen, were forced to live such a primitive existence, devoid of the trappings of a civilized world . . . if he were forced back into a society, centuries old in its backwardness, in its unawareness of civilization as we know it today?

The protagonist of *Nuni*, John W. Harper, a Caucasian, age 57, an assistant professor of English, is translated into such an atmosphere. Professor Harper is returning home to his wife and three children after a reunion with his brother at a military installation in the Philippines. The airplane on which he is traveling develops difficulties and crashes. Professor Harper is the sole survivor, being washed ashore on an uninhabited Pacific reef. He later finds his way to a nearby island inhabited by aborigines.

Nuni, meaning "world" (and indeed it is the only world the natives have ever known and, in their gross lack of knowledge, the only one they desire to know) is the name of the island. The novel is in two parts, the first being "Nuni"; the second is "Vanua," the name of a village on the island.

Pitted against the ignorance and cruelty of these savages — who believe that life is predestined to be a vast kaleidoscope of darkness, sadness and pain, and that death, when it comes, is the ultimate keynote of jubilance ("We leave you in sunlight," Rauka, the sorceress, intones at the burial of a fellow tribesman, "and we go back and wait in shadow.") — Harper risks dignity and sanity in the struggle to uplift himself from this primeval quagmire of destruction.

In his quest for a separate peace, he combats the native indifference with cognition, and offers love as a solitary defense against inbred hates, fears and interdictions.

The premise of *Nuni* is an interesting one, and Griffin constructs it on a tableau of immediacy and universality . . . time is static; the native language has no past tense. The novel is written entirely in the present tense and first person; the never-varying focal point of the professor's stream of consciousness moves graphically from plateau to plateau, emitting a religious ardor, a spiritual mystique in its climb.

Nuni, above all else, is a complex and concentrated study of the values and abuses of individual freedom (what difference is there after all between slavery to elemental nature and slavery to mechanized nature?), set in a never-never land whose anthropology is as soundly and certainly frightening as the fact that *any* land could change overnight — within the slow ticking of a second, even — into a living nightmare of horror and anguish if all vision is fused inward . . . if apathy is allowed to grow unguarded.

The book was dedicated to Griffin's wife, Elizabeth Ann, and his two oldest children, Susan Michelle and John, Jr.

The text of the selections is that of *Nuni* (Boston: Houghton Mifflin Company, 1956). Chapter 8 is from pages 50–59 and 60–61 of that edition; Chapter 9 is from pages 64–65; Chapter 10 is from pages 66–68; Chapter 11 is from pages 69–73; Chapter 18 is from pages 115–118; Chapter 20 is from pages 131–163; Chapter 21 is from pages 164–168; Chapter 23 is from pages 176–186; Chap-

ter 28 is from pages 229–244; Chapter 29 is from pages 254–261;
Chapter 30 is from pages 267–268; Chapter 31 is from page 280 and
pages 282–288; Chapter 33 is from pages 305–310. The selections
from Griffin's journals are published here for the first time.

Journal Entries

Saturday, December 12, 1953

The stitches out of my feet yesterday, and sedation that kept me from working. But good work on *Nuni* today.

A strengthening and quiet evening. Piedy* and I alone in the house working out our Christmas card list with the radio's soft murmur in the background. She put my pajamas on me early and I lay on the couch in front of the fire, my feet propped up high on pillows, half-dozing, answering her questions, talking, but thinking of the book and the chief character's presentation — a kind of day-dream.

What do sighted people see? How much do they see? Do they really use their eyes or is sight for them like the long-married wife — a thing one uses because it is always there, dully. I have noticed often that I can locate things with my hands, know where they are and then have some sighted person come in and be unable to find them at all. This astonishes me each time. How much do they see that never registers? Do they actually see the details of a tree, the exact colors and shapes of windblown grasses? The differences between morning light and noon light? Since I generally visualize these things vividly in my mind, much more so than I used to when I had sight, I cannot discover, with the long years of forgetfulness, whether my blindness is a handicap or an aid in writing. Do things remembered take on unreal and tangential visual characteristics for me over the years? Do I describe details too much instead of de-scribing the whole muffled view? I know I work very hard to write so that no reader could guess my lack of sight. What direc-tions will this take? Will I ever know?

I remember, and it haunts me, my shock when Austin Olney at Houghton Mifflin told me that my descriptions of the island of

* Nickname for Griffin's wife, Elizabeth.

Nuni, the sea, the reef, the sun and the night were almost like abstract paintings. I was secretly pleased because abstraction, if it is right, gets to essences; but secretly alarmed, too, because I had thought my concepts were described in a life-like visual manner. Austin's remark brought the fact home. Like the narcotic who discovers he has become an addict, I hadn't realized I had "gone that far," and thought this might occur sometime in the future when my memory of sight would have become more abstract, less tangible.

Is there such a thing as compensation for the lack of what we consider an essential in the creation of art? Beethoven wrote his sublimest sounds while deaf. And now, Martinu, deaf too, is writing the finest of his music. So why not write better without sight? Sight can limit as well as instruct, confuse and turn concepts ordinary unless one uses it as the miracle it is.

Monday, December 14, 1953

Tears destroy the need to work. I have felt this many times in *Nuni* when I would become so moved over a scene that I would find myself weeping; and the weeping would destroy the fire of the work and it would then come out dull and forced. Today, lying on the bed, listening to the canaries and parakeets in the aviary outside my door, I worked out a scene in the book — the scene in the bedroom with Harper's wife — and I was overwhelmed by some tremendous desolation in the fact that Harper would never again have that. A pressure of tears came to me, but I held them back, climbed into my wheel chair and rolled over to the desk and began to type. Although it took longer for that to bring the relief that comes from tears, it eventually did precisely that. Perhaps art is produced as the product of this intense transferal — perhaps art is the unshed tear, the brushstroke that evolves from the same speck of tension and energy as the tear and is put into form rather than into the evaporative liquid.

I feel more lost, more helpless than ever in my life, and weaker — so terribly weak physically and morally — and yet I write constantly, as though pushed by some demon of relentless force.

God blinds and maims some physically, some morally, some spiritually — again the bruised seed that must bear healthier fruit. I think of Vincent, of Bill Bomar, of Rattner, of Milton, Beethoven, Landino; and wonder that the rebellion of the soul, its vomitings and acceptances of the great wall should provide the compulsive tension, the desperation and longing, the outcry that forms the spark of experience necessary to produce art.

Later — Night

I decided to come back over here to the barn-studio and work. Piedy is up at my folks' house watching TV. Since I cannot sleep with her, due to these feet, I shall spend the evening here working and then sleep in the single bed where I have slept so many times before in all the years I worked and lived down here.

Strange feelings, full of warmth and gratification to return to this place tonight, knowing that all my family are up at the main house well and happy and safe, and that I am back in my old room doing precisely what I have spent so many evenings in past years doing, when this nighttime and this studio and these bookshelves knew my every emotion from Sunday night jubilation while listening to a concert to the nights when I was driven almost wild with despair and loneliness. God, I am grateful that I am married and that there is no longer that kind of desolation; but since I am safe from that now, this return has all the allure of something precious — the return to the past without the griefs of the past.

The night is cold outside. I sit here in a wheelchair, the radio on low volume to a program I scarcely hear, my stove warming the small stone-walled room, my wire recorder turned on and buzzing in the background, ready to read back to me the dictation of the day. How slowly it goes! How much I type and then throw into the wastebasket. Is there any way to learn to bypass the slush that one writes, and to write only the bone, the marrow, the essence of a scene?

June 13, 1954

Long stay in the hospital and now I am able to walk slightly again. Great relief to have gained some mobility. They can give the feet no more X-ray, however, and they deteriorate with the growing tumors.

Am immensely emptied of strength. Each step is like walking a long distance and I must think now, and wait for the moment of strength in order to undertake the project of walking across the room.

I am close to *Nuni* today. I am aware perhaps that I am putting the problems of my life into the lap of Professor Harper and I am desperate for him to solve them. I am stripping him of everything that men generally consider necessary to a man's ability to function at the human level — family, friends, even clothing, and plunging him into a world he is ill fit to live in. With me, the prospect is similar, though I never mention it aloud. First my blindness, then this near paralysis and loss of mobility, the uncertainty of the prognosis. It must drive us to turning into vegetables of frustration or it must drive us to God or an equivalent thing above and beyond us, to abandon ourselves finally, after all the self-delusions of seeming abandonment, to the great "Yes" (as the French call it), to the *fiat*, and only after passing through that can we begin to live again as functioning human beings.

June 16, 1954

My thirty-fourth birthday, a swampy, steaming morning, reminding me of the tropics with all of the parakeets screeching outside. It is like *Nuni*. What did I do there? I got up from my mat of palm fronds on the sandy floor and padded across to remove the heavy boar spear from my window. The window flopped open and a pattern of mottled sunlight and shadows from the trees entered cool into my hut. I stepped over the sill and out into the morning stillness. Low huts with thick roofs of thatch slumbered in irregular patterns throughout the compound, only partially visible through the foliage. Everything looked and smelled clean, from the blackish-green jungle that rose high on all sides into impenetrable denseness around us, to the disordered neatness of the huts, to the sparkling brilliance of the stream that borders the compound in a frame of tall grasses.

Sunlight pours through at slants, and for the moment there is no odor of smoke, no soapy smell of coconut milk and betel. Tombani's hut casts its shadow toward my feet. The laced bamboo window is closed. What do I do? Morning refreshes the earth. I walk swiftly around the back of my hut and into the fringes of the jungle. I pick a betel from one of the low bushes and tear off its husk — a fibrous material a half-inch thick. Holding it open like a lemon peel, I put the fibrous part against my mouth and brush my teeth. I drop the nut into my hut for later use.

With the leafy, straw-like taste tingling in my mouth, I get my coconut half-shell and go to the spring to fill it. I drink two shells of the icy water and turn back to the compound to replace my cup at the entrance door.

Happy to be alone awake at this hour and not needing to be too careful to avoid being seen, I step again into the jungles behind my hut and follow an almost imperceptible path into the swallowing gloom of underbrush and tall trees; there to finish my morning needs in some unused spot. I can see nothing but greenery rising on all sides of me, dark because no sunlight can penetrate it.

When I leave, my body trembles from the wetness of dew that has rubbed off on me. At the pool, I stand on the bank and brace myself against the chill of the water before diving head foremost down the five-foot incline.

When I fight my way back to the surface and clamber out, the air feels tepid and my body is blue from the cold, but the sensations are delicious. I return to my hut, wringing the water out of my beard.

Later

Good work all day. The tremendous happiness of good work. *Nuni* could be a million pages if I would allow it. Can I never have a villain? No, only the circumstances serve as a villain force; my characters do villainous things sometimes, but they are not villainous themselves. I am filled with such love for them, with such tenderness for all of them that it is impossible for me to write unsympathetically about any of them.

Suddenly I think of Piedy at home, resting now on the sofa probably, our child growing within her.

Tuesday, January 18, 1955

Therapy every day now, on the legs. They get some better, I think.

Very good work. *Nuni* draws to its close and absorbs all my thoughts.

Epictetus: "Tragedy inheres not in the condition but in man's concept of it."

That has become the key to it and to my own problems. I have learned to look at myself not as lacking the things that other men have — sight and mobility, but as simply being unlike other men, and yet living in the world of other men and therefore having to work much longer and much harder to accomplish the same thing.

This morning there have been no interruptions. It is cold and getting colder, raw and getting rawer. The weather has knocked the telephone out, thank God, so I need not worry about the interruption of telephone calls. This morning there has been the peace of steady and satisfying work. A vile and wonderful day, making me happy to stay in by the fire and concentrate. Now, my brain is milked dry. I must go bathe and shave. But I fall from sleep. Only three hours last night.

April 18, 1955

At night. I have just finished wrapping and mailing *Nuni*. I have stayed awake almost every night — napping an hour occasionally — for a long time doing the final draft. Parts had to be redone twenty or more times. Piedy has fed me and bedded me and been marvelous in letting me go through this final draft period as the energies came.

Now, a hot and sticky night. I sit here in a near daze, in my shorts, listening to the quietness of the woods. The birds are silent and there is no sound except the distant passing of a train. Is *Nuni* any good? God only knows. I have worked at it three years, too long, and sent it away with fear and trembling. Harper found himself along the lines of humanity rather than those of civilization. Stripped of everything that we think makes a man a man, he in fact became a man.

Now it is gone. Now to come out of it. They are all gone now, all of these characters who have been more real to me than many people I know during these past years. They walked out the door with stamps on them. I can work with them no more. I do not regret it. There is neither jubilance nor sadness. There never is when I finish a work. Only a dullness, an overwhelming fatigue, a need to go and just be quiet with my wife and child, perhaps to bake some bread or help her cook a meal.

BOOK 1 — NUNI

⟶

John W. Harper, assistant professor of English at St. Thomas Academy, is aboard a plane returning to the United States after a visit with his brother, an army colonel stationed in the Philippines.

At twilight, Harper's thoughts drift to his wife, Susie, his daughter, Cindy, and his two sons, Georgie and Timmy, as he anticipates his homecoming. He stares through the window for some sign of life on the Pacific reefs below.

As the dinner hour approaches, he decides to go to the restroom to take a drink of whiskey from the bottle his brother slipped into his pocket at take-off.

As he walks toward the restroom at the back of the plane, the floor drops from beneath his feet. For a dazzling moment he is aware of flames. When he recovers consciousness, he is in the water, his vision fascinated by a star overhead that appears to bob violently with the waves. Breakers move him toward shore and deposit him on an isolated reef.

Half-unconscious from shock, he drifts into profound sleep, to awaken later wondering where he is, if he is the only one washed ashore.

In the next days, his life is a growing nightmare of thirst and anguish as he searches the reef for other life, for water. As the days pass, he begins to hallucinate, seeing water everywhere and running after it. His deepest agony lies in his inability to feel anything for his wife, whose face he cannot call to memory. He realizes he must forget in order to endure. "I would never have believed it of myself that because the needs of a man's heart cannot be met, his heart itself will change rather than suffer death."

He reconciles himself to this, certain that when he has found water and heard the voices of people, the faces of his wife and children will return, and his feelings for them will revive.

Chapter 8

I suppose I have dozed or fainted, for the sun has changed positions, and my left hand, which lies open beside me, has begun to swell so that I can hardly close it. I place the burned hand inside of my coat.

Through the layers of stupidity, an image of memory taunts my brain. I attempt to shake it from my being, to look about and think of other things. There, over there is a trackless path, formed by the downward rush of water during centuries of storms perhaps. An image of memory when I was a boy and had a dog. Over there the crazy pattern of nature that allows a chunk of coral to bend over like a naked man with his head touching the ground in prayer. Memory of the dog's death by poisoning. Yes, memory of the living sounds that followed me for weeks afterward when I would hear the dog's panting and the click of his footsteps on the sidewalk behind me, hearing them so vividly that I would turn full of hope and stare at the empty sidewalk. Sounds heard often enough become habit and can be heard even when they no longer exist.

But the rooster's crowing? Yes, I remember, and my footsteps become aimless wandering. At home I was awakened every morning by crowings from the neighbor's barnyard. How often I complained to Susie that I could not sleep for hearing the roosters crow at dawn? For years I complained of that sound.

The world settles into utter stillness about me as I stagger on. I refuse to think of it, but it is there in the sniggering memory of how clearly I once heard a dead dog's panting on the sidewalk behind me.

Salt sores dig into the quick around my waist and between my thighs, and all of the bruises and stiff muscles, forgotten in my joy of discovering life this morning, pulse to the foreground of my consciousness now that the joy is dead, now that I realize the crowing was only a mirage of the hearing.

Heat clamps a breathless fog about me and fills me with a pressure that demands escape, immediate escape. The beginnings of panic tear at my chest and I search wildly for a shaded spot. A segment of green simmers in freshness through a low spot in the plateau. The ocean is escape, calm in its halcyon reaches, and I am drawn to it across sunlit wastes that blister up through my shoes.

My ankle turns dangerously against a sharp projection of coral and my shoe rips open as I regain my balance and flounder down the slope. At the bottom, I fling my glasses into my pocket and pick my way toward the water. The horizon tilts from side to side as though I were viewing it from a rocking plane, and waves flick foam against my face as I wade into the deafening cacophony of the surf. My shoes fill with the water and my ankles are wetted in its promise of benediction to my whole body. Lifting my feet high into the air, I march forward.

Waves, sucking under and furling over in mountainous cascades of white and green, thunder at me with impersonal savagery. They knock me off my feet at first until I learn to ride atop them and float downward in their wake to regain my footing. When they pass, I am left standing in water only knee-deep.

Ripples catch sunlight and slash it into glittering fragments, all of them aimed directly into my eyes. I drift forward with my knees bent double, scarcely supporting myself on tiptoes in the water's heavy buoyancy.

When I get to my feet again, I lean forward and stare down through the unreflected clarity of my shadow. Pocked hollows of coral seem to gaze back at me like eye sockets of coruscating skulls. Traces of spume minnow pass, touching my eyelash with their fragile bubbles.

The beach, when I drag myself from the water, is strewn with grayish lumps of crystallizing seaweed. I sink down and bunch some of the damp strands about my head to protect it from the sun, gratified with this hint of inventiveness and encouraged that I am fulfilling in some way the role assigned me.

Lying here on my back, surrounded by the flat odors of wet sand and brine-soured clothes, I think of the picture I must make — an overstuffed Bacchus, his face cherub-red from the sun, water streaming from his clothes, his balding head crowned with a diadem of tangled fibers. Professor John W. Harper. Classes in Literature at 10 A.M.

The moisture in my clothes evaporates to coolness, calming me, and I am again struck by the idea that under different conditions, all of this would be ravishingly beautiful. Yes, all of this that I see as frightening and hateful is in turn a miniature paradise depending not on it, but on the conditions of being here. If there were people close by, even on some neighboring reef, with the assurance of companionship, this would become a gem of whiteness and cleanness, bathed in the serenity of soft tropical colors, brushed by a perpetual breeze. It would be an ideal retreat. Then I could leave my people and come here and experience the health of removing my clothes and bathing in the ocean and basking naked on the beach and thinking and dreaming. But now, because there is no one else, every act against modesty becomes a reminder that there is no longer any need for modesty.

Every moment when I close my eyes, then, becomes the recreation of humanity, of its fragments in static portrait as they assault my brain through all of my senses simultaneously, without order, images crowding images — the healthful odor of barley soup on a winter's afternoon; the touching sight of a woman, momentarily hideous and ovarian as she crawls from sleep in the morning; the sound of footsteps running to answer the telephone upstairs and the sudden sweet idiocy that comes into my son's voice when he realizes that his girl is at the other end of the wire; the quick, hesitant touch of midday July rains stippling the backs of hands; the private night-mellowed taste of another's breath before dropping off to sleep — fleeting sense images gradually settling into place to give a more consistent portrait which takes possession of my consciousness with the tenacity of a trancelike dream.

The breeze stirs a vagrant strand of seaweed about my head and brushes it down to tickle my nose. I flick it away without being able to flick my attention away from the dream, and my vision locks itself to a reality beyond the distant present, to a reality over which I seem to have no control.

It gathers its distangled segments from the mists of lingering tropical sunlight and sound and swims into focus that is static, like the people in a Utrillo painting, posed and unmoving, caught in motion and petrified for the moment, without regard of the preceding moment or the subsequent actions. It shows me a room with another me, a stout and placid fifteen-year-old who needs to shave once a week, a youth who leads two separate lives. He lies bundled up now between the quilts and blankets of his four-poster iron bed with its brass roses carved at the headstead. He does not move, and I must supply in my dream his actions. One life has taken him through the day, through the morning hours in the community school and through the afternoon hours working in his father's country store. Now, after supper and homework at the kitchen table, his second life has called him to his room at the end of a long hall, to the secret hours of solitary night that are the most perfect of his existence. He has already skinned out of his clothes and into his nightshirt in the stoveless room, and has carried his underwear to bed with him so that it will be warm when he puts it on before getting up in the morning. He has opened the door of his marble-top night stand, and fumbled beside the porcelain chamber pot for a match to light his lamp; and after adjusting its wick, he has moved his clacking jaw close to the polished glass chimney to gather its feeble warmth.

He lies in bed now, and when the heat of his body has penetrated the blankets, he rolls over on his back, pulls his nightshirt up around his chest and arranges his books upright between his legs, using his knees for book ends. And while winter settles over the countryside, he turns to his private world of discovery in the peace of knowing that the stock is bedded down in straw against the cold and that all is well within the house. Holding his book against his chest so that his arms will stay covered, he becomes part of the drama of Stevenson and London, or bastes his ignorance in the gentle science of Paré's *Journeys to Diverse Places* and Dr. Chase's *Receipt Book and Household Physician*.

Occasionally he stops on a word he does not know, puckers his lower lip out and seriously copies the word down in his notebook. Then he looks it up either in Dr. Chase's Glossary or in the dictionary, memorizes it, and repeats it again and again to himself with much eye-closed concentration and head shaking for emphasis.

As the rustlings of the house calm to quietness about him, the overtones of the day die to remoteness and the realities of the night grow in fascination. Within the intimate protection of these flickering walls covered with latticed designs of giant red poppies, and with the shutters drawn against the world outside, childhood becomes adolescence and tentative manhood, manhood filled with the unrestrainedly noble passions for knowledge, for faraway times and places; but most especially filled with the amazements and fearsome joys of a new strength growing within his body and soul. This beginning awareness of manhood insinuates itself into a magical background for all he thinks and reads, groggily suggesting problems as yet neither forbidding nor familiar in the occasional dreams at dawn. He is only vaguely conscious of these things, conscious of a latent force within himself that is distantly connected with health and vigor and nobleness, coloring his little circle of lamplight with a tonality of exultation as the printed words close to his face fade away with the last vestiges of his daily life and he leaves all of this to become part of a better delight. He is the companion and apprentice to Paré, being chosen to accompany the venerable surgeon to sixteenth-century Flanders to treat the ailing Marquis d'Auret. He walks at his master's elbow in the castle gardens and hears him pray to God to bless his medicaments and his hands, to give him the grace to cure the dying marquis. He stands beside Paré in the sweating, stonewalled antechamber of the sickroom and assists him in making a refrigerant for the invalid's heart, eagerly measuring out the oil of water lilies, the ointment of roses, the pinch of saffron, dissolving them in rose vinegar and treacle and spreading them on a red cloth for the surgeon to administer. Or, his path takes him into the more immediate comfort of Dr. Chase's generous friendship, where he listens, filled with wonderment, as the old man explains to him what a womb is; touches him on the shoulder and tells him that the art of baking good yeast bread is the key to a happy home, and that young boys must train themselves with much exercise, hard beds and cold baths into the habits of temperance and continence as preparation for vigorous manhood and virtuous marriage.

When the room has grown colder and the page returns to nothing more than printed paper, blurring this time only under the pressure of drowsiness, he will push all of the books to the far side of the bed and blow out the lamp. In the sudden riotous blackness, he will crawl lower between the blankets, spraddle his legs out, adjust the pillow about his head and fold his arms across his bare chest.

Closing his eyes, he will force himself to say his prayers, not because he wants to, but because he feels incomplete when he does not; and then, in the same prayerful cadence, he will go over all of the new words he has learned, drifting to sleep on the whispered litany of "metatarsus, consecrate, nutritious, scrotum, ephemeral, aromatic . . ."

I can taste true affection for the child in the bed, but he is different when I close my eyes again. He sits, dressed in a college student's clothes, bending over a writing table in a tiny room in Poitiers. He is becoming convinced that he must make some sudden bold choice between the animal and the spiritual. His soul desires to enfold another in the ancient dream nurtured in him by Dr. Chase — the dream of health and homemade yeast bread, but his body drags the dream down into a swampy vision of a whore's belly, seen again and again in devastating reality of touch and sight. He smells the reek of humanity, seeing it only as frailty, and he hates it with all of his love, his body and soul distilled into a concentrated essence of loving. He looks out and sees the cooking fires of supper smoking upward from networks of chimneys, and each chimney tells him of a family inside, going about their tasks, secure in their protection of body and soul in the nest of affections born of themselves.

The rooms downstairs in this silent boardinghouse give off a different reek, the molding reek of loneliness, of people who sleep alone, who putter about their rooms in half-existences, knowing no one in the shared embrace of familiarity and being known of no one. To him there is the obscenely impeccable neatness of death about such lives, a ceramic odor of unshared propriety, of scrubbed affections, antiseptic hearts and waxed souls. He bends over his journal and his hand moves, scratching a cheap pen against cheap paper:

> . . . to break away, to become bigger than loneliness, for there is such a state. Somehow I know there is. But the dream of a newspaper and a woman's soft crying and a toothbrush and a thousand other things holds me back. It is decency, mediocre decency and not love, decency that binds me and will not let me break away, dividing the hope of heaven from the desire for hell. But decency

clings softly to the soul — the body rejects it in its own prowling way. Will I ever know the answer? Will I ever know it without first knowing my own children?

And that hand is scarcely finished before an older hand replaces it, a hand with deeper wrinkles across the backs of the knuckles, a hand stained with the scuffed layers of experience, a hand moving a better pen against better paper:

> The night has turned very cold, with rain blowing in gusts against our windows, but the fire has kept the bedroom warmer than it really needs to be. I have been up several times to fill the vaporizer with tincture of benzoin compound for Cindy, who sleeps with almost no congestion now, and to add logs to the fire. In spite of my sleepiness, there is some profoundly intimate pleasure in stirring about and doing things to keep Susie and Cindy comfortable while they sleep unaware of the storm. These are the secret things of a man's heart, and sometimes, as tonight, they break through the clutter of my life, shed their dullness of familiarity and overwhelm me as though I were living them in all of the startling clarity of newness, so overwhelm me that I catch my heart pounding with disbelief and gratitude. How many times in how many countries have I walked outside of homes, my heart breaking with the knowledge of what went on inside of them — the families, the loves and the quarrels, the bodies and the hearts, all of that shared in livingness behind those curtained windows.

. . . The sweet odor of a bedroom fireplace vanishes. The soft dampness of vaporized tincture of benzoin compound is throttled in the raw dampness of vaporized sea water.

My hand finds my beard and the crusting dryness of my lips, and all freshness vanishes to a view of the cliff overhang. The sun has disappeared around the corner of the reef, throwing me into the cavelike somberness of deep shadow. Time for dinner, time to bathe and dress for dinner; time to shave and comb my hair and change this filthy shirt. My tongue feels glutinous and clumsy. I won't be able to eat much. Maybe just a bowl of cold rice and cream.

If I hate the sun, I hate the darkness more. I begin climbing back to the top where it will be lighter, stopping midway to catch my breath and to toss aside my soggy crown of seaweed before moving on. I must have light to locate my twin bushes so I can find my way back to my cove. Strange, even its windswept emptiness is a familiarity to which I cling now, as though this familiarity imparted some faint aura of warmth and recognition.

My pants rub the insides of my legs raw. At the top, I drag myself to my feet and gaze about me for some sign of my bushes. The reef lies bathed in warm cobalt tints of dusk, misted with yellow and rose. The sun is a crimson disk, cleanly outlined without radiance and no longer threatening as it hangs near the horizon. Again I see a shadow far in the distance, flat and formless, rising and falling with my eyes' pulsation, a flickering cataract in front of the sunset. What is it, some twin reef as desolate as this one? . . .

Chapter 9

"Is this the second night? — the third night? — the fourth night? Will you tell me?" I roll on my side. Granules of sand bite into my wrist and my weight compresses my ribs against my lungs with dull pain.

How many days' growth of beard and with what filth on a body full of sores? Think beyond, think of something else. It is wrong to die in filth. Words of St. Teresa of Ávila: "If a man had only five minutes in which to prepare himself for death, he would spend four of them making himself comfortable." No, he would spend four of them washing his body, combing his hair, shaving himself. I feel it, you hear? — I hate to die his way, not hating to die, but hating to die in filth.

How is it that I smell so strongly of the odor of sweating when I am blistering here without a trace of sweat on my face or body? A knot draws to tightness at the base of my brain and I wonder how a tree looks. All things assault my somnolent brain as though I were seeing them for the first time. I think how miraculous an ice cube is. A toothbrush — when did I last see one? A drain plug in the bathtub? Morning coffee and a cigarette? The marvel of life that is somewhere back there, magical now even to its smallest detail.

Did I ever sit in an easy chair? — ever? How did it feel? How do
newspapers smell on a veranda in August? And what about classrooms at the end of day? — empty chairs and desks still vibrating
life, rooms still carrying moist odors of youngness that is no longer
fresh after the long day. Did I ever really know all of that? Miraculous. To lie in bed when sheets are clean and smell of summer
sunlight. To enter a library or church and be greeted by some subtle density of atmosphere that demands walking on tiptoe and
whispering the moment you open the door. To hear talk from
someone else's lips . . .

God how remote, how remote and foreign all of that seems tonight.

Chapter 10

There is the coral always and always the sun, and I must walk always in search of water.

I try to remember how many days — three? four? five? Five
days is the limit. Five days and a man sees the sun through a glowing mist and then his eyes recede and he dies.

Thought no longer exists but there is hope. The closer a man
approaches nothingness, the more he refuses to admit it. And there
is tenderness, even when there is no longer the image of a face . . .
there is tenderness until tenderness fills every crevice of being and
a man loves gigantically. And the love is his hope.

There! There! A sandcrab far from its hole. I jump into the air
and land on it with the heel of my shoe. Its legs rake furiously as I
crush it into the sand. Restaurants of the world. Pressed duck with
burgundy. Baked pompano. Roast pheasant. Crab in agony.

The sun, the ocean, the universe gyrate somewhere in the background, but I don't pay any attention to them. I can live. The
beach is full of sandcrabs. They swarm in all directions.

I reach down and pick it up. Its claws are not distorted in death.
It lies perfectly whole in the palm of my hand. None of its liquids
are lost!

Exultantly I place it between my teeth to break its armor. It cracks and I taste grit between my lips and gums. Surprised, I take it away to look at it. Focusing carefully, I see it become a grotesque and lifeless chunk of coral. I let the thing fall to the ground. The others no longer swarm. They cast shadows, motionless shadows. Five days and how many have passed? For the life of me I can't remember.

I climb to the highest point on the reef and stare in all directions. The shadow pulsates on the horizon. For a brief instant, it is brought close to my eyes, inhabiting the smallest corner of my vision, like a miniature seen through the wrong end of a telescope. It is covered with trees. Blanched coral beaches fade into a wild, moss-colored jungle. The tops of the tallest trees are made luminous green by the sun and the lower growth is lost in dank shadows. All of it is motionless, a mass of static color. My eyes ache with the effort and I am aware of the white ground and the white bushes around me as though seen superimposed. I look away and then quickly back. Now there is nothing but a flat shadow once more on the ocean's horizon. Some trick of the lenses, like the crabs . . .

I begin walking again. My pants brush against a dew-drinking bush, and drunkenly I bend down to examine it. And I am bending down in a garden in Holland and there are morning mists and tulips and my pants are comfortable gray flannels that do not eat into the ulcers of my genitals and legs. Clusters of giant purple grapes cling to the stone wall. Globules of morning dew drip downward from one grape to another and plash into the sparkling grasses below. The pockets of yellow tulips are filled with rainwater and the soaked air is gently perfumed with smoke from chimneys nearby.

I examine the leaf for a long time. My hand is incredibly red and wrinkled against it. I stand up straight and begin to walk. A searing breeze from the ocean nudges at my face. I raise my hand to rake sweat from my forehead, but my forehead is dry. Waves crash against the reefs below. Then I see the ground coming up to meet my face.

Chapter 11

The wind blows through a shuddering forest, deep and far away.

Someday I will get to my feet and walk again.

Is this the fourth day? God! Is this the fifth day?

I do not move. The granules of sand beneath my eyes pulsate and draw closer and then swirl away. They fascinate me. In a while I will walk some more.

The sun sets and stars cluster overhead. They are like the sand. They move. They fascinate. They are so young, so terribly young and I can hardly believe that they will go on like that, glittering every night on a world that knows nothing of my existence.

I sleep some of the time, with dreams of verdure, dreams of healthful green countrysides and clear unreflected lakes. I lie on my side with my legs drawn up and with my hands between them, not needing to move, not needing to think. Strange. A point is reached where even thought becomes waste spilled out on the hem of eternity.

But there is no waste to memory, and no thrift and no time. Somewhere back there a freshly ironed dress, face powder, the face without features from a lifetime ago when I knew her and loved her.

The fifth day? Is it? God.

The waiting, the moments of waiting when there are no more seconds. The moments between life and death or between two sleeps. Moments suspended in time, not counted in seconds.

I think that I must turn to my wife, and with sudden youthfulness, mingled with age and passion into a fragment of tranquility, ask: "Do you remember the days? — the days when we first started together? — those wonderful days?" and read in her body the answer and feel strangely full of guilt. We are together, then, for a new time in the nest of our bed, breathing the humid air that accumulates beneath the covers, hidden from the world, from the night, safe, pressing against one another to express some mysterious security of pardon; pardon because always when two people love, they

must be forgiven one by the other, constantly, without other reason than that love demands it — the security of perpetually renewed pardon born of the delicate balance forever re-establishing
itself between two people become one but remaining two. I roll in
my bed. My arms reach out to encircle warmth, to find the complete union after all these years, still seeking to have only one heart
with hers, only one body, only one painfulness.

The sky is full of night's sharp clarity and there is no warmth of
her body in my arms, but I am profoundly comfortable in the silence, the emptiness. I am filled with the realization that I am a
fleck of unknown livingness in a world where nothing else lives,
and yet tonight there is joy and comfort in all of it.

But I wonder why eternity keeps me waiting in this timeless hole.
It surprises me that something that important could be laggard.
You expect it to be punctual, immaculately punctual. I lie here
waiting, feeling strangeness.

To my left, light glistens from coral diamonds. It is a fine illusion.
Perhaps here is the flame that is supposed to blaze up before my
eyes recede into my skull.

Fiery reflections slither and dance. I let my head be raised on its
tendons. Far away, through the clean blackness, pinpoints of flame
cast a glow upward into the sky. Numbly I listen. There is no
sound and I am too wonderfully comfortable to move.

And yet the irritating distraction is there, floating beyond my
intimate world of now. And then I recognize it and I turn on my
side and put my blistered hands against my blistered face. I need
water for one tear or I will suffocate. I remember campfires glittering through timber at night when you return after a long day's
hunting, and they were like these, glowing in the distance and made
close in the clarity of night. These have probably been there every
night, bringing my phantom shadow on the horizon close to me,
but I could not see them from my cove below.

I struggle into an upright position thinking to shout; but no, that
would be useless; to build a signal fire; but no, there is no flame
here. The coral shallows that follow an underwater path to that
horizon? But it is too late. Lights roar before my eyes, splintering
all vision. I cup my hands into a telescope over one eye. I stare at
hundreds of tiny lights until they join in sight to become ten or

twelve, dotting the blackness without design and casting a glow upward to the lowest stars.

"Hey!" But the seal on my lips refuses to break. "For the love of God, hey!" They will never hear my mumblings. Faint odors of night mingle with my own reek. I try to separate my lips. They feel like wood bark to my trembling fingers.

I no longer try to call out. I crawl, dragging my distended belly like a packsack beneath me. Stars allow paleness to glint about me. I stop at the edge of the western cliff and peer out into its black hole. Invisible breakers foam up beneath me.

Sitting with my legs dangling over the edge, I telescope my hands again. The fires are still there. How far? A thousand yards? A thousand miles? I can feel my face draw up into a grin, a weeping grin in which there is no moisture. How far? And what choice? What difference is there between dying on this chalk-dry cliff and dying in sea shallows? The one is certain, the other less so. If I don't think about it, don't try to —

Blind impulse pushes me to lean forward and I teeter over the edge knowing only that I will go as far as possible. My feet touch the ground, my legs buckle wildly and I am sitting with my nose tingling numb where it has bashed into my knees. The surf bellows forward in crescendo and water lashes around my seat and ankles. I stretch out and allow it to cover me from the neck down. Its tepid wetness seeps into the fever of my body, massaging me and clearing my head a little.

My brain swims off into sleep and I am jerked back to wakefulness with my head lolling on my neck into the water. Lumbering to my feet, I straggle forward over the pocked shallows, bracing myself against the long walls of phosphorous turnings that fling the tinsel of breakers at me.

My senses withdraw against the onslaught. How far to the lights? As each breaker roars on beyond me, I can see the fires over low waters and the fixed grin returns to hurt my face. With each step forward, I place my foot carefully, in the prayerful knowledge that I may be stepping down not on the rough ground of now but into the smooth plane of forever.

Slowly, carefully, I shutter my senses deep within me and move forward automatically, feeling nothing, my body senselessly obeying the obsession of its brain, the obsession of those lights.

Suddenly the last fire disappears, cut off by some object, and I am moving with the waves in total darkness. And then there is a swirling envelopment as I am lifted away from the terrain into warm nothingness. I hear my voice from within, moaning "No . . . no . . ." and turn to whimperings of despair as coolness pervades the air of my somersaulting flight. And there is no more solidness beneath my feet.

Harper comes to consciousness on the beach of the twin reef, struggling through the haze of his shock to swallow a liquid that is being poured into him from a halved coconut shell by a naked black child, Veedlie. When he tries to thank him, Veedlie runs away.

"The child is gone, leaving no trace. I wonder if this is not another illusion, but no, a roughly halved coconut shell lies still glistening beside me, and when I reach beneath my head, the pillow that has supported it is the other half of the shell," Harper observes. "The weakness grows on my comfort, like some distant flute song played from the end of a long corridor. I will get up and move later, but now I listen to the weakness that tells me I must rest for a time."

Harper begins a new existence on the island. Each day food and drink is brought, usually when he is asleep, and left beside him on the beach. His total possessions include a tattered book of Great Essays *that was in his coat pocket, his clothing, and a locket with his children's photographs.*

Within a few days, some of the younger islanders approach him, apparently driven by curiosity. An elderly patriarch, Tombani, comes each day and begins to teach Harper the language of the island. No suggestion is made that he can leave the beach for the island villages. As he learns the language, he learns that he is held in contempt. But Tombani softens this with attentions that surprise Harper, who finds him completely inconsistent.

After weeks on the beach, Veedlie arrives one day, his hair dyed white with lime juice. Veedlie explains casually that his hair is dyed because during the night his father, Maigna, died. According to local custom, whenever a man got too old or too weak to walk

*a certain distance, he had the privilege of ending his life, usually
by opening his stomach with a bone knife. Harper tries to understand how Maigna, Tombani's son, can be old enough to die, but
Tombani is not. Veedlie explains that Tombani can still walk the
required distance and therefore has "no right to die."*

*Veedlie then informs Harper that he is to accompany him to the
village to celebrate the death of Maigna. In preparation, he starts
a fire, places a coconut shell wrapped in banana leaves on the coals,
and begins to boil water with a sea slug in it. Harper understands
nothing about this.*

BOOK 2 — VANUA

Chapter 18

. . . "Why do I go to Vanua?"

He reaches back and slaps his upper thighs like a bird clumsily
flapping its wings, in perfect mimicry of Tombani's habitual gesture of exasperation. His face is almost against mine and his neck-
lace dangles free. He stares at me as though I were stupid beyond
all hope. His breathing rattles through his congested nose in mounting fury.

Then, sighing exaggeratedly, he stops spanking himself and
clasps his hands behind him while he begins the painfully patient
explanation in a chanting tone of voice that sounds so insulting
when his grandfather assumes it.

Tombani calls me to Vanua for the feasting and dancing of
death, Veedlie intones, his wiry, nasal voice rising and falling in a
monotonous cadence. The unmated males who are beginning to be
pubescent have gone to hunt the wild pig, all except Fat Oai, who

is now to be mated and who has no spirit left in him for pleasure.

"Fat Oai doesn't want to be mated?"

Veedlie recoils and spits to the side with such revulsion that the vein at the side of his neck swells and pulses. The monotonous chant is replaced by a rapid staccato stream of language that fills the cove with sounds like a monkey's chattering. I can understand little except that nothing is so terrible as mating, that a man has to make babies, and each time he lies with a woman he loses some of his manhood, and that is "zagata," no good. He spits the word "zagata" out with such a violent turn of his head that a streak of saliva glistens across his cheek from his mouth to his ear.

"If he doesn't like it, why does he do it?"

"No one likes it," he cries in an agony of explanation. "But everyone must do it when the hairs come on the body. Everyone is mated, and if you do not make a baby from one rain's end to the next, you are zagata, tabooed and driven into the forest never to return to Vanua."

"But it is good to lie with a woman," I protest.

"Taeega!" [1] he screams. "It is bad, bad." His eyes glaze over like Tombani's and become inhuman. He spits again and makes a pathetic gesture, drawing away, covering his genitals tightly with both hands and hunching his shoulders forward defensively as though he were protecting his manhood from even the idea of its ever being shared with a mate. His gaze wanders fearfully toward the towering palms, making me feel ashamed that I have frightened him with a truth he can probably never understand. The grotesqueness of our situation makes me even more ashamed. Here I am, an elderly man and father, arguing with a child who cannot be more than five or six years old about the goodness of sleeping with a woman. Past habits of thinking make the scene appear almost depraved, but to Veedlie there is obviously no shame in it, only outrage that I should be perverse enough to think such a thing could be "good" when everyone knows it is "zagata." They marry then, without any desire for it, considering manhood synonymous to sexual potency, seeing the act of mating as evil since it makes man lose some of his manhood, but necessary in order to prove his potency by producing children. Not to have children

[1] No. (Ed.)

would prove sterility, which is a disgrace sufficient to ban him from society for the rest of his life.

"I go to Vanua for Maigna's death and for the feast to celebrate Fat Oai's mating?" I ask, looking into his agonized face and turning the words around to make sure that I have understood correctly, to determine if the marriage is not, after all, the real reason for the feast.

"No!" he shouts, almost sobbing, "for Maigna's feast."

"Good," I say, reaching up and patting him on the cheek.

"Thank you," he barks. He turns away from my touch and stalks toward the fire, his body in a tremble. Wrapping another navundi leaf around the shell, he lifts it from the fire.

When he deposits it on the ground beside me, I see that a thick, greasy substance has risen to the top of the water. It catches rainbows in slithering streaks of color. The child lifts the scum off with a twig, leaving the water clear, with no sign of the sea slug in the bottom. He tosses the refuse aside and steam-smoke hovers around it until it cools. I rub some of it between my fingers; it is soft and grayish and leaves a film on my flesh like chicken fat.

Veedlie stands beside me and pours the warm liquid from the shell into my hair, drop by drop, with one hand, massaging it in with his other hand. My head begins to itch and I reach up to scratch it and feel the sparse matted hair full of thin suds. We are washing my hair. When it is soaked and rubbed to Veedlie's satisfaction, he pours the remainder of the liquid on my beard and repeats the process. I am more than ever mystified. Are they that fastidious — that I must be shampooed head and beard before attending the feast? Veedlie leaves me and sets off at a jog trot for the river, returning in a moment to bring fresh water for rinsing the soap out. He makes the trip seven or eight times. The stuff leaves my hair as clean as any shampoo I have ever used and takes the wiryness out of my beard.

"We go now," he announces when we have finished. "We go to Vanua."

"Do we come back here?"

"No, kulangu," [2] he says, wiping sweat from his forehead with his hand. "We stay in Vanua." . . .

[2] Friend. (Ed.)

As the two proceed through the jungles toward the village of Vanua, Harper discovers one of the taboos. Veedlie leaves him and goes far into the brush to urinate. When Harper questions why, the child becomes terrified that he may have been seen in this functional act. Veedlie explains that anyone who sees another in the performance of a physical function thereafter has control over the other's spirit. Only children who are not yet old enough to be tattooed and circumcised escape the taboo.

Eventually they arrive in Vanua, a village of thatch-roofed huts. The village is deserted as the local inhabitants hide themselves from the visitor. Veedlie takes him across the compound toward the hut that will be Harper's home. It is an old structure, almost hidden in the trees, with stained bamboo-woven walls and a roof of thatch that is almost black. It has only one opening at the end, a window that serves also as a door. Harper learns it is the hut formerly occupied by Maigna, abandoned when Maigna died. It is dark inside, unfurnished except for a woven mat which will serve as his bed. It is only slightly larger inside than Harper's bathroom at home in America. "The tightly woven walls let in a faint lattice design of daylight from the outside."

Veedlie leaves, explaining he and his mother will go live in the hut of Fat Oai, his brother, soon to be married.

Harper goes to the back of the hut, sits down on the mat and waits for what is to come. The villagers come into the compound and prepare for the burial of Maigna and the feast to follow.

Harper thinks about his new home. "I breathe the reek of the hut's past . . . What have these walls and floors known? — what bodies, what hungers and pains, what passions and revulsions, what bewilderments? It looks as much like an animal den as a human habitation . . ."

Tombani and some of the other men come into the hut, carrying food, symbol of his acceptance at last into the life of the island. As he eats the potato-like vegetable, the other men sit in a circle and take betel nut.

Finally stuffed and drugged by the heat, Harper is left alone. "I

*am back in a world that is somewhat akin to the world I have
known — the world of man, no matter how primitive — the world
that tells of man's appetites and his needs. I am no longer exposed
to the stark language of nature. I can hear voices of men and
women and children. I am in a home, in my own home, and living,
breathing, mortal humanity surrounds it."*

In the afternoon, covered with sweat, he makes his way to the
spring-fed pond near the edge of the compound where the villagers
bathe. However, before he can get into it, he is called to the funeral
service for Maigna. At the service, he meets Fat Oai and, among
others, the local sorceress, Rauka Tataolagi, the most powerful person in the village. She is a *"withered old hag . . . who stands tiny
and hunched with her chin resting on gnarled hands which are
crossed at the top of a tall branch staff. She consumes me with her
jeweled gaze. If it were not for her long, empty breasts flapping
down below the crease of her abdomen with their elongated nipples
pointing to the earth like purple sticks inserted in the flesh, I would
take her for a shrunken old man . . . Her eyes are inhuman in
their phosphorescent brightness . . . as she stares at me with such
intensity I must look away."*

Veedlie explains that the rauka is the strong one — it is she who
performs the tattooings, reads the omens and does the circum-
cisions. *"And she keeps serpents in her hut which it is taboo to
look upon."*

They go to the hut where the body of Maigna has been prepared
for burial. The body has been gutted, drained of blood and then
wrapped in a soft bark that appears rather like the wrappings of a
mummy. Two men carry the light weight through the village,
past the pond and into an open field of yellow buttercups where
a shallow grave has been dug. The chanted service is long. Rauka
ends it by saying: *"We leave you in sunlight, and we go back and
wait in shadow."*

After each villager tosses a flower on the body, it is covered and
all return to the village for the feast of death — roasted pork,
bananas and taro-like roots. Gaiety returns after the somberness of
the burial. Laughter floats through the forest.

Turning aside, Harper makes his way to the pool, undresses and
drops into the icy waters. *"Chill invades feverishness . . . seeping*

*into the depths of my entrails. Without moving a muscle, I drift
with the moment as my toes rake gently across the frozen pebbles
of the bottom."*

Chapter 21

Without being aware that I have slept, I find myself awake. My
vision is diffused in all directions around and about and beyond the
face above me. Briefly, I glimpse the shaded underfoliage forming
a high arbor above the black silhouette that peers intently down at
me. A child stands in the grass at my head, hands on hips, bending
far over me and gazing into my face. Through the muffle of drowsiness, I cling to one thought. I must do nothing to frighten this full-
cheeked infant away. Smiling, I speak a soft greeting and move my
eyes back in my head to see that it is a girl.

She ignores my greeting but lowers her head closer to mine, en-
grossed in the upside-down view of my face.

"What is your name?" I ask.

"N'gari kikiki daoka," [3] she says in such childish accents that I
must guess more than I actually understand. And I notice that her
skin is smooth and fresh, that she has not yet been tattooed and
therefore has not been named, being called simply "girl baby."

The grass is cool against my back, and I am glad for this sleepi-
ness that deadens my heart to the acute rise of hope that the child
inspires in me.

"You sit with me?" I suggest.

"I sit with you," she answers.

I stretch out my left arm and she hops around to the side and
kneels in the hollow of my armpit, sitting back on her heels in the
way of these women, with her knees drawn together and her hands
folded primly in her lap. Gazing sidelong at her, I allow my arm to
encircle her back. She inches forward until her knees are pressed
into my ribs.

And she is like any other child in the world, without even the
tattoos to give strangeness.

[3] Girl baby. (Ed.)

"You are pretty, child."

"You are pretty, Jon," she smiles, dimpling her cheeks in a shy overcoming of timidity.

Seeing her and feeling her flesh touch mine with growing ease that is devoid of any hint of repugnance, I have no doubts as to how I must behave. I am at home in the world of childhood and all constraint evaporates from my chest in the blessed relief of familiarity. I can be natural with her, for she is like all children and with children there is never the need to fear the spontaneous intelligence of the heart.

"Do you want a name?" I tease, feeling authority and liberation return to my stunted bloods.

Her eyes open in blank surprise and her head starts forward in a movement of expectancy.

"Since you are no bigger than a finger, I name you Ririkinger."

Her hand flies up to my chest. I sense its faint weight through the thick mat of my beard.

" 'kinger?" she whispers.

"You," I say solemnly, "are not N'gari kikiki daoka. You are Ririkinger!"

" 'kinger! 'kinger! 'kinger," she laughs.

"Is that good?" I ask, drawing her close to me, fingering the folds of her feet beneath her infant buttocks.

"Good and very good," she explodes ecstatically, repeating " 'kinger, 'kinger, 'kinger," and thrusting her face forward to giggle into my beard.

Moving my right arm across my chest, I grasp her beneath the armpits with both hands and lift her into the air, as I have done with my own children so many times. And like them she grins with elation and screams when I swoop her from side to side and dive her downward to kiss her on the cheek. The clearing is transformed into a world where all is guilelessness, all is innocence and gaiety, all is centered in the child's amusement, and in the unfoldings within man's withered heart when he becomes the child with no other change from childhood than the forgotten perspective of years.

"Oof," I grunt in fatigue, lowering her to rest on my stomach. Her tiny legs flail against my belt and she melts the crusts of stagnation within me with her gaze, clear of the cautious dregs and full of that expression of pure joy that is reserved to the eyes of infants.

"You," I announce with mock majesty, "are Ririkinger."

" 'kinger!" she sings, planting her fists on my chest and rising up on stiff arms. She puffs her jaws out in imitation of my pompousness.

"You are pretty, Ririkinger." I slap her behind as she tumbles forward against my chin.

"You are pretty and very pretty, Jon," she says with sudden drowsiness, and I feel her muscles turn to mush almost instantly with sleep. I cradle her body to me in a rocking motion from side to side as my nerves absorb the gentle nourishment of peace.

"She is woman."

My body convulses in spasm at the unexpected whispering. My eyes fly open and I am staring into the rage-distorted face of Tombani. I clutch the child to me as he transfixes me with his slitted glare.

"It is taboo to touch female," he purrs cunningly, tainting the atmosphere with subtle viciousness.

"But a child," I protest, stupefied. Surely he doesn't think I would defile —

"She is female!" he bellows, stepping over my head in a fleeting perspective of underthighs and wobbling genitals. He sweeps the child up by her arm and flings her through the air to one side.

I plant my elbows furiously in the grass behind me, rising up in defense. The child thumps to the earth with a breathless grunt that becomes a deep inhalation, then a scream. Tombani tenses over me, lifting his club into the air. His dripping lips curl away from his tushes and he weaves over me with an insane leer on his face that throttles all intelligence within me. I wait, unable to move, sickened by the raw horror of viewing feverish eyes in which there is no hint of mercy. And a sudden devastation of light floods my insides with the certitude of death. The sky above is infinitely blue, trailing scattered white clouds with underpuffings of gray; two sun-pinked cockatoos float serenely from tree to tree in the stratospheres beyond.

All of it is intensely real, lifted from the context of time into the timeless motion of a dream until his club trembles and arcs toward me with the full sweep of his body. The movement obliterates my paralysis and I flounder to one side as his leer wells to enormity before my eyes. The clap of wood against bone reverberates through my head, and the child's screaming is abruptly silenced. The skull-cracking pain sears into my brain, cross-cutting nerves to the quick of agony and then shifting to numbness. My head lolls painlessly to the side, but I have the impression that I am terribly hurt. I feel myself sinking downward, sinking into mists. Saliva bubbles from the corner of my mouth and the sinkings gather momentum, hurtling me through nothingness.

Harper regains consciousness and stumbles back to the village wondering if they think him dead, if they will menace him further for having touched the girl. In the village, they ignore him as though nothing had happened. He sees Tombani who gazes at him with an expression of sympathy.

In his hut, Harper lies on the mat and drifts to sleep as the odor of burnt hog floats to him. He hears the villagers' laughter and shouting.

Chapter 23

"Come, friend."

His voice is distant, mingled with the pale ocean of my beard.

"Come, friend."

A ragged toenail scrapes against my rib, catching in underarm hairs. How long did I sleep between the first call and the second? I brush the foot away and abandon myself to the pressure of drowsiness.

"Come," he insists, and I recognize the childish voice of Veedlie.

"What do you want?" I ask, without opening my eyes.

"You do not eat."

"I am full and very full."

"You eat."

"I am sick. Go away." His toe grates into my armpit again, and I open my eyes to the silver glare of twilight.

"You come, kulangu," he says again, with no inflection in his voice. "You eat betel. Fat Oai takes his mate."

"Does Fat Oai ask me?"

"Fat Oai asks."

Strange gratification awakens me to the courage to move. There was something in Fat Oai's glance after all, something that makes him request my presence at his marriage. I climb to my feet, dumb with a headache but touched that I am wanted.

Following Veedlie through my door, the freshness of evening air settles over my shoulders. In the somber light of dusk, I see that all vestiges of the feast have disappeared and that the earth is once again swept clean. Against the background blackness of the forest, the inside of the cooking hut glows full of the pinks of an invisible fire. I stand still, stretching myself to full height and inhale the balm of jungle stagnation, cool and moist, dampening the foul after-odors of the feast.

A shadow crosses the compound, hurrying from the cooking hut to Oai's hut where the villagers are gathered.

He arrives before we are half across the compound and I watch him drop to the ground and blow sparks from the punk he has carried. A flame crackles in green wood, expelling a column of thick white smoke straight into the air and lighting the undersides of bellies and flanks and breasts that mill around in the half-light.

Little Veedlie leads me around the group to a point near the opening of Fat Oai's hut where Tombani squats on his haunches against the flickering wall.

The old man glances up at me, his eyes reflecting firelight and removes his pipe long enough to say: "You sit here, friend," patting a place beside him on the ground. His voice is soft and cordial, with no undertones of apology, but simply as though nothing had occurred between us earlier. In my dullness, I reach up and finger the bruised lump which fills the cup of my hand, wondering for a moment if I have not suffered the violence in a dream. He replaces the tiny pipe between his teeth and pats the ground again. Shaking my head in bewilderment, I squat beside him and lean back against the retained warmth of the wall.

Behind us, the hummings and screechings of night creatures and the croaking of frogs begin to float out from the jungle. The fire of green twigs, perhaps symbolic of puberty, pops loudly and shoots its sparks in all directions. Rauka parades toward us with her long staff and I see the giant silhouette of Oai trailing after her.

The crone plants herself directly in front of us, facing the crowd and all motion ceases in the firelit semicircle. Fat Oai and a girl stand together before her, the three of them forming a triangle. Faces are stoic, expressionless in the firelight. I watch the flames through the wide opening between Rauka's legs.

Without moving her feet, and without speaking, she turns the upper part of her body toward Fat Oai, who steps forward so close that I can hear his dolorous breathing. He raises his left arm and she places a thin armband of braided bamboo around it above the biceps, weaving the loose ends together with rapid manipulations of her fingers. Then she turns from him toward the girl, whom I cannot see; but from the writhings, I judge that she is placing an armband on her also.

"What is she doing?" I whisper in Tombani's ear, my voice cold with the reticence of our recent violence.

"She mates them," he answers, turning his head to speak quietly to me, but keeping his eyes averted to the ceremony. I draw back from the bitterness of his breath.

The crowd relaxes into fidgetings as Rauka secures the girl's armband and steps back away from her. Tombani rises to his feet with a grunt.

"We go," he says down at me, nudging my elbow with his knee to urge me up. Irritation throbs into the ache of my head at the gesture.

"It is finished?" I ask, pulling my arm away from his knee.

"It is finished," he says, his voice assuming the resonance of something profoundly final, more like the announcement of death than of a marriage ceremony. The hush taints the atmosphere, felt from the hearts of all, a longing, a sadness of accomplished pain.

Rauka turns, glares down at us and hurries past the fire into the night. She is followed by the jostling backsides of all the other women except Oai's new mate, who steps over the door beside us, a specter of loneliness.

Oai stands motionless in the firelight, his head lowered, his gaze indrawn in his own isolation as no man speaks to him, no man laughs and pats him on the back and congratulates him. The other males are arranging themselves in a large semicircle extending from the sides of the hut in an unbroken line around the front, sitting cross-legged before the fire and facing the open door.

Peering above their heads, I see the shadowy figures of women disappearing through the gloom into their huts, leaving the compound deserted except for our firelit circle.

My pain, my fatigue are blanketed as my attention becomes absorbed in the black hulk staring dejectedly into the flames, and I am drawn to speak to him, to say some encouraging word in his ear.

All of the men are in place except Tombani and me. They give off an aura that gradually penetrates to my intelligence, an aura not of rawness or severity, but one transformed by portents of pity, of sympathy, swelling in poignancy when young Oai stirs himself and waddles to the door of his hut and climbs inside. I squint after him, squint at the black hole as the door swings shut replacing it with a barrier of solidity, alive with dancing reflections from the flames.

A movement at the end of the circle attracts my attention. Betel nuts and branches and the bamboo shoots are being passed around. Tombani's grip closes around my elbow and he shoves me toward an empty space near the center of the circle.

"Why do we stay here?" I ask, pulling my elbow away from his clutch.

"To keep evil from entering," he answers glumly, nodding toward the closed door.

In the earthbound simplicity of his words, I am stirred with a first hint of real sympathy for these men. We do not sit here in celebration, there is not the slightest trace of ribaldry; no, we form a circular wall before Oai's door to assure him that evil will not get past us to threaten him this night. Expressions are sober with understanding, sober with the duty we perform sitting out here helping the children bend themselves to an awesome conformity demanded of life. Rauka's gummed words come back to me: "We leave you in sunlight, and we go back and wait in shadow." And in the waiting, all obey the commands of living, the shadows of existing.

Tombani shells a betel nut and pops it into his mouth, folding the fibrous husk and laying it on the ground between his thighs.

"You take betel," he says through loud crunching.

I obey, choosing one and passing the rest to the thick-lidded man on my left. He accepts them without smiling, without looking into my face.

"We stay here all night?" I ask Tombani, peeling the nut and tossing the husk away.

"No, when it is over we go."

Veedlie has jumped up and retrieved my discarded betel shell. He holds it between his hands and brushes it vigorously up and down on his teeth and Tombani explains I must use the fibrous inside as a toothbrush, to clean my teeth. Little Veedlie hands the salivaed shell back to me, and I imitate Tombani, placing it on the ground between my thighs.

"Eat," Tombani commands impatiently, his brows lowering over the shadows of his eyes. I drop the large kernel into my mouth and bite down on it. Bitterness freezes my jaws for a moment, but I chew until it crumbles, filling the space between my lips and gums with fragments that have the taste and texture of green peanuts.

Tombani is dipping a straw into the bamboo shoot and bringing it to his lips. He tells me it is poki, a fine powder made from pulverized sea shells and that I must take only enough to sweeten the betel or it will blister my mouth. I dip the straw into the black hole of the shoot and feel it contact softness. The powder begins neutralizing, not sweetening the sourness in my mouth, and I bring it to my lips on the wet straw several times until the bitterness has turned into a flow of bland saliva that must be swallowed in tricklings.

"Keura," [4] Tombani announces more amiably, handing me a tree branch. When I hesitate, he tells me to bite off some of the bark and chew it up with the betel and poki mixture in my mouth. I place it to my lips, feel the wetness of others' gnawings and tear off a strip between my teeth. Spicy fumes fill my mouth and nose with a coolness that burns, and I see that it has turned the contents of Tombani's mouth blood red. A dry scorch is clamped over my ears and cheeks as I swallow and chew in a movement of my jaws that becomes almost hypnotic. Senses are thrown into a tangent and concentrated as the fire begins to separate in my vision with the rise of fever to my face, becoming two fires and then fusing into one

[4] Name of a tree. (Ed.)

and separating again in a constant swivel of fusion and separation. Reaching up, I pat my cheeks with the palms of my hands. My jaws react as leather, stiff and nerveless. I move my head on the creaking ratchet of my neck, toward Tombani, who is watching me closely, and his face separates into two and flows back together again as the fire did. Drunkenness rises up, rolling in vast clouds through my brain.

God forgive me. I'm getting drunk at a funeral. No, a wedding. I'll do something wrong and get bashed in the head again.

"Are you all right, friend?" I hear Tombani ask.

"I am dizzy."

"It is betel."

"I see strange things."

"It is betel. Things dance. Sight dances and tongue dances and head dances."

It is like bolting a bellyful of whiskey on a hot day. I cling to reality with intense concentration.

"You like?" Tombani's voice penetrates an underthrumming of deafness.

"I like," I say too loudly. "It is good."

"You have enough?"

"Yes."

"You tell legend?"

"What legend?"

"Legend." He smiles in double images of kindness. "The tongue dances and legends are told."

His information is late and far away. I think, with tremendous intelligence, that I must tell a legend, but only the grossest images come to mind. I must not, I tell myself firmly, I must not tell grossness. I must not mention woman.

A legend is being told. The first native on the right, an elder, scoots on his behind up to the fire and speaks in a chanting tone of voice, not singing, but speaking his phrases in cadenced monotony.

. . . *goes in full day to the top of the great hill where bushmen live, goes alone, and at the top of the hill he stops and sees below the cliff a serpent in curl. He gnaws through a branch and takes away the leaves with his hands and bites through its croppings with his teeth until he has a pole with two legs.*

Pain streaks through my ear, but I am grinning, swallowing back the urge to ask: "Pardon me, kulangu, but whom are you speaking about?" Cheapness, all is cheapness within me, cheapness wells up and abounds in my private night.

. . . *and he holds the pole before him and leaps from the cliff, burying the pole legs in the earth on each side of the serpent-head with such force the branch pierces his side. Then he takes the live serpent and carries it to Rauka, who places it in her basket to guard us against the bushmen. Each day she puts fire to the snake to make it hate, and when it hates she shows it the head of the bushman she keeps; and one day we know she sends the serpent back to the bush and the serpent finds a bushman and hating him for the burnings, kills him.*

That's a noble and dull damned story, I think, swallowing back words as blood warms to tempest in me, and we are telling legends wherever men are gathered, but not legends of snakes. A party of men sitting around and drinking and telling legends always of ass, always gurgling and giggling, somehow sure that laughter is good and makes the legends good until the white-bellied ones come in and sneer and call it cheapness. Cheapness, they make it cheapness, the whited ones. What is good, you call cheapness, Reverend Mackay, with your shame and your platitudes. Our great struggle, friends, is to overcome our lower natures. Overcome, hell. And where is it so low, and how is it so low? Overcome? No, cover up, Reverend, cover up ass in your cheapness.

And here and now — no ass and no cheapness — stars are out and when you look up they separate and draw together in swarms. The sky's full of them, God, full, close there, spread out over the treetops.

What's he talking about? I focus on his fire-streaked face, on his chanted words, earthbound and guttural, eerie in the night, tying heaven to earth.

. . . *and the bushman comes and takes his child's head away and Maigna waits for him in the night, waits for him to return, waits sitting against the wall with his boar spear. He hears the noise in the night and he rises to his feet and waits for the door to open and he pushes his boar spear through the bushman's body, and in daylight he carries it to Rauka who takes the head from the body and*

smokes it for her hut, tying it to the ceiling, and Maigna drags the
body into the river for the gators to eat.

I wonder what Fat Oai and his lady are doing in there. Looking
up at the blank door which pulsates with my heartbeat I feel myself
grinning again; but the grin fades once more in my loathing for this
thing that I have become. Is it the betel? — the concussion?

Concentrate, I command myself. Concentrate and seek to revive
right feelings. Think of the night and the lonely, lonely world behind those latticed walls; and let compassion crowd out the cheapness.

A giant moth sweeps into the light, fluttering silver above the
flames.

They take their turns, narrating their endless legends of heroism
which has no other motivation than duty. All of it is duty, all acts
and all emotions foreordained by the sterile compulsion of duty,
never of pleasure or desire or free choice, making all things that
would be nourishing in freedom become tasteless because of their
slavery to elemental nature. What will I tell them when my turn
comes? Will I tell them about the great heroes of history and fiction? Will I slump to the earth and be dead drunk before they get
to me? . . .

When Harper's turn comes, he mumbles a long monologue about
love, a quality he cannot find among the people of Nuni. At the
end he takes another betel and sinks into a stupor. Heavy rainfall
awakens him later. The wait is over. The others have left him
where he lay.

The following day, a yaw in Veedlie's eyes distresses the child
who keeps scratching at the scabs. Harper, remembering the oil
scum atop the water in which Veedlie had boiled the sea slugs, pre-
pares a treatment. He boils a sea slug, cleanses the open sores, puts
the grease on them, and prohibits Veedlie from scratching. This
works and soon he will become renowned for his ability to cure
the yaws.

After lunch, he naps while Tombani fans the flies away. When
Tombani leaves for a moment, the children come and lie close to
him, with Ririkinger on his stomach.

When he returns, Tombani chases the children away. Harper pretends to sleep, expecting to be beaten again. Tombani does nothing. Harper tells himself that he must not hate the patriarch so much, "but he becomes the cause not only of my loneliness, which is bad enough, but even worse, the cause, too, of my cowardice, driving me to be ruled by the body's fears rather than the heart's hungers. I know that he is turning me into the animal the rest of them are, nullifying the sum of my past existence, turning me back into a thing that I am not, through the pressures of the body's fears."

The sorceress Rauka comes to the village again with a child she has tattooed. Harper learns that so many children die from this practice that no child is named until after the tattooing. Rauka is hostile to Harper, because of his cure for the yaws. She begins to cast doubts about him in the village.

That evening, stupefied by betel, Tombani, Veedlie and Oai torment Harper. They suggest that since he cured Veedlie's yaws, he must be a sorcerer, a rauka. Thinking it might earn him some respect, Harper admits that he is a rauka. Oai moves away from him in horror.

They accuse him of being a female, since all raukas are female, and prohibit him from sitting with any males again. When Harper objects that he is a male, that they have all seen his body, they accuse him of being able to change sex to fool the men. Otherwise, they reason, why does he continue to wear clothes when no one else does; obviously to hide his sex so he can change it at will.

Desperate and humiliated, Harper denies this. The thought of being cut off from contact, even with the villagers, sickens him.

"I am rauka and I am a male," he insists.

When they ask him if he can make babies with his manhood, he says yes, and tells them of his children.

Tombani orders him to prove it by bringing the children to him.

Unable to explain that there are other worlds beyond the waters, Harper is subjected to the vicious threat of Tombani, until he is driven to take off all of his clothes and remain naked in the future to prove that he is not changing sex.

Stripped now of everything that connected him with his past, Harper verges on mental collapse, unable to find any human dig-

nity in himself, filled with self-loathing at his apparent cowardice. Tombani spreads Rauka's doubts about Harper's manhood. He is believed to be a male rauka, now that he does not hide his sex, but he is hardly accepted in village life except as a curer of yaws. He spends most of his time alone, making little bark dolls to give to the children of the village, reading incessantly the few pages that remain of the book, Great Essays.

The rains have come, turning the compound into a quagmire. The darkness of the days, the mud everywhere, build depression in Harper.

One evening, driven by a desperate loneliness to seek human companionship, Harper goes to Tombani's hut to eat betel. The child who has shown him the only human emotion, Ririkinger, is being prepared for the tattooing. She hangs by a stake, her feet touching the ground, in the shadows at the rear of the hut.

Chapter 28

I bite into the betel nut's bitter kernel and try to forget the child in the corner. From time to time she babbles her pitiful pleas to the shadows. With the back of my hand I wipe saliva from my lips. Myopia floods mind and vision quickly and I must force my eyes to focus on Tombani who sits motionless, ignoring the infant. Rain has slowed to a faint mist and the last light of day sifting in the open door silhouettes the old man's skeletal figure.

Why?

But no, I wrinkle my forehead, shutting out the question, refusing to beg again for what must be given if it is to have any value, waiting for Tombani to speak, waiting for him to show some sign that at least he tolerates my presence. Others lounge away from us there in the bog of slush at the back of the hut, near the child.

"Why? Why Ririkinger?" I hear some part of me daring to ask, while other parts cower in their separate cells.

Tombani's eyes open wide in puzzlement, and I realize he does not know I have given the child that name and must think I am asking: "Why? Why finger?"

"Why her?" I say, nodding in the child's direction, cherishing the frail interest that enlivens me.

The old man, his protruding lips dripping betel juice, stares at me in scorn; then, shrugging his shoulders, he explains that the matriarch, Rauka Tataolagi, will begin the cutting tomorrow. She will open small designs in the child's face with a sharpened bone and pack them with blue mud from the —

"I know how it is done," I hear myself mumble, thinking of the mutilations I have seen on the swollen faces of the other children. But not Ririkinger. God — her flesh should remain smooth and soft. I shake my head against remembering Oai's explanation that they do not give their children names until after the tattooing because so many die from it.

Beyond the door, to my right, twilight filters stagnant through wet jungle foliage. I chew my betel and glance at other villagers, vague shadows in the early evening as they wade humming across the quagmire of the open compound and disappear into the safety of their huts for the night. Sitting here, a cross-legged bundle of beard and nakedness, I reach up and feel the bruised lump, raw and tender, above my left ear. Wind shudders high in the tops of trees and there is the subtle movement of night descending on the jungle.

I try to keep my eyes averted from Ririkinger, wishing now that I had resisted the temptation to seek Tombani's companionship against the lonely dusk; but again and again I catch myself peering past the supporting pole into the gloom of that corner.

Her hands are bound above her head with strips of bark to a stake driven into the ground. Her body hangs listlessly, scarcely supported by buckling knees. The screech of a nightbird echoes through trees, quickening me to reality. Why should they bind her like this? Surely she would not run away. For a moment the blank daze of fear dissolves from my chest as I lick my lips and turn to Tombani to ask him for mercy for this infant. But the movement causes pain from the lump on my head to shimmer through me and chokes back my words. *The end of that route is even greater blackness,* I hear from retained memory. My shoulders sag forward and the betel is not enough to make me unconscious of my shame.

"Keura," is all I can say. Tombani's arm detaches itself from the shadows and he places the twig in my hand. I brush mud from a spot and tear off the bark with my teeth, chewing grit into the betel and poki mixture. I am driven to it, driven to sink into my betel dream and forget the child — my child — in the corner. But no, she is not my child. I want to forget that child and all children as I forget everything else.

My head droops forward while I chew and swallow, waiting for the familiar betel numbness to turn me into leather. No one speaks. Through the thin black walls, a single cricket livens the air with its presence; its warm sound in the desolate evening. Cricket on the hearth — God — an old home full of autumn fire in the hearth, full of the smells of waxed furniture and dinner's lingering aftermath, and the chirping of a cricket on the hearth. The scene is abstracted into calico and warmth and a rose-cheeked infant lying on the floor in the gross pleasure of food's digestion, reeking of decency and security and livingness. The child looks at me and smiles, safe in her regard for me, and I smile back down at her and reach out my foot to poke at the bottom of her shoe in a gesture of reassurance.

The pole bites into my cheek through the tangle of whiskers as my head falls to the side, and I tremble with the chill of mud beneath my seat. Far away there is a jungle listening to all the live things. Here, close by, there is a cricket. Cricket on the hearth, full of cheer, awakening old instincts, long dead, returning them to pierce the thick shell of forgetfulness. I am here and now. I am in the presence of the infant Ririkinger, hanging from the stake, but I am also in the presence of my own Cindy, long ago, sick and feverish in a bed of white sheets. But I am another John Harper, a different John Harper, hovering over her bed, my hands suddenly too large and clumsy, not knowing what to do with them. I fold them across my lap. My beard scratches, turning back on itself in the hollow of my throat, and I am floating in the world of double images, myopia, floating through images that shine with life, counterpointing the *then* and the *now*. It is Saturday night — God — and I am polishing the boys' shoes in the kitchen while Susie irons Cindy's dress for church tomorrow. It is Sunday afternoon in the amusement park, with the carousel music and the orange and raspberry and lime snowcones and the children's sticky fingers being wiped on my handkerchief. Strange — God — strange, I see them only as children, not as the adolescents they have become, and yet I loved them no more then than I do now, love their adolescence, love their . . . I am listening to the cricket with such concentration it is nullifying the present, turning me back into the other John Harper, completely different from this betel-drugged derelict who sees all things through watering eyes and who trembles with anguish, like a child, before the infinite reaches of loneliness.

Time and betel dulled the sharp edge of memory until tonight when palaces of orgy are replaced by a cricket on the hearth, when a swollen-bellied black child becomes my own white child of long ago.

I raise my head and focus on Tombani through the blear. "Damn your filthy soul," I mutter in English.

He grunts. My cheeks burn with an upflushing of fever and I carry my belligerence into dialect. "Why do you bind her like this?"

The old man bends forward and stares at me, with that expression, sometimes so poignant, that knows nothing of ignorance. His explanation is the monotonous chant of derision, but the night, the wetness, the inseeping hush of drizzle alters his tones into whispered softness.

"The cutting is painful. The pain kills one so young. To save her from the pain, she is kept on her feet and awake for three days and three nights. When time is ready for the cutting, if she is still alive, she sleeps and feels nothing . . ."

His voice joins with the silence without seeming to have ended the sentence. He lights his pipe of twist with a coconut punk which turns his face orange and glows through his silhouetted fingers when he blows against it.

A mosquito drones close to my ear. I wave it away and concentrate on the approaching drunkenness.

It is getting too dark to see. Tombani grunts a command and young Veedlie detaches a handful of twigs that are suspended from the ceiling on a bark cord to keep them dry and brings them over to light a fire on the floor between us. I stare at the sparks as he blows hard, his face close to the earth, holding the coconut husk against the kindling and working with it until the entire underside of his face, chest, belly and thighs is outlined in the brilliant brushstrokes of firelight.

From the corner, a whimper floats to me, thin and fragile, a flower born of silence. Tombani does not react in any way to it; he stares serenely at the play of firelight on the stained weave of the walls. My glance shifts to Ririkinger. I can see red flames, caught in tears, rolling down the mute child's cheeks. My own child lies in a bed of white. The white image of the white child fills me with tremblings of pain for the black child. Reality strips away its mask and flaunts its rawness to my brain, telling me how she will hang there all night in mud up to her ankles, surrounded by bodies that sleep, that snore, inhaling the foul accumulation of smoke; hanging there alone and perhaps flickering out.

"Let me have her," I hear words from my lips, distant words and cracked, harsh words and sobbing. My head flops up in my total astonishment to hear what I have said. Tombani's thick eyebrows lift. He exhales a cloud of twist smoke through his nose in a snort, as though such an idiot request did not merit even so much as an answer. I sit stunned by the radiance that flashes through me. They care nothing for their children. It would mean nothing to them. Radiance returns the words beyond my volition to torment my lips, pouring forth on the impulse of my own salvation — not so much for her as for myself.

"Let me have her," I plead, my voice steadying itself on the focus of some distant hope, some giant hope. I can feel myself sinking, sinking into the swirling vortex of nothingness, held to the time and the spot by the magnetism of that faraway hope. I listen to drippings from the eaves into puddles beyond the smoke-fogged door, to the silence of a dying drizzle. I listen to Tombani's feet suck through the mire as he pulls his knees up in front of him; and I watch all things in the magnificent assaultings of radiance; I watch the uppuffings of turbid smoke from the fire, watch pink reflections on his knotty shinbones. His face twists into a smile around his pipestem and his eyes glint a thousand subtle understandings.

"She must be cut," he answers softly.

"You filthy pig," I whisper, stupefied by his callousness. "You filthy son of a bitch," but my words are in English, mottling emotion, parroting courage; words symbolic of a man, uttered by a ghost. Cheapness scores my intestines with unbearable clarity, the cheapness of cowardice.

Abruptly Tombani's mood changes. He closes his fist around the tiny bowl of his pipe and removes it from his mouth, spitting vermilion saliva into the mud between his bare feet. Outside, the rain has completely stopped. The old man points to the door, his arm casting a dislocated shadow on the woven wall behind him and tells me to get out.

I pull myself up against the supporting pole, determined to stand my ground. Soupy mud from my buttocks trails down the backs of my legs. I falter again, hating the faltering as some strange moral debasement. Through layers of smoke I locate the black hole of the door. No, I must stay here and protect my Cindy. I struggle away from it, struggling back, hating the strange debasement that drags me toward the black hole.

"Let me have her."

With a flick of his hand and a belch he dismisses me.

Betel saliva fills my mouth. He has gone too far in his derision. *I could step forward, but why? I could roar my bitterness down at him, but why? I could take my Cindy from him by force and surprise, but why?—and flee with her into the jungle, but why? I could vomit out this trembling, no longer trembling of fear but of idiot debasement, but why? I could raise my arm and strike out and there would be magnificent liberation from the debasement and the cringing, but why? I could, but there is the white wall of my own pain, the unknown consequences, the unknown payment. They would kill me.*

The body, then, holds and the soul must accept its greater pain through fear of the body's lesser pain. New redness settles into old whiteness. Without looking back, I plow through the smoke and out the open door: grief-stricken no longer for the child, but for the defeat of the father, my own defeat.

Night air is clean against my face. I stop and lean against the soaked wall of the hut. Washed night is a well of immense purity and gentle reproach. I inhale the purity in gulps and I am inhaling my own reproach. The clean gives remorse to the unclean. I mourn the loss. I mourn the vividness of my realization, for I was close to the victory of the soul over the body's fears. I would have won if my body had not been ligatured by fears of pain, of death. This prison of cheapness, of cowardice, unbearable to the soul, would have been destroyed by the one grandiose gesture I could not make.

Placing one foot before the other, I shove myself outward from the wall and stagger toward my hut across the compound. Later, later I will win, but I know that there will never be a time later except in greater difficulty, and that will come only when the driving despair to escape the prison goads me beyond myself toward the ultimate cowardice of annihilation, not the noble ideal of freedom.

On all sides, sodden huts cluster in protection from the jungle beyond. Water rushes over logs blocking the pond from the river. I look up to a clearing in the sky, to a pool of fledgling stars surrounded by rolling cloudbanks that are lighted at the edges by an invisible moon. I brush my hand across my eyes and the heavens become distorted in myopic grandeur, with two outlines for every image. All of it accuses, every sound, every health of savage movement, every animal movement in the jungle, every odor, every star, every silvered puddle — all that is good on this earth. I am accused by universal goodness this night, and it turns me into a solitary chunk of loneliness.

It must be escaped. Crickets burden the stillness with their tinseled raspings. I want to close myself away from night's purity, to fall asleep, not to rest but to be rid of consciousness.

Inside my hut, I bolt the door with my heavy boar spear and stand listening to the heartbeat that throbs in my ears. Numbness creeps across my forehead, dulling thought. I allow myself to sink to the earth as dazzlement rolls over me. Why? This is not the betel. *Let me have her.* But no, it is not that either. Let there be at least no such lying to myself. As long as there is truth, the splotch of hope can remain. Now, the dazzlement fills me with the vertigo of hope. I must not pretend that I am experiencing the noble grief of a father over the fate of his child when it is really the grief of my own debasement. I cried "son of a bitch" but in a language no one could understand, and with cringings.

Loneliness fights numbness like a duller light fighting blackness. I must get this straight in my mind. There must be no hiding of my real grief of debasement beneath the noble grief for the child, unless the noble grief can become the real, dominating and hypnotizing. *Let me have her.* I have not drowned the needs of my heart in betel drunkenness. Let the nobler grief persuade. Let me sink into it until it fires my soul above my body's dreads. Let me think of the child at the stake, of the long night alone for her, of the mysteries within her veins and organs that may never know another night.

A humming catches overtones in my brain. It spins, gyrating, building slowly, mercifully driving out thoughts. I turn on my side, drawing up my knees and cradling my paunch in my hands. Outside moonlight fades to gathering mists within me. The humming builds its crescendo, ever louder, like some giant mosquito gone mad inside of my head.

Mists and moonlight. Mists and sunlight. Light transpiercing prayers. Shafts of light bursting through the roar of insects in my brain. Cockatoos floating white against blue skies, full of screechings from tree to tree, and the expanding chest of a white man, not cowering, but holding the child high on his shoulders and walking full of pride, carried forward on the flow of tons of heartsperm, tons of soulsperm, tons of spiritsperm, slashing out and crushing with great dignity and greater tenderness, pushed onward by his strength; and then a raised club, a leer and mists forming before the eyes and a sniveling sun glimpsed through a veil of red . . .

Mists swirl and I roll in my drunken dream of power and intense liberation. The humming accelerates into cheapness. *Everything is on sale today, everything cheap.* The humming comes through the loudspeakers of the cheap sale and people are listening to it, waiting for more band music while they finger the cheap objects and the cheap coins in their pockets and speculate *Is it worth a dime? Everything costs so much. I'll take this child at the stake and this crude little hemp-and-bark doll, and that gold locket over there and five or six —*

The confused thought blasts through with such force that the humming in my brain stops abruptly. I am not sure what I will do as I drag myself up and jerk my pants from the overhead beam. Concentration centers on standing upright while I fish through my pockets. And outside in the silence, no other sound but the cricket's thin chirping —

I drop my pants to the mat and turn about slowly, trying to locate the door in the stippled blackness until I see a frame of moon-light seeping around its edges.

I throw it open, showering my belly with water. Moonlight fil-ters through trees into puddles. I must not think, must not let it accuse me until I can stand beneath it without guilt, or lie dead beneath it, but sweetly, without cheapness. I stagger across the compound, closing out the desire of panic to turn me aside, wishing for some reason that I had brought my glasses.

Reflected firelight dances in liquid brightness on the mud before Tombani's open door. Placing my left hand on the door strut, I step inside.

And I am staring through a choking fog of smoke down into a face blank with astonishment.

"Let me have her," I command in a voice of wavering authority. "Let me have her. I'll give you this." I swallow my heart and hold out the locket by its thin chain.

Tombani's eyes dilate and fix on the golden disk while he un-winds himself and rises slowly to his feet. In the background, be-hind the supporting poles, other members of the family stir and look toward us. My glance shoots to Ririkinger. She hangs mo-tionless, suspended from her frail arms like a black tear. Her head lolls forward on her neck in an attitude of death. The fire shifts into a dozen fires, and agony that I am too late crumples my insides. Before I can fall, a pain sears across my palm as the locket is torn away.

I lock my knees to hold myself up, squinting to focus my gaze on Tombani. I think how carefully I have kept it hidden from savage eyes, always going into the jungle before pressing the button that opens it, always looking about to make sure I am not being watched before taking out the faded snapshots of my children. Now, the locket with its pictures of everything I love in the world is clutched in the mud-caked hands of a man who would sit by and let a child die.

Without emotion I raise my fist high in the air and bring it down with all my force. The old patriarch crumbles like a decayed leaf. I rip the locket from his hand and stand above him reeling. I have done it. It is too late to turn back now. The fire is coming up to meet me. I am sinking. Regret and pity and the magnificence of absolution from my guilt of cowardice flame as I seek to retain my balance. I am squeezing the locket until tendons in my arm are rigidly knotted. The fire rises to consume all of my attention, the fire and the elongated navel of the gasping native and his little clay pipe which lies in the mud where it fell beside him.

A whimper softer than silence reinforces me, jars me back. I catch myself, holding to the supporting pole, and peer into the corner. Through the haze, I see Ririkinger's head sag to one side as her small hands clench and unclench. Smoke tartness, flame tartness fill my eyes with tears. I am staring open-mouthed when a movement to one side makes me turn. Veedlie is handing his grandfather the club of the patriarch. The child splashes back into the shadows as I transfer the locket to my left hand and wheel around. Tombani, clasping his club, is crawling to his feet.

I look through the smoke fog for the door, but my eyes delude me and everywhere I see the white child alive and breathing in the black child's pain.

Could Tombani ever be placated now? It doesn't matter. I listen to the child within me, to the child's destruction of cheapness, releasing me from the bondage of cowardice. I raise my fist above my head again. The old man ducks and crouches defensively. We stand across the fire from one another, a naked patriarch and a naked derelict, splattered with mud and grayed in smoke. I glimpse the reflections of scattered coals through the slits of his eyes. And then his eyes open cautiously in an expression of vague bewilderment.

"Let me have her," I urge hoarsely. "I'll give you this," extending the locket to him again. His shoulders tense and he holds out his hand, palm up. I allow the locket to dribble through my fingers on its chain and step back from the fire. Placing his club between his thighs, he lifts the locket to his face with both hands, glowering at it, smelling it, and then it is as though the expression of brute ferocity were suddenly stripped from his face to reveal his true expression of childish delight. Without taking his fascinated gaze from the glistening metal that reflects red spangles all over the hut, he nods brusquely in the child's direction.

"She belongs to me?" I ask, feeling perspiration detach itself and dribble down the diagonal crease in the back of my neck.

"She belongs to you."

I stare, full of open-mouthed incredulity as tremblings settle into exhaustion in my stomach, for I am no longer looking at the proud, scornful patriarch, but at a white-haired old man with withered flesh; an aged child with grinning betel-red lips over stained tushes, absorbed in the play of firelight on gold; his eyes bright orbits of wonderment as he cocks his head from side to side.

A sigh from the child brings me to my senses and completes my exhaustion. I move and act in automaton, incapable of assimilating my feelings. The fire's warmth touches my legs as I step over it and slosh to her corner. My hands are steady when I untie the soft bark liana that binds her to the stake.

She collapses into my arms and I carry her past the bustling knot of Tombani's family who ignore us in favor of the locket.

The night, then, is changed. The moon is low behind the trees, pouring through in slants to mottle the earth. As I trudge wearily home, I hear the old patriarch shouting to his villagers, calling for fires and betel nut to celebrate his new fortune, filling the compound with his jubilant voice.

All I can feel is the unbelievably light weight in my arms, and the surge of relief that she is safe and that some cheapness has been flecked from my heart, a relief so immense, so attached to the guiltless night and the guiltless universe that I am incapable of reacting to it except quietly, in stunned preoccupation. They run from their huts, preparing to celebrate as I ease myself over my door. They have new fortunes, and I have a child.

Soberness returns me from the pulsings and fadings of myopia. I deposit Ririkinger on the mat and massage her wrists. If there were tears left in me, the smallness of her hands would bring them to the surface, but now there is only the numbness of fulfillment, nothing else. When warmth returns to her fingers, I spread my coat over her and lie down beside her. A peculiar timidity makes me lie away from her, completely in the mud, with my hand resting on her shoulder. But she stirs and moves closer to me. I inch over onto the mat, cradling her head in the crook of my shoulder and allowing my fingers to explore her sleeping face. The flesh is soft and smooth, the way a child's flesh ought to be.

The two of us are alone in a world apart as the outside noises of celebration pour through the thin walls of our hut. An old man and a child. After the long loneliness I once more have a daughter to hang my life to. I lie here listening to the laughter and shouting and chanting; and watching the flickering specks of red and orange from the celebration fires that seep through the cracks of our hut and dance on the opposite wall. I lie here holding the child close.

The following morning, Harper is awakened by Rauka Tataolagi who furiously demands that the child be returned for tattooing. Harper refuses to allow her into the hut. She storms away.

Harper cares for the child with a new spirit of purpose. She has saved his sanity. He sees Tombani, suffering from a hangover, and even feels affection for the patriarch.

Tombani asks him, as a rauka, to cure the pain in his head.

Harper tells him to go to Rauka Tataolagi for the cure.

"No. She says the hurt is an evil to punish me for giving you the infant."

"She cannot cure such evil?" Harper asks.

"No one can," Tombani tells him. "Rauka says the hurt will stay in me until you are dead."

Harper assures Tombani that he can cure the hurt, that he is stronger than Rauka Tataolagi. He intends to put hot compresses to Tombani's feet and cold ones to his head, an old family home cure taught to him by his grandmother. In order to make the cure look complicated, he crushes leaves from the field of yellow flowers into the coconut shell of water he is preparing to boil. Then, telling Tombani to watch the child Ririkinger, he goes into the brush to gather some large banana leaves to wrap the coconut shells.

Chapter 29

. . . Ducking beneath the wilted leaves of an overhanging branch which has been cracked and dragged down by the storms, I strike out along the river path in search of a banana leaf in which to wrap the shell for boiling water. On the way, I cache my handful of buttercups behind a tree, at the juncture between two of its snake-rooted tendrils . . .

Speckles of banana green, pinpointed through the jungle gloom, attract my attention, and I turn to my left from the path. The mud is soft in the eternal twilight of the forest, so soft I can make out another's footsteps leading toward the sunlit area before me.

Through the brush I see a miniature clearing which is enclosed on all sides by a wall of banana trees, broad-leafed and luxurious. No vegetation sprouts from the black mud of the tiny perimeter, now churned and drying with cracks in it, but a wretched lean-to cringes beneath the full blare of sunlight. It is so constructed, with a low shed roof of thatch, that I think for a moment it must be a privy with a full door at the left of the front side. A man my size would have to stoop almost double to walk about inside.

Something stirs beyond the door and I squat back behind the navundi screen. Gnats swarm beneath me, between my legs, giving a ring to silence as I watch through leaves. The movement gathers form from the substance of obscurity and assumes the cramped features of Rauka Tataolagi at the opening, her tufts of hair pointing outward in white cones above each ear. Dragging her staff on the ground, and with her head stretched out on her scrawny neck, she ambles into the brush at the side of her hovel.

I listen to her body sloughing against leaves until she is beyond my hearing.

Insects underline awareness of my nakedness, cumbersome and flaccid. I brush them away and rise up for a full view with my cheek touching the uplifted fingers of a banana stalk. The forest is silent, motionless; ropelike vines drape in and out of foliage. All of it waits in the suspension of some distant storm threat.

Crossing the few feet to her door, I place my hands on each side of the frame and bend far forward. Heat and dampness breathe into my face, full of flies, full of permeations of old smoke, old nauseas and old urines, full of rot and yeast — the stench made more purulent by a contrasting hint of sweetness, like perfume on carrion.

Holding my breath, I glance about the cluttered interior. On a large mat, a young woman, her belly enormous in a pregnancy that must be almost immediately deliverable, lies spraddle-legged, snor-

ing in a mire of sweat. The idea of her being brought to such a
pest hole for her birth throes appalls me.

The back end of the shanty, to my right, is a jumble of woven
baskets piled on top of one another; and in the green-spotted obscurity above them hangs a silhouetted object so strange I am both
driven to flee and at the same time drawn through the door toward
it.

With my head retracted between my shoulders, I stoop and step
over the sleeping woman's body into the corner, stirring up a vast
activity of green glints as flies effervesce disturbance.

I study the object closely before perception of what it is confirms
my suspicions and fades all other details into the background, oblit-
erating sounds and odors when I come to realize that I am staring
almost directly into the closed eyes of a head which dangles from
the rafter on a two-inch cord of bark, the small and serene head of a
young man, smoke-blacked and mummified, but not shrunk, not dis-
integrated. I am gazing in awakening awe at the symbol of eternity
which changes the chemistry of all things — of my body, my soul,
of the land and the time — slowly, almost imperceptibly, making of
all things new things, and I am seeing a bundle, a leathery balloon, a
ball, a thing that once lived and breathed and ate and drank and
slept and roamed these forests, and most probably was intimate with
violence; and yet all of that is dispersed and I am looking on blankness, on a blackened parchment where nothing of his living and
breathing and eating and drinking and sleeping and roaming is transcribed, where nothing remains except a fragment of smoke-cured
flesh sculpted into features to tell of the years of living that went
into its development, and where violence is nothing more than sur-
mise in this mask of repose, this mask of tranquility.

I react without shock, without disgust, without sorrow — his
face does not evoke these things. No, it evokes rather an ineffable
calm that flows out from him into me, muting stridor to a quiet and
secret tenderness for all that has its place in living; for the earth and
its parts and the seasons and their parts, and the sweats and the flies;
for every emotion, for every joy, yes, and every sorrow; for all that
was once tied up in the making of this bundle; for all that is given
me to live — even those dimmest and harshest things — in view of
all that is suspended for him.

His presence communicates to me a shifting of knowledges wherein the logic of eternity once again supplants the logic of the moment. He makes me see that the tattered perceptions of my human condition, those perceptions that have led me into such anguish, must transform themselves around the same human condition — through a perspective of eternity — to lead me into joy; showing me that tragedy is not in the condition but in man's perception of the condition; that while I am heavy with years and suns and trees and storms, he is gone from years and suns and trees and storms — that while I must rake sweats from my eyebrows, there is only dust on his.

I close my eyes wearily, and when I open them again the vividness is gone, and I am gazing at an impersonal mask and seeing there nothing more than any other bundle, any other leathery balloon, any other black ball. It has dismissed me, I whom it never even recognized, to the new miracles of mud and heat, letting me see their conformity to the rules of all the older, more obvious miracles.

Flies are dribbling over my body and I am brought back to the moment and to the squalor, but changed now; heightened in tone to a dimension of benevolence, for I am seeing these things, smelling them, feeling them, living them, not in errant space, but as a part of the passage of time that will lead me to his estate; and they are rendered intensely precious because he dangles here at my shoulder no longer seeing these things, smelling them, feeling them, living them, no longer involved in the parts of time, but only in the whole of eternity. That which is out of all time tells me of the miracle of these clacking cycles where all is zoned in hours, minutes, seconds up to that final fraction of instantaneity which leans against the wall of forever, that which is out of life tells me of the miracle of living — tells me that it is as black an ingratitude and as great a stupidity to cavil over any of the many-mooded conditions of time as it would be to cavil over the single-mooded condition of eternity. The reality of heats and smells, the buzzings of flies, the stained grays of bamboo return to the foreground of consciousness in that peculiar sharpness of detail summoned by moments of profound peace. Guarding the emotion, clinging to it as a gift of truth so intangible it might dissolve back into blankness, I turn and step over the sleeping woman, hearing my feet suck liquidly from the mud.

Half-blinded by the slap of outside glare that makes trees look violet, I draw up short before the stooped blear of Rauka. I scarcely make out her features before my mouth is filled with the foretaste of nausea spurting up from my throat. Sinking to my knees, I pour out my insides against fissured crusts of mud, dimly aware that thin black legs are stalking away and almost immediately returning. The upblaze of reflected heat burns my cheeks and eyes. Her body swims before me, spangled and transpierced by shafts of light caught in my tears. I croak that I am sorry for having invaded her hut.

She props her chin against her staff and extends a wavery streak of arm to offer me a banana leaf. Wiping my mouth with it, I realize that to an onlooker I would appear to be in an attitude of obeisance, kneeling before her. When I am finished, I lumber to my feet and brush my forearm across my eyes.

"Thank you, friend," I say, my voice altered to a deeper bass by the acids of nausea.

Without giving the traditional response, she swivels slowly around the pivot of her staff, following my every move with eyes that glitter from heavily folded lids.

"Thank you, friend," I repeat, discarding the banana leaf at her feet in a faint gesture of defiance. Again she makes no pretense of giving the required answer. Her mouth is closed in a thin line of toothless gummings, creating pockets at each side of her lips. Her eyes dance above her delicately flared nose, constantly fluctuating between expressions of gloating and innocent amusement and hatred; all of it in a face so shriveled the wrinkles look as though they were inked into the flesh.

I cannot decipher her changing expressions. Is she enjoying this triumph of catching me in the taboos of looking on her hut and vomiting — that intimate act which presumably makes her the possessor of my spirit? But from the sparkle of intelligence in her buried eyes, I have the impression that she does not believe in such taboos any more than I, that she is rather reveling in the victory she can manipulate through the ignorance of others, through this complication of innocence which becomes first mystery and then guilt in the minds of those who cannot unravel the truth from the fabric of fact.

"Thank you, friend," I repeat insistently. Refusing to answer, she flexes her jaws in more rapid chewings that stretch tendons into a frame for the ribbed hollow of her throat.

We stand here, a bearded and aged white man and a shrunken and ancient black woman, both naked beneath the nakedness of the sun in a world no larger than this enclosed perimeter where all is baked mud and navundi, exchanging clothed emotions, testing strengths; and my confusion gathers itself into the focus of admiration for her, for I recognize in her something superior to the dullness I read on the faces of all others here; and I know I would experience a certain dejection if she weakened and deigned to answer, much as a general would if an opposing general were to show cowardice or falsity; and indeed, I am awakened to a brief hint of exultation that comes with the discovery that one is to be tested at his best by an enemy of stature; and I realize that this wizened crone is an aristocrat, an indomitable woman, but one of vitality and the irresistible charm of a certain toughness that makes her even more feminine.

And yet I am bewildered as to what this will bring. She is a person of too much quality to castrate an enemy, she would not degrade me by being lenient — no, she will, as she should, use my every mistake, my every fault to her advantage. She becomes immediately more formidable and more attractive; the consequences of mortal threat cannot alter the enormous sympathy I feel for her at this moment, a sympathy of union in our understanding of all these unspoken things. I gaze down at her and feel my own face relaxing into a smile, certain that we would be friends if circumstances had not contrived to turn us into enemies.

She leans on her pole, her head at the level of my chest, scrutinizing me, and her eyes boil up into vivacity as she disengages her hand from beneath her chin and reaches out in a rapid movement. Before I can react, two stinging tugs at my beard coincide with jerkings of her sinewy biceps.

Stepping back, I attempt to penetrate her expression, to read some clarification in a face puckered into a simultaneous smile and frown, and I think that there should be words that explain, words that would communicate understanding and warmth, words that would permit the wisdom of negotiation to arrest the ignorance of action. But the language is void of such nuances.

I hear myself chuckling as I gravitate toward the path by which I came, brushing gnats from my stomach. In a nearby tree the cicada frictions dryness into raspings that broaden silence, raspings that give tone to the time and the place and the woman — perched and static and bright.

"I go, friend," I taunt affectionately, stripping a banana leaf from the closest tree and waiting for her to answer. She is hunched over her staff, her lower jaw loose-hinged in chewings, her eyes fixed speculatively on me as though she were seeking to pierce my covering of flesh and hairs in order to evaluate the dimensions of my brain and heart. When she does not answer, I turn to retrace my footsteps toward the riverbank, carrying with me the image of the old woman in her statuesque pose which is nevertheless so animated, wondering at the mysteries of her life and cult as indicated by the misery of her hut and the head dangling above the baskets, wondering too if it is the head of the bushman the old native was describing in his legend. If so, the baskets probably contain the snakes . . .

He finds Tombani almost prostrate with pain and begins to apply the compresses which soon bring relief. Tombani can hardly believe the rapidity of his cure. Harper takes advantage of the situation to insist that Tombani tell the villagers that he is a stronger rauka than Rauka Tataolagi, that Tombani's pain did not come from giving away the child and that Rauka Tataolagi lied.

"Tell them, too, that I am a male rauka," he adds.

As the days pass, Harper brings Ririkinger back to health. He warns the child to run to him any time Rauka Tataolagi approaches. Most of Harper's time is spent cleaning up the hut where he lives with the child, making bark dolls for her and seeing after her needs. He misses his handkerchief, but thinks nothing of it at the time. He washes the sleeping mats and places them on the roof for the sun to dry.

Chapter 30

. . . Realizations halt me in my actions. My God, how far have I come? — how far have I drifted from the man who would probably be preparing his classes at school about now? — anxious for Fridays to get here so he could spend them with his family. What day is this? What month? Is there ever again to be a weekend, a Sunday? There need to be Sundays in a man's life, and indeed Mondays and all the other days which have their own special colorings and tonalities.

What would today be? — just from the feel of it? Perhaps Saturday with the housecleaning and with the general aura of relaxation throughout the compound. Saturday at home, sitting on the veranda and listening to the baseball games, drinking a cup of coffee.

How far have I come? How far have I drifted from all of that? And yet this is real. What is coffee? A name, a word with but faint overtones in me now. What is a veranda, or baseball? But even when these words will have ceased entirely being image-makers, the days will continue to evoke their own peculiarities, and today is most certainly Saturday.

Smoothing out a square in the back corner, I print SAT. in the mud with my forefinger, deciding that I will keep my own calendar, that each day I will erase the spot and print SUN. or MON. or TUES., for there must be retained some connection with the other John Harper, even though I am no longer he. That is the change and the vague shock to me — and also the relief. For such a long time I have been that other man, playing a part, trying to fit it in, calculating every move and every reaction from his background; but imperceptibly I am becoming Jon, a rauka, a naked and bearded man, beginning to live again, beginning to love again, beginning to live and love on another level as my thoughts center around the soft nucleus of the present instead of the past, around the sparkling clarity of morning outside, around my responsibilities to the child, who fills the center of my being during these moments when I putter around in our home and attempt to bring some cleanliness and some order to it. . . .

Tombani sends for Harper to tell him that in the village of Zinai there is much of Veedlie's yaws sickness and that Harper must go there to cure the villagers.

*Immediately suspicious that this might be some plan of Rauka's
to get him away so she can get to Ririkinger, his fears are calmed
by Tombani, who orders him to leave at once. The patriarch promises to guard Ririkinger, tells Harper to gather the cloth he uses
to cure the yaws and get on his way.*

*Harper mentions that he cannot find the handkerchief. A silence
falls over the group.*

*Harper is informed by Tombani that the disappearance of the
handkerchief means that he will soon die. The rauka must have
taken it, the patriarch reasons, to torment her snakes. It was believed that she kept snakes, that she would torment them, then let
them smell some object belonging to the intended victim, and when
they had made the association, they would be released and would
strike the victim.*

*Harper laughs at the threat, explains that such a sense of smell
and association are impossible with snakes, and adds that in any
case — if Rauka took the handkerchief, it would smell as strongly
of her as of him.*

*His apparent lack of fear in the face of death impresses the vil-
lagers. Harper leaves, asking them to warn Rauka that if she attempts to touch Ririkinger, he will kill her.*

*In the village of Zinai he treats the villagers for several days.
One evening, Veedlie appears to invite him to return to Vanua for
the feast — the death feast of Ririkinger.*

*Shocked profoundly, Harper grabs Veedlie's arm and demands
information. Veedlie tells him that Ririkinger is not yet dead, but
that she is dying and will be dead in a few hours.*

*Harper forces Veedlie to return with him to Vanua. On the way,
he learns from Veedlie that Ririkinger is in Rauka's hut and that
Harper cannot go to the hut, since it is taboo for any male to go
there. Veedlie assures him that Tombani guarded the child until
she fell ill. Then the patriarch had called Rauka to cure her. The
child had drunk some of the sea slug water Harper had left in a
shell, fallen ill with dysentery and developed a high fever.*

"Then she will not die," Harper says.

*"She dies," Veedlie affirms. He explains that despite her illness,
the child will be subjected to the cutting, the tattooing, and that in
her weakened condition, she cannot survive it. The boys have*

already gone out to hunt the boar for the funeral feast. Tombani sent for Harper, not to save the child, but to participate in the feast.

Harper asks why Tombani allows the cutting. Veedlie tells him Tombani can do nothing because the taboo nullifies his power, and that the cutting is to take place the following morning.

Veedlie pleads with Harper not to go to the hut. He says Rauka will kill him with the snakes. They hurry through the darkness.

Chapter 31

. . . He slithers forward, his weaving body little more than a rain-slaked shadow before me, dim in the night. I flounder at his heels, lashed by soaked leaves, the two of us alone in a universe of underbrush and rain. An image returns again and again to my mind, the image of that terrified woman's eyes this afternoon, dancing in her skull, pleading for mercy, in helpless need; and all of that is transferred to the guileless eyes of the child, hanging there at the stake in Rauka's hovel, full of the mystery of livingness that will soon be murdered, tied up in the filth of that place throughout these drizzling nights with no other companionship than the mummified head and the sorceress with her snakes. And the idiot logic, the idiot logic of these people, sending Veedlie for me not so I might save Ririkinger, but only so I might be there to help celebrate her death by participating in the feast.

The eyes dancing in the skull are stippled deep in my consciousness, in some core of infinite tenderness and fear, casting the future before me, the future nights and days alone, the future returning to the past when I had no human to hang my life to. Now that I have been granted Ririkinger, the thought of living again that solitary existence, of breathing alone the airs of my hut, drives out the immediate pains of roots cutting into my bare feet, of scratches and slaps against my naked body, and I plod on at Veedlie's back, goaded by the terrified eyes.

. . . We are not far from the pond. Catching up with Veedlie, I grasp his shoulder and bend to shout in his ear that I want to take the path leading to Rauka's hovel.

"It is taboo, taboo," he argues. "I cannot look on her hut."

I tell him he will not need to look, but simply to lead me to the edge of the banana grove, and then he can return to his dwelling.

My respiration becomes short as we grope our way forward. Now that we are here, calmness rustles into uncontrollable tremblings, requiring me to breathe deeply.

Veedlie stops before me in a dim seepage of moonlit rain and I can make out the giant folds of a banana leaf beside him.

"It is there," he whispers mournfully, keeping his face averted from the clearing.

"Tell no one you bring me here," I command. "Go and sleep." The moment I release his arm he is gone.

I push back the banana leaves and gaze into the miniature compound. The scene is like an ancient and faded photograph, with no dimensions of light and shadow. Pale through sheets of rain, Rauka's solitary hut is etched in faint outline, standing silent and infinitely peaceful.

I rake dribblings from my eyes and slosh across the open space to her door, deadening all thoughts, deadening all feelings, blanking my mind to all possible consequences. Above the flurried freshness of the rain, above the ozone freshness of the air, the hovel's stench filters out to surround me.

I take a deep breath which sucks water into my nose, and stooping, shove my head through the door where the immediate clatter of rain is muffled through thatch above me.

The interior is a black hole, full of chill dampness and rot.

Dropping to my knees, I inch forward with hands outstretched, wishing for a momentary flare of lightning to orient myself, but the downpour drones steadily without thunder.

My knee touches flesh and flesh is quickly withdrawn. I kneel motionless in the mud, waiting for an outcry, but hear only a vague settling of movements as Rauka probably changes positions and drifts into renewed sleep. I hear no whimper, no sound except water from the eaves bubbling into puddles at the open door behind me.

Rauka is to my right then, and beyond her there would be room enough only for her clutter of baskets and the head. Ririkinger, if she is still alive, if she still hangs from the stake, must be back to my left. Reversing myself, I waddle through the mire on my knees, with my hands outstretched and following the soaked weave of the wall opposite the door. My fingers guide me to the corner seam where the wall turns, and between the seam and me, flesh touches my wrist, flesh that is on fire.

Muscles melt in my legs, obliging me to sit back on my heels as I bring my other hand to the fore and trace the body of Ririkinger hanging motionless, not responding to my touches but burning with fever and therefore still, thank God, alive.

My hands follow her arms up to the knotted bark above her head, tied not to a stake, but to one of the low ceiling beams. My fingers tear at the knots, manipulating them loose. She sinks forward and I bring her fevered body full length against my rain-chilled flesh, holding her tightly and trying to cool her. Kissing her cheek, it is as though I could see clearly her face, see clearly her eyes closed, see clearly her head wobbling to one side on her neck, see even the expression of utter peace on her unconscious features. How similar to the look of death is the look of sleep.

A loud rattling, as though a stick were raked across a corrugated surface, causes me to jerk my head up. A blow cracks against the back of my neck. I am jolted forward, squishing Ririkinger into the mud beneath me. Hugging her tightly with one arm, I roll to the side and see the door full of dribbling grays. The pole rattles again across beams, accompanied by Rauka's screech, and thumps into my ribs as I lurch for the opening.

Rain from the eaves sloshes cold across my neck and my free hand sinks into water up to my wrist. I rise to my knees, struggling to my feet as the pole drives hard against my kidneys, sprawling me forward again. I twist in midair and land splashing on my back with Ririkinger on my chest. Rain streams mud from her head into my mouth.

Rauka appears in the doorway. Her screams are faint above me, faint through the sizzle of rain, faint through the sizzle of pain in my kidney.

She bounds toward me, a gray form emerging from the slanting backdrop of rain. Covering Ririkinger's head with my hand and pressing it into my beard to protect it from the blow, I kick out with my right foot, kick out so violently my entire body slides forward. I feel my foot contact her belly and her wailings are abruptly silenced. The pole streaks inside of my thigh and falls on my stomach. She is skittering backward, flinging out her arms.

I struggle to my feet and hobble toward the wall of banana trees, unable to straighten up for the pain in my kidney.

As the first broad leaf slashes across my face, I reach up and break off a handful of bananas, and without glancing back, plunge into the jungle.

The deserted compound huddles rainswept, a shallow lake when I wade across it to my hut.

Inside, I bolt my door with the heavy spear and rip down my bundles of clothes until I find my shirt and coat. I dry Ririkinger as well as possible with the shirt and hold her high up against me, listening to the faint regularity of her heartbeat with my ear pressed against her chest, and hearing the counterpointing pounding of my own.

I shake her gently and talk to her, my voice hoarse and lost above the thuddings of storm, until, of her own accord, she lifts her head and groans.

Wrapping her in my coat, I lie down and place her on my stomach to keep her from the mud. I wait, expecting to hear Rauka come battering at my door at any moment. I wait, sleeplessly, with my arms around her as pains within my own body filter one by one into consciousness; the incessant grinding of my kidneys, bringing exaltation that I have saved the child; the pain across my ribs, bringing further exaltation, and then the pain at the base of my skull, changing exaltation into a vast and spreading fatigue. I wait, feeling the rise and fall of the child's good sleep against my chest.

I close my eyes and hug her to me, listening for Rauka, remembering another life in another world where children are protected, where I slept in a night of dry sheets and the comfort of another body that was equally mine. For a moment the sheer discomfort of lying in slime, the sheer exhaustion of pain, the sheer starkness of this land where Rauka prowls always in search of death, unhinges my exaltation and brings me to a view of desolation. But the mummified head of the other afternoon is highlighted in the sinkings, dangling above me again, telling me that at the door of many years from now whether I have slept in a bed of slush or one of down, whether in pain or comfort, will be seen as having little importance, and that it is folly to mourn over the momentary wetness or dryness, fruitfulness or fruitlessness of a night when there is a lifetime of nights to be lived. The recollection persuades me to the goodness of all that seemed torment a moment ago; and I lie here subjected to the invasion of peace, beginning to understand a phrase I once memorized because it bewildered me, the haunting phrase of ancient Lamachus, blind and paralyzed, answering Phrynicus the Poet, who consoled himself in captivity by saying that at least he still had a view of the sky through his dungeon window: "What is your patch of sky to me, Phrynicus? — I who am without eyes or legs?" I think for an instant and the answers swarm back, a thousand things to astonish and enchant me this very night of storm when creatures huddle deep within the woods against the elements; when I can feel and sense and become a part of every huddling thing out there, and see, yes, see — see fish suspended in brooks, see owls facing into the rain with their eyes tight shut. How much richer are your fortunate guards and my fortunate landlord, pacing about their rooms this night, seeing everything and therefore nothing, hearing everything and therefore nothing, waiting for an end to their boredom, their eternal boredom?

Above the drizzle, above the stench, an aura of health pervades my being, and for the first time since childhood I do not need to voice words in order to be praying: my emotion is prayer, the night is prayer, the relenting storm outside is prayer and the protection within is prayer, quietening the afterflush of emotion, quietening all thought and all rebellion as I wrap the splattered coat more closely about Ririkinger.

Chapter 33

The air is rich with the crusting odors of pork. They are going ahead with the feast then, and this time the fatty smell unhinges ravenous hunger in my belly as I stand before my hut, cradling Ririkinger, and watch the festivities in preparation, watch for some sign of Rauka among the women.

The sun reflects from a small sheet of water caught in the center of the compound, casting ripples of gold on the face of Tombani's hut and on the trunks and underfoliage of the towering trees beyond.

It touches me with some regret that Rauka Tataolagi is not here, and the vision of her huddling alone and crushed in defeat pushes into the soft corners of my being. If I should go to her and placate her she would only begin again. We will never be safe from her. No, it is better to leave her in her misery, to let her accept in her own way what has happened to her. But all the while I find myself preparing words and phrases in the dialect, words and phrases that might explain to her and help her to salvage her self-respect. It is better to have a lively enemy than a crushed victim. I am conceding points. I am degrading the quality of her opposition, but to bring her from shame is more important than the ethic of our enmity.

I putter about my hut, attempting to forget her, attempting to read. Giving that up, I go and kneel in the corner and wipe out the faded letters where I printed the word SAT. for Saturday. That was the day I left for Zinai. Today must be Thursday. I print THURS. with some excitement, waiting for Sunday, waiting to know Sunday again.

In the brilliance of morning, villagers go about their occupations preparing for the feast, carrying in firewood, spreading banana leaves on the ground and gathering in knots to chatter. Tombani sits in full sunlight, his back against his hut and his clay pipe between his teeth, ignoring the world.

Surely in all of this day, in all of these lullings and hummings of joyous calm there could be some way of bringing Rauka to an understanding that would allow us to live peaceably here in the same village.

Shoving the mat to the highest ground in the room, over the word THURS., I place Ririkinger on it and arrange her into a comfortable position before heading for the door.

The path is filled with undercurrents of tranquility and quietness made light by the unrestrained chirpings of birds. The buttercup meadow sparkles deserted and full of color when I pass the pond, drawing me to it.

And again there is a strange detachment when I limp stiffly through the shadowed grove toward the green speckles of sunlit navundi leaves with its surroundings of birdsongs and leaf rustlings, detachment as I see myself from another perspective: a bearded and naked old man hobbling toward the miniature compound, a man who will attempt to explain his love for his child to a shrunken black crone with tufts of white hair who stares desolatingly at her feet, defeated in her benevolent designs to kill his child and murder him.

Pushing aside the large flat leaves of the navundi, I squint, adjusting my eyes to the new blaze of sunlight, and gaze toward the door of her shanty.

The sights and sounds of a doorway filled with the thrumming iridescence of flies quieten my heart and make me wish I might drop the navundi branches back in place and leave this area to the secret and sacred reclamation of nature which is being carried out before me. But she cannot be left there to join in her own proper time with the earth and the skies. She must be buried.

I walk slowly across mud crusts that blister into my feet. She lies on her face at the entrance of her hut in the mirrored pool which has been gutted from the earth by constantly dripping rain water from the eaves. Kneeling beside her, I see a line of silt and dust tracing across her face where the water has receded in evaporation as the pool has become shallower. She drowned apparently without ever regaining consciousness after I kicked her and sent her reeling back to knock her head against the door jamb, for there is no indication of writhing or struggle.

I retrieve her pole from the congealment of drying mud and start back to the village to tell them they may have the death feast for Rauka Tataolagi. But at the navundi wall I turn, drawn back to her, remembering the laughter and clowning that accompanied Maigna's burial. I could not bear for her to suffer that indignity. The urge to bury her myself surprises me and grows in me, the urge to bury her secretly and decently, to bury her gently and kindly, to bury her reverently, as a friend, and then never to tell anyone about it, to let her death and resting place become a private affection I shall carry through my days.

But first I must return to the village.

At the cooking hut, I pick up a coconut husk and light the edges of it from the fire, gasping for breath in the smoke-filled, pork-filled interior where others are nothing but shadows. Quickly I wrap the fire inside the husk and escape before anyone can question me.

In the center of Rauka's little compound I kneel and break through the thin crusts with my fingers and begin scooping out a shallow grave.

I reach water about two feet deep, water to which my own pouring sweats are added. I line the bottom of the grave with navundi leaves, sober in my task and filled with a peculiar gratification that nullifies all somberness, all macabreness.

Her emaciated body is as light as though it were made of paper. I carry it to the grave and lower it to its bed of green leaves, arranging her mud-caked staff beside her. With the sun full on my back, I straddle the mound and begin covering her when I remember the mummified head. Bringing it from the hut, I place it with her and kneel in the blazing heat to cover them both, repeating again and again the words of the Requiem: "Rest eternal grant them, O Lord, and may the perpetual light shine upon them . . ."

I work, drunk and dizzy from the heat and the effort, mumbling the prayer above the cicada's distant raspings.

When the churned mud of the grave is level with the surrounding earth, I stumble back and pick up the smoldering coconut husk. Holding it against the ragged eaves of the hovel, I blow on it, seeing the black ash turn pink with each respiration. My throat aches from the effort and I am almost ready to give up when an upshoot of orange flame crackles into being and spreads, shooting off sparks and enveloping the rotted roof of thatch until its roar silences the cicada, silences the birds and drives me out of the clearing.

Needing desperately to get some food into my belly and to get into the pool, I rip off a handful of bananas and limp away from the holocaust of flame and smoke, fighting against the vertigo that sweeps over me.

At the pond, I drop my bananas on the grassy mound and with my last strength fall face forward into the chilling waters.

The scent of flowers floats to me from the meadow when I climb out on the bank. I sit down and stare at my flesh, blue and stippled from the refreshing coldness. Peace drifts to me on the lively twitterings of birds overhead, on the return of heats to my body as I begin to eat my bananas.

Sunshine makes the surface of the pond sparkle through leaf shadows. Smoke from the fire in Rauka's compound mingles with smoke from the cooking fires of the village and casts a faint bluish haze over the meadow. The jungle will reclaim the ashes of the pest hole, the compound of the raukas. Already it seems no more insidious than the field of yellow buttercups stretched out beneath the sunlight before me.

From Vanua I hear the bawling of a baby and the lazy chattering of a mother. And the atmosphere is new, freed of the taint of evil, freed of constraint and fear.

Rising stiffly, I head back toward the path, back to my village and my hut and my child, back to erase the word THURSDAY and print the word SUNDAY in the corner beneath Ririkinger's mat.

PART V

Selections from Land of the High Sky

Notes

⟶

Land of the High Sky is a comparatively short book that traces the history of the Staked Plain area of Texas. It opens with the 1849 territorial exploration of Captain Randolph B. Marcy (who was seeking new routes to the West) and concludes with a panoramic appraisal of life in the region in 1959.

The book, Griffin's first nonfiction work, was written to commemorate the opening of a new building by the First National Bank of Midland.

Although highly praised and required reading for many students of Western Americana, it is the least known of all Griffin's works due to the fact that it was published in limited edition; and this is regrettable, for it is a fascinating account of a land and of the men and women who wrestled it into civilization.

History comes alive in its pages, a century ago becomes again only yesterday, for Griffin's narration is one of liveliness and believability, a style that avoids the pitfalls of turgidness usually expected (and most often found) in anthropological studies of this type. It is in the fine tradition of J. Frank Dobie, a writer Griffin knew and greatly admired. As W. P. Z. German observed, *"Land of the High Sky* . . . is a story of virility and cruelty, timelessness and pathos, sublimity and earthiness the like of which we do not before recall having read . . . Griffin has managed with skill and even a certain daring to create a story worthy of reading and re-reading . . ."

The text of the selections is from *Land of the High Sky* (Midland, Texas: The First National Bank of Midland, 1959). "Preface" is from pages iii–xi; Chapter One, "Eighteen Covered Wagons," from pages 1–17; and Chapter Seven, "Cowboy," from pages 93–110. (One selection, which I have entitled "The Love Letters of Bessie Love," did not appear in the published edition of *Land of the*

High Sky. Originally written by Griffin as part of Chapter 7, "Cowboy," it was deleted by the publisher because of the book's space limitations. It appears here for the first time.)

An interesting sidelight of Griffin's activities at this time is shown in his journal entry that follows. Dated October, 1958, it documents his discovery that the first church in West Texas was founded by a small group of Carmelite monks.

Journal Entry

————————————————————————————→

October, 1958

In 1880, a German Catholic, John Konz, made a trip from Kansas to Texas in search for a good location to establish a Catholic Colony.

At Fort Worth, which was then a rapidly growing cattle shipping center, he met W. H. Abrams, land agent for the Texas and Pacific Railway. It will be remembered that the T. and P. was laying rails westward across the thirty-second parallel of Texas, through what had until recently been Comanche country. The T. and P., knowing that its future profits depended largely on the people who would settle the frontier and make use of the railroad, had inaugurated a tremendous publicity program to get settlements established in the West Texas plains area.

The publicity had to counter two widespread misconceptions about West Texas. In the first place, most believed it to be a barren desert. In the second place, even though the Comanches had been subdued, many continued to regard them as a terrifying menace. Abrams persuaded John Konz that the land was fertile, and that the Indians were all on the reservations.

As a result of this visit, five men arrived at the Grelton Station, one of the loneliest spots in the world, on August 15, 1881. At that time the Grelton Station consisted of nothing but a section house and telegraph station. It was the extreme Western frontier. Of the five men, three were Carmelite monks — Fathers P. A. Peters, Albert Wagner and William Fuhrwerk. Anton Kleber was a lay brother. Adam Konz, son of the John Konz who had made the original inquiries, was the only layman.

They soon petitioned to have the name changed from Grelton to Mariensfeld, meaning "The Field of Mary," and the Texas and Pacific, anxious to please the advance-guard of what they hoped would be a large settlement, immediately complied.

The men had two small tents, 12-by-14 feet each, which they pitched where the Martin County courthouse now stands. These tents served as living quarters for the little community and as a place of worship.

On the second Sunday after their arrival, they celebrated their first Mass in this lonely land — a solemn occasion, indeed, and certainly a contrast to the violence of the Indian wars that had preceded them.

The men labored hard most of the day, building and preparing for the colony that would eventually come to join them.

When they slept in their tents at night, they heard the cry of the coyote. They quickly learned to conceal all their edibles from the lobo wolves that roamed the area.

The first years were good. The colony grew. They built a church, a monastery and schools. The monastery served as a theological center for several years. The Texas and Pacific Railway Company, eager to cooperate in the settlement of these lands, sowed 20 acres just south of the present water tank in wheat, barley, rye and oats. For a time rains were plentiful and the yield impressive. Encouraged by this, the unique colony cooperated with the railway company in advertising the merits of this area as a farming country.

Father Boniface Peters even went to Germany and brought back 17 students. By 1885, the community numbered eight priests, eight lay brothers and 20 clerics.

Their ministry covered a widespread area. For many years, priests made their calls on horseback from ranch to ranch, administering the Sacraments and giving instructions. If night caught them on the prairies, they slept in the open with their saddles for pillows.

During the splendid years of 1884 and 1885, when wheat from the colony won honors at the World's Fair in New Orleans, hope ran high. The pious community looked forward to a secure and peaceful future in this vast, meditation-inspiring land.

Then, the historic drouth of 1886 and 1887 destroyed them. Family after family was ruined and forced to abandon its home and farmlands. There was simply not enough food to go around, nor sufficient money left to bring it in by rail.

Mrs. W. F. Fahrenkamp, one of the survivors, wrote:

In 1885 the grass was plentiful, being almost knee high, while wheat and cotton were fine . . . In 1886 the drouth began. What before had been green fields was now burned and withered stubble, and sandstorms reigned supreme.

After this devastating drouth, which forced so many to leave, the German colony began to lose its Catholic identity. New settlers came into the area, and in 1889, under the influence of a strong Protestant element, the name of the town was changed from Mariensfeld to Stanton, the name by which it is known today.

Records for this period are incomplete, but it is to be supposed that the school closed that year, for Father Peters was removed to start a new convent in Louisiana, and Stanton was left to a sub-prior.

Thus, it can be historically documented that the first church in West Texas of any denomination, was established by the Carmelites. The incident is little known in history, because the colony had come and then been wiped out almost before other West Texas towns were well started.

That its origins have fallen into obscurity, even among some of the people who today live in the town, was demonstrated to the writer in a poignant manner.

Having run across these records during my research for *Land of the High Sky*, I asked numerous questions. No one knew anything about the exact location of the Carmelite buildings, and I supposed they had long since vanished. One day, at a luncheon in the nearby city of Midland, I mentioned this to a man at our table who had informed me he was from Stanton. He not only knew about it, but he assured me the old convent and parts of the church walls remained.

Taking my wife and children, I immediately drove to Stanton. We passed through the business section toward the modern building that serves as the hospital.

Then, to the right, at the top of a gently sloping hill, we saw a large two-story wooden building, obviously old and in a state of disrepair. After having passed the modern buildings, this stately ruin so plainly showed its age we could not doubt we had found the right place.

Driving through what was left of the once fine entrance gate, between square pillars of red brick, one now nothing more than a stack of rubble and the other leaning at a dangerous angle, we approached the house through a surrounding field of dusty, autumn-browned weeds.

As we drew closer, details became clear. A porch encircled the second floor, above the first floor porch. Some of the boards had fallen away, and we noted the outside stairs leading to the second story were boarded up, obviously to prevent some curious visitor from going up and perhaps crashing through the rotted flooring. Some of the siding boards, long since dried and showing only faint traces of paint, had warped badly. Strange, rather fat Gothic windows, so dust-fogged we could not see the glass, encircled the upstairs, while taller ones, at close intervals, lined the downstairs façade, under the portico.

An impressive quiet hung over the place. We got out and began walking around the grounds. A small arbor of stunted trees, undoubtedly where the monks had walked to read their Office, stood a few feet opposite a side door. We quickly found a crumbling wall of mud and rock, the remains of that first church. A small pigeon-house stood almost intact. Looking up into it, we saw through a veil of spider and cobwebs, the perches and nesting places and the round holes where the pigeons entered. To the side, a rather large foundation had been laid for some building. Beyond, in all directions, stretched the fields.

We turned back to examine the main house more closely, noting the debris of more recent civilization — beer cans scattered here and there, a whiskey bottle or two, a crushed cigarette package.

At the corner of the porch a few old pews, hand-carved, stood ruined by the winds and rain. The wood was silver-gray and defaced by long cracks where the grain had separated from being exposed to the weather.

The early Carmelites seemed near, indeed. One felt the calm that lingered from their occupation of this monastery. Even my children stopped asking their questions as though awe-stricken by the evocations.

We walked on the porch around to the other side. My wife and I heard a faint, muffled sound that stopped us in our tracks. It came from inside.

"Is that music?" she asked.

I stepped closer to the window and we listened.

With our footsteps silenced, the music came out clearly and we heard the frenzied beat of rock and roll blaring somewhere in the depths of the old Carmelite monastery.

My wife said, "Why, someone's living here."

"Well, it's sure as hell not the Carmelites," I said.

We stood absolutely dumbfounded at the incongruity between what we saw about us and what we were hearing.

I tried to peer through the dusted window, but could see nothing except old-fashioned lace curtains hanging inside.

After discussing it a moment, my wife urged me to knock on the door and make inquiries. The Gothic windows, the obvious age of the house, the abandoned pews — all of these things made me certain we had made no mistake, that this was in truth the old monastery. But the music . . . I thought perhaps some indigent had simply moved in to occupy the deserted building.

Finally I knocked and a rather irritated man opened the door. The music surged out.

"Pardon me — but is this the old Carmelite monastery?" I asked.

"What?" he said, frowning. I repeated my question.

"No — it's a private residence," he said.

"Are you sure? I've never seen a private res—"

"Of course I'm sure," he said. Then — "I don't know anything about it. I just room here."

Since we were obviously going to receive no information from him, we got in our car and drove away. Down the street we stopped and asked a lady if "that big house on the hill" weren't the Carmelite monastery.

"I think so," she said. "I know it used to be something Catholic."

I told her the man who roomed there denied this.

"Well, he's wrong. I know it's something Catholic," she insisted.

Further inquiries quickly revealed that this was the abandoned monastery. It had been sold to an elderly man who occasionally rented out rooms. He had apparently left the exterior untouched, but had "fixed it up nice inside."

I traced him down. He was cordial, but rather vague about the monastery's past. He told me he occupied only the lower floor, that he had closed off the upstairs "where they used to pray up there."

I asked him if there would be any chance of my going upstairs.

"No . . ." he said, shaking his head. "It'd be too dangerous. You wouldn't want to go up there. Nothing up there but just some of those old — you know — Catholic things — statues and things like that . . ." he grimaced. "Nothing up there worth seeing."

I suggested that nothing would interest me more than having a look at those old "Catholic things" but did not insist. He gave the impression of being so old and so tired that the matter could not be pursued further.

He expressed his regrets that he could not be more helpful and I left.

We drove back to the site, and looked over the brown weed fields up to the beautiful but dilapidated remains that stood imposingly at the top of the hill. The monastery appeared serene and lonely and peaceful. I thought of the days when Carmelite monks labored to build it, when they gave lessons to seminarians in German, when they walked in the little circle around the oasis of trees reading their Office, when they worked in the fields or saddled their horses to go out into the vast, sparsely inhabited country to carry the Sacraments to Mexican sheep herders or to visit with the isolated ranchers. I thought of the days when premium wheat swayed with the breeze in fields now covered with scrub weeds.

But the illusion was forever destroyed for me.

I could not forget that the rooms that once housed monks now housed men who did not even realize this, that the monastery was now a run-down rooming house.

Nor could I forget that the prayerful monastic silence of former days was now cruelly shattered by the racket of rock and roll.

PREFACE

In the summer of 1958 Sam R. Bloom of Bloom Advertising in Dallas telephoned me about a writing project in West Texas.

The First National Bank of Midland, he said, was in the process of constructing a new building. To help memoralize the opening, the bank's Board of Directors had decided to sponsor the writing and publication of a history of the oil-rich Permian Basin area of West Texas, of which Midland serves as the trade center.

A visit with John P. Butler, President of the bank, and A. N. Hendrickson, Chairman of the Building Committee, clarified the issue. "Do a thorough research job on the history of the area from its earliest days to the present, and then write a book telling its story," they said in essence. "We'll give you all the help possible." They left the book's contents and organization in the author's hands.

Why should there be a history of the area? True it had a colorful past. Prehistoric Midland Man had roamed the area in search of food 20,000 years ago. The nomadic Comanche had lived here and fought off all intruders for almost 400 years. The Forty-Niners had struggled across its hostile grasslands on their way to California and many had died of thirst or been slain by the Comanches. It had grazed tremendous herds of buffalo and wild mustangs and later some of the finest cattle produced in the world. It had helped form the cowboy and the Western type. And it had more recently been the scene of oil's overwhelming drama.

But what distinguished this from any other area in the West? Obviously its great oil wealth.

Attorney Robert Turpin of Midland soon pointed out another distinction of utmost significance, one that had extended the area's importance far beyond its geographical boundaries even before the land was explored or surveyed.

In 1845, when Texas was annexed to the Union as the twenty-eighth state, the Texas founding fathers found themselves in possession of vast lands but no money. They were, in fact, $8,000,000 in debt. Their annexation agreement with the Union stipulated that they retain all their lands and also all their debts.

Penniless, they used lands to build for the future. They set aside large tracts, the revenues from which were to benefit the Common School Fund and build a "University of the First Class." Other lands were for the benefit of veterans and public welfare, and finally — realizing that a land without transportation was worthless — they set aside over 5,000,000 acres to pay for building a railroad. Later, in the 1880's, they continued the practice by bartering acreage in exchange for the Capitol Building at Austin.

Most of these lands were in the Permian Basin area of West Texas which extends approximately 100 miles in all directions from present-day Midland.

So this land, once considered worthless and uninhabitable, paid for the State Capitol at Austin, for much of the rail transportation system in the state; and after the discovery of oil, it substantially contributed to a $65,000,000 plant at the University of Texas and benefited proportionally Texas A. and M. University. In addition, it contributed large sums to the Public Free School Fund and to public welfare.

The founding fathers hoped for future development, but they could not have dreamed these "wastelands" were to produce such wealth.

My first research for the book was simply to familiarize myself with the land.

I asked Mr. Butler and Mr. Hendrickson to find me a place untouched, a place that would be as nearly as possible the way it had been when the first settler came to the Midland Country in 1882. I wanted to live alone with the type of equipment he might have carried. They contacted rancher Foy Proctor, who arranged to have me "deposited" on one of his ranches. They fixed me a bedroll, and I took along a coffee pot and some sandwiches. They left me at an isolated spot near a water hole where a stunted mesquite tree provided the only shade.

The immense silence emphasized my isolation. Grass-covered land stretched flat to all horizons. I left my bedroll at the pond and

walked many miles that afternoon. The only sounds were my footsteps loud in the stillness and the occasional chirping of birds and a
slight breeze in the brush. The sun baked down, but the breeze had
a cool undercurrent.

When I returned to the pond at sunset, I sat on my bedroll and
began making notes. I built a small fire of dead mesquite branches
and cooked coffee with water from the pond.

At dusk, the jack rabbits came to the pond to drink. I looked up
and saw them reflected in the still water. By 7:15, the sun had set.
A luminous pink glow hung over the countryside and the breeze
died to utter stillness. A full moon rose before the pink had faded.

Noiselessly a large sorrel horse appeared from the brush beyond
the pool. He stared at me and after a long time he drank. Dampness and chill settled and the air grew fragrant with odors of sun-
baked sands, animal scents and the smoke of my fire.

The horse left at a full run, a shadow dashing through the brush.
I listened to his hooves rumbling the earth long after he had disappeared.

I rolled out my bedroll, put my clothes under the canvas cover
and slept in the chilling night. Throughout the night I made notes.
One read:

11:30

I slept heavily and awakened. It is cold and still, though a faint
breeze blows from the south. The moon is high now, but it does
not obscure the stars. I added a log to the fire and it flames
brightly again. Strange what a fire does. In this great deserted
area, in these Carthusian silences, the circle of firelight dispels the
forbidding aspects. However, the country, the plains stretch out
beyond, and you cannot forget they are there. It is easy to erase
the present, for nothing here is contemporary, nothing is changed
from what it has always been. One feels joined to eternity, somehow. I begin to sense something of the hold this land has on people
like J. Frank Dobie and Walter Prescott Webb — men who love
its spaces, its silences.

I recall a letter from Dobie, in which he said: "Many times I
feel more closely akin to the land and its native wild life than to
people. Very few understand or care to understand the 'Bach Harmonies,' the rhythms of the earth in its Wordsworthian 'diurnal
round.' "

Like the desert or the ocean, it throws a man face to face with nature stripped of all distracting elements — no mountains, no trees, no beautiful views, though its very simplicity is more than beauty. It overwhelms. To stay here, a man must face himself and the realities of life and death.

I told myself this was the essence of it. Often I returned to the land and always its evocation grew more powerful. I could understand the early day rancher's love for it and the cowboy's, as I could understand another's hatred of it.

My next research led me into old newspaper files, court records, birth, marriage, medical, church and death records. A panorama began to unfold.

The researcher's greatest joy is this growing familiarity with the lives of men and women who have now passed into history. He picks up a fragment here, one there and begins piecing them together, and his own life and affections are altered by the process.

Perhaps this process is more immediate and clear in passages jotted in my journals during the actual work on the book.

Here at Mr. Hendrickson's office, late at night, I have been working on the daily life of the early settlers, the foods, how they did the laundry, problems of bathing, bread baking and burying, etc. All of it comes alive in the strange stillness of this office. I read the drugstore inventories and smell the odors of asafoetida, iodoform and arnica, mingled with turpentine, vanilla extract, camphor, sweet spirits of nitre and tobacco that were so common in the drugstores of those days.

Odd how digging into the details of daily life brings the past, the unknown past, into focus. You find it in a thousand different places. You search and eventually stumble onto something that clarifies the picture. I start with a name, nothing more — a man long dead, who ran a grocery store here. Someone describes him. "He used to come home from the store every night, remove his shoes, sit with his stockinged feet close to the fire and read until bed time."

What did he read? I find some of his books, and see the passages he marked: Epictetus — "What disturbs men's minds is not events, but their judgment of events." Or again: Heraclitis — "Man's character is his fate." Years ago a grocer read at night and underlined passages that impressed or delighted him, and tonight they show me a side of him, and he comes alive. I learn about these people from such hints, from the things they saved, the things they underlined . . .

Yes, this is the strange transformation that takes place here each night. I lift heavy old handwritten record books — court, crime, birth, death, marriage, church records, etc., up to my desk from stacks all over the floor. I open them and pieces and fragments come together to make a picture, and from all of these impersonal pages, I become personally attached to these people long since dead. I follow them through all the episodes of their lives.

I find them, one by one, and some of them come out whole and alive, and then I go out and spend hours where they lived, see what they saw, smell what they smelled and eat whatever recipes I can find that I'm sure they ate. I get menus from people who ate Jennie Scharbauer's famous plum pudding on a Sunday after church. I get others from people who ate at boardinghouses that served the cowboys when they came in for their "frolics" after spending long periods of hermit-like existence on the plains.

So, from around four in the afternoon, until seven or eight in the morning, while the rest of the town sleeps, I have the almost unique experience of living in growing intimacy with people now gone. This is so true that when I go to the cemeteries to check an occasional date, I find myself suddenly out of my role. I am no longer a researcher, but a friend, often knowing them more intimately than anyone else now alive, often more intimately even than their own friends did in life.

When you work like this, you become easily saddened that time leads people to forget something precious in a heritage of the past. You feel as though men should walk more softly, that they should take time to be aware of these evocations.

I think of Van Wyck Brooks' statement in *From a Writer's Notebook:*

> Americans, more than other people, feel that they must be up to the minute, as if this last minute were more important than any of the great realities of life and death . . .

This is not the only period, nor are we the only people who have been aware of the importance of "living in the present." But there is no doubt that people who felt this in former times were also aware of their forebears and of the past. It was their reading of the Bible and the classics that saved them from time-provincialism; and having, in consequence, equipoise and a standard of value, they knew their present better than we know ours.

I make my notes, I dictate them and correlate them. And then, around three or three-thirty in the morning, I hear the elevator door open on the floor. In a moment I look up to see Mr. Kirkpatrick, the night maintenance man at the bank, peer speculatively around the door at me.

"You about ready for some coffee?" he asks.

He has a lonely job, and he guesses I have, too, although he has no idea what it is. He isn't interested. All he knows is that around three in the morning a man gets hungry and coffee-thirsty. So, I go down with him, in the elevator, past darkened floors, into the warm atmosphere of the basement, with its huge heating equipment, its tubes and valves and compressors and what not. Every morning we have a cup of black coffee, crackers and longhorn cheese and some grapes before I return to my desk.

Since he is an elderly man, our talk remains of the past. He tells me the details of traveling in a covered wagon, the stories of frontier life as he has lived it, and he answers many of my questions.

Finally, at dawn, I hear trucks rumbling in the street eight stories below. I go to the window and see the flat expanses of the country, sometimes misted, sometimes clear-cut in a brilliant streaked dawn. Skyscrapers take shape and the country comes to life. It is always a vague shock. I return from the past to the present. I return from a Comanche camp, or from a cattle drive, or from an early morning breakfast with cowboys of another age, or from an early-day meeting of the Time and Tide Club, or from the tobacco-chewing circle of men sitting around the old stove in the original First National Bank — I return from all of that to the present, to the clean high skyscrapers whose windows glisten gold and pink at sunrise.

*

Clarence Scharbauer, Jr., and Foy Proctor took me to their ranches and allowed me to observe cowboying and handling cattle; from the early-morning breakfasts, through the day's work, to the night bath and falling into bed. They answered all of my questions and allowed me to experience the cattle business first-hand — and they showed me a warmth and hospitality such as I have seldom before experienced.

Finally, I began to write —

I wrote everything in the first draft of the book. The manuscript exceeded 1300 pages. Then, I began to think of the viewpoint I must use to give the book some cohesion. No matter in what direction I turned, a phrase from Virgil recurred to me: "Nature first gave those customs." The very nature of the land had so impressed me — as it has many men before me — I began to wonder what effect it might have had on the various cultures and civilizations that had known it, inhabited it.

The viewpoint of the book crystallized then on the land and the peoples who successively lived on it and were formed by it: from the prehistoric man to the modern oil man and industrialist.

My principle aim has been to show the various civilizations that inhabited this land in the past and the manner in which one succeeded the other.

Finally, I hope that when the reader comes to the end of the book, he will see the land not just as brush and grass and oil tanks and super-highways, but that he will see the whole panorama: Marcy's men singing at twilight, Comanche camps, buffalo hunters, lonely trail drives, cowboy camps, early oil explorations and all of those things of the past that give us a perspective of the present and future.

EIGHTEEN COVERED WAGONS

---→

The sun of October 1, 1849, raised sweats on the men and lifted from the earth the dry sweet odor of ripened grasses. Its warmth penetrated the covering sheets of wagons and turned their interiors into ovens. The reek of bedrolls, clothing and leather trailed each wagon.

Members of Captain Randolph B. Marcy's eighteen-wagon caravan sat in saddles or on wagon seats and watched the passage of a land new to the eyes of white men.

Blond grasslands of the southern Staked Plain of Texas stretched treeless and level for hundreds of miles. The country lay so flat the sky took up most of the view, and the men could see as far as their eyes would let them.

Harness clanked and wheels screeched — new sounds to a land whose immense silence had been softened only by the twitter of birds, the knitting of grasshoppers, the rumble of Comanche ponies, and at night, the howl of wolves and coyotes.

Oxen, three yokes to the wagon, pulled toward the next permanent water. Their mouths slavered and their eyes blared as they hooked and kicked and sometimes broke pace, maddened by clouds of hornflies.

Marcy's caravan advanced in a low dust haze along the Great Comanche War Trail immediately south of present-day Midland, heading for an unnamed spring reported a few miles northeast. The surface of glaring white caliche and pink sand had long since been pounded hard by Indian war ponies. It formed a wide highway over which the Indians made their murderous raids on Mexico each year.

The rains had been good in that year of 1849. Occasional buffalo wallows reflected the sun from their stagnant waters. The sight of water reassured the men, for they traveled an unknown land. Fear of thirst was as great as fear of the Indian.

Marcy remarked how the previous morning, when scouts brought in news of a shallow, rain-filled lake, that "it appeared to inspire our men and animals with renewed vigor. From the cheerless silence of the last two hours, the aspect of everything changed in a moment to humorous jokes and boisterous merriment." [1]

Water was the important thing. Men traveled not directly but where they could find water on the route. No man dared move off alone and unguided, for if he missed the water he died.

If he found the water, he risked losing his life to some youthful Comanche who hoped to become a brave by taking a scalp back to his village. This was soon to be felt cruelly in the caravan.

Grouse and quail, fat from the seeds, lifted heavy bodies on a loud flutter as the caravan passed. Blanched skeletons of buffalo and horses littered the trail.

This was a good year for the grasses. Comanches and Kiowas would winter handsomely on pemmican and jerked buffalo meat in their tepee villages.

For this land belonged to the Indian, the mustang and the buffalo. This lonely land that evoked in men a sense of eternity and peace was the violent and feared *Llano Estacado* (Staked Plain) so named probably because Mexican traders and hunters are reported to have driven stakes from one water hole to the next. It extended hundreds of miles through western Texas and eastern New Mexico and was a country of such hostility and so little surface water that white men seldom ventured into it. Even the Indians had more than once killed their horses to drink the blood.

Among the members of Marcy's party, adventurous Larry Gooding, eighteen, sought to forget his homesickness in the new shepherd dog he had bought when the party left Santa Fe to begin the return journey to Fort Smith, Arkansas. The dog, Shep, trotted alongside Larry's "splendid little pony" which was almost worn out from the long trip. The boy took pleasure, too, in the Mississippi rifle Lieutenant Buford had entrusted to him when the officer had left the expedition at Santa Fe. [2]

Marcy viewed the passing scene from a position flat on his back

[1] *The Report of Capt. R. B. Marcy's Route From Fort Smith to Santa Fe*, published in *Reports of the Secretary of War*, Senate Executive Document No. 64, 31st Congress, 1st Session (Washington, July, 1850), p. 207.
[2] "Across the Plains in 1849," *Dallas News*, May 14, 1911, reprinted in *Frontier Times*, Vol. 1, No. 11 (Bandera, Texas, August, 1924), p. 4.

in one of the wagons. An attack of colic had forced the 38-year-old commandant to leave his saddle and travel in a wagonbed where, as he noted, "every slight jar of the wagon sends the most acute pain through my whole system." [3]

The hardships of his present life contrasted to his former life in New England where he and his wife, Mary, had enjoyed a civilized existence.

But this was not the first time in their twelve years of marriage they had undergone separations and hardships. They had spent their honeymoon in a primitive frontier camp in Wisconsin. Mary Marcy had proved that she could transform any place into a pleasant home. [4]

Such hard and impoverished living was a part of the military life. Marcy took it with cheerful and even temper. He was a large man in every sense. He stood more than six feet. Though he had not won outstanding marks at West Point, he was large-minded, with unquestionable sincerity and integrity. He commanded both respect and affection. In addition he possessed personal and intellectual dignity balanced by a sense of humor.

Exploring a new country aroused his finest qualities. The present expedition was to mark the beginning of his fame as an explorer and Indian authority.

It was also to make known to the world the Midland area of the Staked Plain.

It is important to note why Marcy was in this particular area at this particular time.

II

In 1849, Texas had been the twenty-eighth state for only four years. Its sparse settlements lay far to the east of the Staked Plain Midland area.

With the discovery of gold in California, however, men swarmed westward. Between them and the Pacific lay the Plains, an area Marcy described as "The Great Zahara of North America." [5]

[3] Marcy, *op. cit.*, p. 207.
[4] Hollon, W. Eugene, *Beyond the Cross Timbers.* (University of Oklahoma Press, Norman, 1955), pp. 14, 19.
[5] Marcy, *op. cit.*

Waterings were uncharted and uncertain. Emigrants to the West had to pass through country overrun by Indians who counted it both a duty and a joy to slaughter and scalp intruders.

III

For almost 400 years the Comanches had ruled the Texas Plains, killing or driving out all interlopers whether white men or other Indians.

This "Zahara," unlike its African namesake, was exceptional grazing land. It sustained the buffalo, and the buffalo was the Comanche's chief means of living. The buffalo furnished him food, clothing, carrying bags, skins for making his tepee shelter and almost everything else he wanted.

The earliest meetings between the Anglo-Saxon Texans and the Comanches were friendly. The Comanches, whose hatred of the Spaniards and Mexicans dates back to the first Spanish occupancy of the country, held out a hand of friendship to the Americans during the first days of colonization.

In 1831, Mary Austin Holley wrote of them:

> Though fierce in war they are civil in peace, and they are remarkable for their sense of justice. They call the people of the United States their friends, and give them protection, while they hate the Mexicans, and murder them without mercy.[6]

The two cultures, however, had little in common. Their practices, beliefs, values, ambitions and traditions differed so drastically that conflict was inevitable.

Characteristically each believed his culture superior and considered the other's merely underdeveloped.

The white looked on the Indian as inferior, childlike, a heartless savage. The Indian, on the other hand, saw the white man as a superstitious fool without character.

As the frontiersman pushed westward in search of new land, the Indian questioned his sense of justice; and when settlements were established in his hunting grounds he saw the white man as an ag-

[6] Holley, Mary Austin, *Texas*. (Baltimore, 1833).

gressor acting in bad faith. The friendship of the two races degenerated into bitter and lasting hatred.

Emigrants to the West, therefore, had little hope of passing through the area safely unless they traveled in large groups, capable of defending themselves against attack.

Accounts abound of instances when individuals, in their foolhardy determination to make time, traveled alone or in small groups and were straightway massacred.

As a step in aiding the westward flow of Forty-Niners the government ordered a number of exploring parties, well escorted by soldiers, to open up new routes.

IV

One of these, the first to traverse this area of the Southern Staked Plain, was the caravan under Captain Randolph B. Marcy's command.

Marcy had been instructed to open a route west from Fort Smith, Arkansas, through Indian Territory to Santa Fe and to return by a more southerly route across the Staked Plain; also to conciliate the Indians and to give protection to any emigrant parties along the route.[7]

The detachment, organized at Fort Smith, consisted of Lt. J. Buford and twenty-six non-commissioned officers and privates of the F Company, First Dragoons, and Lts. M. P. Harrison and J. Updegraph of the Fifth Infantry with fifty infantrymen. The Dragoons and officers were mounted. The rest of the force manned the eighteen supply wagons, beef cattle and surplus work stock. Lt. J. H. Simpson of the Corps of Topographical Engineers accompanied the expedition and prepared a series of maps tracing the route.[8]

In addition to the wagons, they also brought one six-pound iron gun and a traveling forge, each pulled by six mules.[9]

Marcy's guide for the trip, a Delaware Indian, Black Beaver, was noted throughout the frontier for his courage as well as for his skill as a hunter and scout. He had traveled among the western and

---

[7] Acting Assistant Adjutant General F. F. Flint to Captain R. B. Marcy, Fort Smith, Arkansas, April 2, 1849, published with Marcy's *Report*, pp. 169–171.
[8] *Ibid.*
[9] Hollon, p. 60.

northern Indian tribes, knew their character and habits and conversed fluently with the Comanches and most other prairie tribes.

For hunting, Black Beaver used a small reed instrument called a *bleat*. With this he could imitate the cry of a fawn so accurately as to lure eager does within shot. Parker, who accompanied Marcy on a subsequent trip, objected morally to the bleat, since it made "the affection of the mother for her young, the means of her death, a piece of barbarity which I could not sanction, though I must confess my prairie appetite overcame my scruples under the influence of the savory odor of the smoking haunch." [10]

On the trip westward from Fort Smith to Santa Fe, Marcy had met his first group of Comanches, a band of twenty or thirty, under Chief Is-so-Keep (Wolf Shoulder), well mounted on mustangs, wearing red leggings and beautifully beaded blankets, feather headgear and rings on their ears and arms. [11]

The Comanches never engaged a superior force. They attacked only when they were certain of winning an engagement. When, as on the present occasion, they could not fight the white man, they pretended overwhelming friendship.

Marcy, eager to meet with the Indians, had answered Is-so-Keep's signal of friendship and had ridden out to him.

When the two horses came alongside, Marcy offered his hand in friendship. The chief ignored it, leaned over in his saddle and embraced the officer. Marcy reported the incident with considerable good humor:

> For the good of the service, I forced myself to submit. Seizing me in his brawny arms and laying his greasy head upon my shoulder, he gave me a most bruin-like squeeze; after undergoing which I flattered myself that the salutation was completed, but in this I was mistaken and was doomed to suffer another similar torture, with the savage's head upon my other shoulder, and at the same time rubbing his greasy face against mine, all of which he gave me to understand was to be regarded as a most distinguished and signal mark of affection for the American people — whom he loved so much that it almost broke his heart — and which I as their representative had the honor to receive. [12]

[10] Parker, W. B., *Notes Taken With Marcy* (Philadelphia, 1856), p. 103.
[11] Hollon, *op. cit.*, pp. 70–71.
[12] Hollon, *op. cit.*, pp. 70–71.

Marcy's party had completed the first portion of their journey on June 28, 1849, at Santa Fe, "a miserable group of low flat houses all huddled together inside a mud wall." [13] They had come 819.5 miles from Fort Smith in eighty-five days. There, the travel-worn men and stock rested for a month.

At Santa Fe, Lt. Buford had received orders transferring him to California. The officer had entrusted his fine Mississippi rifle to young Larry Gooding whose pride in it departed only when it was used later to murder one of the company. There also the youngster had bought the dog, Shep.

Lt. Delos B. Sackett had assumed command of the Dragoons, replacing Buford. Captain Marcy had hired an extra guide for the return trip across the plains, a Comanche Indian, Manuel, who formerly had served as guide for the noted traveler, Josiah Gregg.

Manuel, whom Marcy found "a man of much more than ordinary judgment and character . . . the best guide that can be found in New Mexico," [14] knew almost every waterhole and stream on the Staked Plain and assured Marcy he could guide the party across.

From the village of Doña Ana, on the east bank of the Rio Grande, sixty miles above El Paso, they had turned eastward to follow the Pecos River to a spot south of the White Sand Hills, near present-day Monohans.

There, on September 21, in order to cross the river, Marcy had devised a ferry boat by attaching barrels to a wagonbed, inverting it and floating the men and baggage across.[15]

They had then proceeded in a northeasterly direction across the Sand Hills and up on the Staked Plain following the Comanche War Trail.

Passing south of present-day Midland, they encamped a few miles to the northeast.

At the head of a shallow draw, a spring percolated into the surface of a pond. "It is about three feet deep, covers several acres of

---

[13] *The Dallas News*, May 14, 1911.
[14] Marcy, *op. cit.*, p. 208.
[15] *Ibid.*, p. 205. For detailed study of Marcy's route from Doña Ana to Fort Smith see Williams, J. W., *Marcy's Road From Doña Ana*, West Texas Historical Association, *Year Book*, XIX, 1943, p. 128.

ground and has rushes growing in it," Marcy noted.[16] He believed the pond contained permanent water, since numerous mustang trails led to it "and as the horse requires water every day he would not likely stay at a place where it could not be found at all times." [17]

Marcy named it Mustang Pond. Later it came to be known as Mustang Springs and the draw that approaches it as Mustang Draw.

The men corralled their wagons into a defensive semi-circular position. The drivers, unhitching their oxen and mules, never failed to enliven the air with their "awful profanity." [18] Parker noted that the ox and mule drivers invariably indulged in "blasphemy" and observed how "ill-timed and unnatural" it was when encountered in the midst of natural beauties "which might fire a dying hermit." [19]

Horses were hobbled and turned out with the oxen to graze. The men pitched their tents and started fires of buffalo dung and twigs.

As they found time, they returned in small groups to the water to bathe. They rarely, if ever, shaved on the trail. Marcy had remarked in his report before reaching Santa Fe that he had not had a razor to his face since leaving Fort Smith and that he was beginning to look barbarous, or rather "anti-barbarous."

However, bathing was necessary. Fine sandy dust raised on the trail penetrated clothing. It could be so irritating that men would break ice on ponds if necessary to "scrub up." The ration of grog Marcy frequently issued his enlisted men, or the tumbler of claret he offered his officers then had added savor.

"Jackass" rabbits came close, showing little fear. They sat like kangaroos, and the slanting sun made their long ears almost transparent. Distances hazed and the air became perfectly still at dusk. A pinkish glow hung over the land. Evening odors of ozone, cooling grasses and animals scented the air.

Silence lay so profound that the whisper of oxen shaking their necks could be heard in the distance, soon underlined by the rattle of frogs on the pond.

Color drained from the sky and the pinkness vanished. A first pale star appeared. Viewed from afar, the camp presented a picture

[16] *Ibid.*, p. 207.
[17] *Ibid.*, p. 207.
[18] Parker, *op. cit.*, p. 22.
[19] *Ibid.*, p. 22.

of peace. White tents and wagon covers glowed in the twilight. Campfires blazed, sending their columns of smoke straight upward to great heights.[20]

Then, as darkness settled, the mood changed. Silence took on a new dimension, softly at first, as voices from the camp floated "Home, Sweet Home" on the air. Men, far from their families, rested in the grass and waited for supper. With the night chill at their backs and the warmth of fires on their faces, they often allowed themselves the luxury of homesickness. For the moment the empty plains and the Indian menace were no more.

Lieutenant Harrison, a young man of "extraordinary amiability and goodness of heart," must have thought of his absent fiancée, Mary Conway. Harrison, twenty-three, had fallen in love with the daughter of Dr. John R. Conway during the first half of the trip when the Conways had traveled with a group of westbound emigrants in company with Marcy's caravan. The young lieutenant was more than eligible. One of his grandfathers was General Zebulon Pike, the noted explorer; the other was William Henry Harrison, ninth President of the United States. Lt. Harrison's elder brother, Benjamin Harrison, was destined to become President of the United States in 1888. Dr. Conway had consented to the marriage. He had stipulated only that Harrison join them in California for the wedding.[21]

To men of the caliber of Marcy and Harrison, who had certainly heard the music of Haydn and Mozart, the simple melody of "Home, Sweet Home" must have seemed fitting for the evening and the place.

The music carried them away and it brought them back. More boisterously, as though to counter the previous sentiment, the crowd bellowed "Hail, Columbia" and "Yankee Doodle," which were "roared out at the top of not the weakest lungs." [22]

If Black Beaver had hunted successfully, he prepared either antelope or venison. Sharpening a stick at both ends, he spitted the meat on it and inserted the point in the ground near a blazing fire. He watched the meats, turning them occasionally until the juices

[20] *Ibid.*, p. 41.
[21] Hollon, *op. cit.*, pp. 65–66.
[22] Parker, *op. cit.*, pp. 81–82.

started to run. Then a portion was cut off, salted and eaten. Parker reported that once tasted it left "a lasting impression upon the palate, light and easy of digestion, and carrying no nightmare with it." [23]

After supper, Marcy and his junior officers frequently discussed the land and the Indians. Lt. Harrison carried a running debate with the other officers. He said, as Sam Houston had before him, that the white man's bad faith and his abuses had incited the Indian's savagery. He insisted that the Indian would respond, as any other man, to confidence and trust.[24]

More experienced officers opposed this idealistic theory. Marcy explained that young Indians could not hold any position in their tribes until they could show a scalp and proof of having stolen a number of horses. He pointed out that as a result of this, two or three young Indians would start out together and sometimes be absent a year, until they could "return with these evidences of their manliness." [25] If one saw Indians, the best plan, according to Marcy, was either to escape to camp or else "preserving a bold front, take care to have the first shot." [26] Despite these admonitions, the youthful Harrison held firm to his faith in the Indian.

Marcy, noticing what appeared to be fossilized sea life, had little doubt the Plains had once been a sea bed, but he scarcely could have imagined that it dated back 200,000,000 years when the Permian Sea covered the area. He could not have suspected that aboriginal family groups once lived at Mustang Pond, hunted small prehistoric horses to eat, and sat around campfires fashioning beautiful flint tools thousands of years before it was supposed man existed on earth — 18,000 years before Christ.

The sick captain lay in his tent, rolled up in blankets on the grass, with his saddle for a pillow. The fires died and all men except the guards retired. The land settled once again into silence.

Marcy knew a great deal about the *Llano Estacado*. He rated it the highest tableland then known to exist on this continent. He knew it had some mineral wealth and could see the grazing wealth. But he could not have dreamed that he was that night lying above

23 *Ibid.*, p. 121.
24 *Ibid.*, pp. 29–30.
25 *Ibid.*, p. 30.
26 *Ibid.*, p. 30.

a great invisible underground basin that would, in less than a century, give up the rich yield of oil that had been forming for millions of years.

He slept that night, one of the first white men to do so, almost in the center of the Permian Basin.

v

The covered wagons rolled over the prairie from Mustang Pond. Lowing oxen, snorting horses and the shouts and whip-cracking of drivers accompanied the caravan's progress toward the next permanent water.[27]

On October 3, after a trip of forty miles, Marcy arrived at another fine watering place, which he named Big Spring.

On October 6, the party camped in a grove of mesquite and wild china on the bank of a creek running into the Pash-a-ho-no, or Colorado. Marcy had noted quail and meadow larks common along the route, but they saw their first wild turkeys at the creek.

They halted for a Sunday rest. Stock and men were exhausted and Marcy once again suffered from colic. After they made camp, Marcy asked Lt. Harrison to examine a ravine two miles distant next morning.

That evening Lt. Harrison borrowed Larry Gooding's Mississippi rifle for his foray.[28]

Sunday, Harrison started out after dinner to examine the ravine. When he had not returned by nightfall, Captain Marcy had the cannon fired, noting that if the lieutenant were within twenty miles he would hear it "as the atmosphere is perfectly still and clear." [29] The commandant was not particularly concerned, since Harrison was a fine woodsman and an excellent marksman.

The next morning, Harrison's continued absence was noted with alarm. Marcy concluded he must be lost on the prairies. He sent Lt. Updegraph and Black Beaver to follow the tracks of Harrison's horse. Within two hours, the searchers reported they had followed the trail a mile and a half beyond the ravine where it appeared Lt.

[27] *Ibid.*, p. 22.
[28] *The Dallas News*, May 14, 1911.
[29] Marcy, *op. cit.*, p. 207.

Harrison had met with a party of Indians and gone off with them to the south.

Marcy, too sick to move from his bed, ordered Lt. Sackett to take all the mounted force and follow the trail until they recovered the young officer.

They searched the grasses and were ready to turn back when the dog, Shep, took the scent. He darted off toward a canyon half a mile away and the horsemen followed.

Fears for Harrison's safety increased when the dog stopped at the top of the precipice and began barking. The noise flushed a crow which flew up from the river bed and circled the bluff.[30]

The horsemen dismounted and walked to the brink. On the rocks below they saw Harrison's body. It was scalped, stripped and mutilated obscenely.

Lt. Sackett sent a report back to Captain Marcy. A wagon was sent out and when it arrived, the body was picked up and "tenderly conveyed to camp."[31]

Black Beaver was asked to "read the signs" and construe what had happened. The Delaware's uncanny ability to deduce a crime from only a scrap of evidence has been recorded.[32]

He reported that the murder was committed by two Indians. They had encountered Lt. Harrison, and seeing he made no move to run or defend himself, had pretended friendship. The three men had dismounted, sat on the grass and smoked together. Here, feigning curiosity, the Indians had asked to see his rifle. When Harrison passed it to them, they overpowered him, tied him to his horse and later shot him in the back of the head with the Mississippi rifle. His body had then been stripped, mutilated and tossed to the rocks below.

As Harrison had been mounted on a fleet horse and was a fine rifleman, it could only be surmised he was determined to prove his theory about the Indians.

Marcy noted the camp was plunged in gloom and that the men, though hardened soldiers, "were seen to turn away their faces to conceal their tears."[33]

[30] *The Dallas News*, May 14, 1911.
[31] *Ibid.*
[32] Parker, *op. cit.*, pp. 29–30f.
[33] Marcy, *op. cit.*, p. 210.

One senses the extent of Marcy's own pain in the restraint of his journal entry: "This has been a most melancholy day for us." [34]

Instead of burying the body there, Marcy had it coated with tar and placed in a box made of wagon sideboards. They packed it with pulverized charcoal before the box was sealed. This primitive method of embalming preserved the body until the caravan returned to Fort Smith late in the winter, where it was buried with full military honors.

Because of Harrison's important family connections, the details of his massacre were widely published. His death not only attracted the nation's attention to the Staked Plain, but it also strengthened the argument for Indian suppression that he died seeking to refute.

VI

This concluded the first of Marcy's explorations.

The return of these men from a journey of 2,000 miles, "believed to be the longest march ever performed by the United States Infantry," [35] excited the curiosity of the country, and many newspapers carried the story.

Marcy mapped and described the region. The expedition was scientific to a degree that perhaps astonishes us today. They measured distances with a viameter and chain, and took compass bearings every mile. Variations of the needle were determined at eight different points along the route. Of historic significance was Marcy's recommendation that his route across the Staked Plain be used by the future railroad to the Pacific. He wrote:

> Throughout the entire distance it would not be necessary to make a single tunnel or to use a stationary engine. There would be but a few heavy excavations or embankments; and for a great portion of the distance, the surface of the earth is so perfectly firm and smooth that it would appear to have been designed by the Great Architect of the Universe for a railroad, and adapted and fitted by nature's handiwork for the reception of the superstructure.[36]

[34] *Ibid.*, p. 209.
[35] Hollon, *op. cit.*, pp. 87–88.
[36] *Ibid.*, p. 89.

His suggestions were not to be put into action for another thirty-three years because of political intrigues and the hostility of the Plains Indians. But he laid the foundations of Empire-thinking and presented them in a distinguished and scientific manner.

Captain Marcy's report described the land in its very essence:

> . . . nature, in her wise economy, has adorned the entire face of the country with a luxuriant verdure of different kinds of grama grass, affording the most nutritious sustenance for animals, and rendering it one of the best countries for grazing large flocks and herds that could be conceived.[37]

At bottom, this made the history of the land. The grass brought the buffalo, and chasing them, the Comanche. It attracted the frontiersman with his cattle and helped him build them into great herds.

But for thirty years more, Mustang Pond and Mustang Draw would remain one of the centers of Comanche activity, a locale from which they planned their raids on Mexico or against Texas settlements.

[37] Sen. Ex. Doc. No. 64, 31st Congress, 1st Session, *Reconnaissances of Routes from San Antonio to El Paso*, pp. 224–226.

COWBOY

→

Perhaps no one in history has been more falsified and romantically distorted than the cowboy. The legend transforms him from a working individual with a highly specialized know-how into a character of many shades.

The frontiersman developed a character rooted in the land and shaped by danger and hardship.

These virile qualities were demanded by the very nature of the West, by its silences and isolation, its ascetic expanses. It sickened weaker natures and drove them to softer and more hospitable sections. An elemental land demanded masculinity.

The land itself developed the unique breed — the cowboy, or perhaps more to the point, the Westerner.

Many a youngster, fired by the fiction about the plains, came West with hope of high adventure.

He found that instead of loafing around "cowtowns" with his six-guns, ready to rescue a lady or drive out the "bad guys," the working cowboy had no time for such things. He found no pistols, no fast draws. He learned that he might be laughed out of camp if he practiced such "silliness."

He did find other skills — more prosaic and useful, such as repairing windmills, staying in the saddle of a fractious horse at dawn on a winter's morning, breaking ice on tanks, repairing fences, riding bog and rounding up cattle smoothly and easily.

The cowboy had to learn to take his pleasures and joys in his work — in the silences and solitude, in careful and patient labor with livestock, in sheer affection for his horses and the land.

Yet, when a man became accustomed to the cowboy's life, he found great compensations. The very silence itself grew important. His life was free to a large extent. The cowboy, if conscientious, was his own boss. Oden characterized the cowboy in this manner:

They (the cowboys) got their education from the school of hard knocks. Some of them couldn't write their names so anyone could read them but the teller at the bank, but their checks were good for any amount they cared to write out. They were practically all men . . . who came along about Civil War time when there were very few schools. Therefore, they had very little book learning. They were men who were not content to spend their lives in sight of the parental roof. Early in life they had drifted West when the West was young, where they had ample time to commune with their thoughts while riding the hurricane deck of a Spanish pony over wide open spaces, or sleeping in their saddle blankets with a saddle for a pillow and nothing but the broad canopy of heaven above. No wonder they grew to manhood with an iron constitution and many of them with judgment equal to that of some of our best statesmen . . . often the cowboys would stay on the ranch for six, eight or ten months riding lines, fixing windmills, sometimes working eighteen of the twenty-four hours. Often they lived more than a hundred miles out of town; so no one questioned their right to a hilarious time when they finally did come in.[1]

A man was not a cowboy merely because he wore jeans and boots and spurs and handled stock. No, the standards were higher. Only the man proficient in all aspects of the business — a good roper, horseman and cattle-handler — was a cowboy. In order fully to qualify, he must have certain other qualities. A show-off never quite made the grade. Neither did the sluggard who failed to do his share of the work and a bit more. The man who "did not get along" with the others was viewed dimly. A cowboy who could not handle men, presumably, could not handle stock.

A subtle honor code governed the elite. A man did what was needed, without being asked. He handled other cowboys with discretion and had to know them a long time before asking a personal question. In the "profession," there was a feeling of brotherhood. A man assisted his neighbor when possible and never kept books on it. A cowboy never said "no" to a man in need except when it would jeopardize the stock under his care.

[1] Oden, Bill, *Reminiscences* — Johnston, Sue Mildred, Master's Thesis, Sul Ross State Teachers College, August 1940 (unpublished.)

Many men came and went in the "cowboying" business, because they found it less glamorous than they had imagined.

Oden tells this pertinent story. When he was foreman of the M Ranch, owned by Crowley, Bishop and Company, and managed by A. F. Crowley of Midland, he was bringing a thousand head of steers and cows to Midland from a Dawson County ranch. A heavy snow forced him to take refuge in a Dawson County bunkhouse where for three weeks he and his men waited, squatting on their heels around the little sheet-iron stove. When the sun finally came out and melted the snow, the men gathered up their scattered herd and resumed the trail to Midland. They were well on the way when a cold dry norther struck.

The cowboys worked valiantly to hold the herd, but no steer could face that storm. The riders' legs were stiff beneath their leather chaps and their fingers so frozen they had scarcely enough feeling to hold the bridle. One man sighted the barbed wire fence of a large horse corral. The cowboys maneuvered the herd into the enclosure and then turned back to search for the ranch house.

The next morning, a puncher, his fingers and ears frozen black, came in to Oden. "I'm through," he announced. "You can get them cows home any way you want to but I'm through. This cowpunching business ain't what it's cracked up to be. I'm going back home to Ma and the farm." [2]

Pictured as either a knight or the most worthless of men, the only time the cowboy appeared pathetic was when he sought to defend himself against either of these extreme portraits. Then, he stoutly maintained he was nothing but an ordinary man, doing an ordinary job.

A more typical attitude has been complete indifference to the opinions of others.

The cowboy of the 1880's and 1890's, and this has scarcely changed today, received the "knight in shining armor" title because of his attitude toward women. His language was his own on the range or among other cowboys, and it could rise to heights when he faced a stubborn steer or a bronc mount. But in the presence of women not one off-color expression was permissible. If a cowboy swore in the hearing of a lady, he had better leave the country.

[2] *Ibid.*

T. O. Woody tells of the time when a cowboy rode up to a ranch house after having spent fourteen hours in the saddle. He was so saddle stiff he could hardly dismount. The woman of the house came to the door and said cordially:

"Get down and rest your saddle for a while."

The cowboy "before he even thought" replied, "Thank you, ma'am, but it's not my saddle that needs resting." [3]

This was considered very near the pale.

A modified form of trail driving continued in the country long after the railroads made the longer drives unnecessary. Ranchers moved herds from one section of the range to another, or from one ranch to another. These drives might take several days.

Each cowboy took a pack consisting of three suggans (thin comforters or quilts) rolled up in a tarp. Two suggans were to sleep on, and one to sleep under. In a flour sack he carried two changes of clothing which, with the one he wore, made three; a carton of Bull Durham tobacco or plug tobacco. Not until the First World War did anyone hear of cowboys carrying toothbrushes. They brought coffee, bacon, beans and flour, a frying pan and a Dutch oven. After the 1890's few bothered to carry a gun. [4]

The drive was adjusted to the habits of the cattle. Since beef sold by the pound, the chief consideration was to avoid walking off valuable poundage. The cattle grazed from early morning until shortly before noon when they began to seek water. The cowboys simply looseherded the animals and allowed them to graze in the direction desired. In this manner, they covered around twelve miles a day, going from watering to watering. Cattle do not lose weight when handled in this manner. They even can gain weight on the trail if pasturage is adequate. Cattle water once a day, and good waterings were located every ten or twelve miles.

The cattle were bedded down at night in the smallest possible area. They lay still until about midnight, when they got up and milled around. At this time the night riders were important, as the stock might wander away and graze if not controlled. The cattle soon became quiet again, and would lie back down and remain still for the rest of the night.

[3] T. O. Woody to Griffin, Nov., 1958.
[4] T. O. Woody and Flop Roberts Interviews, 1958.

Breakfast came before dawn. Dinner was at noon if it was convenient to stop — but the cattle came first. The men ate whenever the herd was quiet and could be managed by a skeleton guard. Supper was at sundown or as soon after sundown as possible.

Each cowboy on a long drive mounted eight to twelve horses — he used two for cutting, one for a night horse and two for evening horses. The night horses were so well trained that if a cow began to move away from the herd they would notice it and quickly turn it back. If the cowboy were dozing, he stood a good chance of being unseated. The horses usually watered three times a day. As soon as a cowboy "unrode" a horse, he led him to water. The horse would roll in the sand and then drink.

After supper, usually in twilight or early dark, the cowboy hoisted his bedroll on his shoulder and struck out to find a smooth place to sleep.

He unrolled the bed with the foot to the wind, so the tarp, which was tucked under the foot-end and loose at the top-end, could not blow away.

Undressing, he put his clothes under the tarp to protect them from the dew and also to protect them from the coyotes, which would eat anything leather including chaps or boots. A cowboy usually slept in his underwear. The last items of clothing removed were boots and hat. He put his boots on the hat to keep it from blowing away.

In the morning he dressed in reverse style, putting on his hat first, and then his boots and finally his clothing.

After a big rain, when the clothing and bedding had been soaked, the cowboy, as soon as the sun came out, unpacked all the wet items and draped them over mesquite bushes to dry.

On longer drives or on lengthy roundups where the chuck wagon accompanied the men, they piled their bedrolls into the wagon along with other supplies.

The chuck wagon was constructed for its special purpose. It had a long deep body covered by bows and a wagon sheet. A chuck box at the rear end contained shelves and bins for supplies, with a door letting down from the top to make a cooking table. A water keg was attached to each side of the wagon. Standard equipment consisted of two grubbing axes, two spades, a small sledge hammer to drive stakes for the rope corral and a sheet with poles to protect the chuck box and fire if it rained while the cook was preparing meals. Of cooking utensils, the wagon carried two large Dutch ovens for baking bread, two iron pots for cooking stews, two pots for heating water and making coffee, and two large frying pans for frying bacon and steaks. Enough tin plates and cups were brought along to furnish a set for each man in the outfit.

The wagon was loaded with more food supplies than needed. Bacon, lard, sugar, salt, coffee, prunes, potatoes and syrup were staple.[5]

The cook and horse wrangler worked together in locating the wagon camps, and gathering fuel for cooking and branding. On the plains, this fuel usually consisted of cow chips, sometimes called buffalo coal or prairie coal.

When the cook and wrangler had located a site to camp, they unloaded the cooking equipment, dug the pit for burning the coals and took the wagon mules to water.

The cowboys never touched anything around the chuck wagon except their bedrolls. The cook was the master of his wagon. With a few notable exceptions, he was also one of the longest-suffering humans ever to function on the western range. He generally provided good meals since most of the ranchers permitted their hands to kill beef as often as needed, and to take the finest from the herds. But he appears to have been unable to satisfy the tastes of the cowboys. He was also generally sensitive to slurs against his offering. It is traditional for the cowboy never to express his satisfaction over a meal, or if he did, to understate it in such language as to outrage the cook.

Every cowboy knew how to cook the traditional cowboy meals of beans and bacon, beef cuts, son-of-a-gun and the inevitable and delicious sourdough biscuits. Therefore, every cowboy had a connoisseur's tastes where these items were concerned. When a cook had worked hours to make a good son-of-a-gun, rich and savory, a cowboy's remark that he liked his with more liver was not welcome.

But if the cowboys seldom expressed their appreciation within cook's hearing, they later recalled chuck meals with glowing praise.

[5] W. S. Willis, former cowboy for C. C. Slaughter, Interviews, 1958.

The western range provided a few first class recipes. Son-of-a-gun, which some hold in contempt, was a masterpiece of ranch cookery, and after a long day's work in the open air, when a cowboy was hungry, nothing tasted more delicious or richer than this dish.[6]

Another staple was sourdough bread or biscuits, certainly one of the world's great breads.[7]

When on the trail, the beef was killed in the evening and hung out overnight. At dawn, before the sun got to it, it was wrapped in a good tarp or slicker and hung under the wagon, where it would

[6] They made son-of-a-gun in this manner: Out of a 500-pound calf, which dresses out at about 250 pounds, the cook saved all the sweetbreads he could get and all the marrowgut, cut in pieces one inch long, and all the brains. He cubed about one half of the heart and two pounds of liver into half-inch pieces and added two pounds of chopped round steak. He put this into a pot, added enough water to cover, seasoned it with salt and a heavy sprinkling of pepper and cooked slowly for four to six hours. Some thickened it slightly with a pinch of flour. Although some people are prejudiced against a dish prepared from such ingredients, son-of-a-gun remains one of the favored dishes of the older cattlemen and cowboys. And whenever it is prepared by a rancher like Roy Parks, who provided the above recipe, or his wife, or Mrs. Flop Roberts, it is a topic of conversation among the old-timers for days. (Courtesy Miss Ted Dickerson, Midland, Texas.)

[7] The most important item in making and keeping sourdough going was a proper container for the starter. The best was an earthenware jar with a good lid, close-fitting but not airtight. A tinned container will cause the souring dough to form a poison.

The starter is the portion that is kept going, sometimes for years. It is made by dissolving a cake of yeast in two pints of warm water, adding two tablespoons of sugar and two pints of flour which is mixed in the crock. It is then left to rise until the starter is light and slightly aged, from 24 to 48 hours, without letting it get too sour or chilled.

To make the bread or biscuits, the cook sifted out a pan of flour, made a hollow in the top and poured approximately two cups of the starter into the hollow. Over this sponge he sprinkled a half teaspoon of salt, a tablespoon of sugar and two heaping teaspoons of baking powder. He would mix it well to a soft, firm dough and turn out on a lightly-floured board. Then, probably using a whiskey bottle for a rolling pin, or else patting the dough out with his hands to a thickness of about a half an inch, he cut the biscuits using a cheap cutter or an empty small baking powder can and put them into well-greased pans.

He set them in a warm place to rise for about five minutes and then baked them in a hot oven, about 500 degrees for 10 to 12 minutes until browned. The heat of the oven was important, though he often baked them successfully enough in a Dutch oven buried in the coals.

To keep the starter going, he added a cup of warm water to the crock and mixed in enough flour to give it the consistency of the first starter. He never added yeast again, unless, through disuse, the starter grew old and died. If it turned sour on him, he added a pinch of soda dissolved in warm water along with the baking powder. The first biscuits from a new batch of starter were never as good as those made later, since the starter improves with age. (Courtesy Miss Ted Dickerson, Midland, Texas.)

keep for several days. Butchering was done on the trail whenever meat was needed, and except for the portions saved for son-of-a-gun, and the actual meat, everything else, including the hide, was thrown away.[8]

II

During the winter some of the boys went to their homes and some to ranch headquarters to work on the corrals, fences and buildings, to break horses and repair gear. Others were sent to isolated line camps to look after windmills, ride fences and to cut ice when the stock tanks froze.

For months a cowboy in one of these line camps saw no one except the man who drove the supply wagon around once or twice a month to replenish his stock of tinned goods, tobacco and horse feed.

Line camps at the turn of the century were primitive. Constructed of wood, they consisted of one or two rooms about ten by twelve feet each. They had shingle roofs and plank flooring, and were raised off the ground on a foundation of stacked stones or posts so the area beneath remained open. They usually had two windows and a door. Furnishings were bunk beds, a table, a few boxes for chairs and a sheet-iron "bachelor's stove." Supplies of tinned foods and tow sacks of oats and chops for the horses were stacked along the wall. The most used items, such as salt, pepper and tobacco were placed on shelves made by nailing a box to the wall. Cooking utensils, a keg for water and a washtub for both laundry and bathing were standard. A woodbox was kept full of "prairie coal" and whatever roots or wood fragments could be found.[9]

In this camp, windswept and isolated, the cowboy spent his winter alone. It was his job to look after the fences, windmill waterings and cattle in his territory.

One of the old-time cowboys, W. S. Willis, recalls that for days he did not speak, did not hear any sound except the wind and

[8] T. O. Woody and Flop Roberts Interviews, 1958.
[9] W. S. Willis, Interviews, 1959.

his footsteps on the plank floor. Occasionally he would talk to his horse just to make sure he could still speak.[10]

On cold winter mornings, the cowboy awoke and hurried from his bunk to fire up the stove and make coffee. He dressed, poured cold water in a pan and washed his face. After smoking a cigarette and drinking a first cup of coffee he planned supper. If he were going to have beans, he put them in a pot with some water and dry salt pork and set them on the stove to simmer all day.

He put on gloves and his heaviest jacket and went outdoors to catch the horse he would use that day. He saddled up and rode off slowly, to give the horse's muscles time to loosen and warm.

At the waterings, he checked to make certain the windmills were working and broke ice from the tank so cattle could drink. He rode the fences and made repairs. At noon, if he were too distant from his shack, he ate jerky or a sandwich he might have brought with him. The jerky, which was thin strips of raw meat dried in the sun, took a long time to chew, but it was nutritious and palatable.

In the evening he gave the horse its head and returned to camp.

He dismounted, pulled off the saddle and dumped it inside the door. Then he fed the horse some oats or chops, put the hobbles on and with a slap on its rump, sent it to graze.

He did his outside chores, gathered in prairie coal and water.

The cowboy butchered his own beef, dressed it out and hung it on the struts of the windmill beyond the reach of coyotes or lobo wolves. If he wanted beef for supper, he went to the windmill and cut off what he needed.

As an evening cold settled he finished and was ready to go indoors. He stepped up into the doorway and inside, closing the door behind him. The wind had subsided, making the room quieter. In the pale light, he saw the cabin as he had left it that morning, the boxes, the bunk, the stove and the tinned goods and tow sacks. Odors of cooking beans, oats and planking mingled.

He fired the stove again and lighted a kerosene lamp. He put water on the stove for coffee and for shaving, if it were his day to shave. And he straightened the room, for he early learned that if a cowboy didn't keep neat quarters, the solitude was demoralizing.[11]

10 *Ibid.*
11 W. S. Willis, Interviews, 1959.

Too, it provided welcome activity, as did the cooking, shaving and bathing when he had nothing else to occupy the long hours.

The sound of percolating coffee and water enlivened the atmosphere. He peeled a couple of potatoes, and fried them. Then he began frying his beef, and fixing his biscuits. Finally, he warmed a can of tomatoes and filled his plate. He carried it to the table, pulled up a box to sit on, and placed the lantern nearby. He ate his solitary meal of beef, beans, french fries, tomatoes and biscuits, washing them down with smoking coffee from a tin cup.

After supper, with the cabin warming and the night turning black outside, the cowboy washed dishes and put things in their places. He left the bean pot on the stove to be heated again and again until empty.

If he had laundry to do, he brought the washtub, scrubbed his clothes and hung them over the boxes and table edge near the stove to dry quickly. He probably bathed at the same time and drew on clean underwear.

When all this was done, the weary cowboy might sit at his table, with the lantern close by, and read. If not, he listened to the silences and the fire until he grew drowsy. He blew out the lantern, crawled into his bunk, pulled the wool blankets or suggans close around him and slept. Tomorrow would begin another round of the same.

If the tedium of this almost hermit-like existence is obvious, the compensations were there, nevertheless.

The nature of the life, without communication, without diversion, demanded that the cowboy develop the patience to value what he could not alter. The silence, loneliness and simplicity of life kept him close to reality and gave him ample time to think. He had to face himself and find peace with himself. Many grew to love the solitude, the silence, the closeness to nature.

At least one of the compensations was certain. Some morning the cowboy would step out and feel a softness in the air. Almost overnight grass would green around the stock tanks. Calves, antelope fawns and colts would show up on the prairies. Unseen meadowlarks would send up their warblings. His horse would grow frisky beneath him and he would sense the regeneration of spring with a delight few could know in such depth.

*

III

In our days humor is kept alive largely by professional entertainers. In the early West, a man's wit was a valued part of his equipment, a measure of his intelligence, and it was considered an art to develop and polish.

The pace of the West permitted a man to spend hours in perfecting the details of a hoax.

The Westerner who had mastered the art of making comedy a part of his day-to-day life was prized. And since all were more or less proficient, those who excelled became legendary. A humorist of the caliber of Will Rogers, for example, had his greatest triumphs among his own people. Long before he became an international star he had created an enviable reputation as a wit while cowboying for Charles Goodnight in Texas.

Nearly everyone knew everyone else. The account of some amusing incident or "wisecrack" covered the distances between camps with remarkable speed.

Such humor was divided into two classes — the impromptu retort or quip, and the practical joke. It required that the perpetrator be what they themselves termed a good "actor." Acting in this sense usually meant underacting. A man was less than an artist if he did not have what vaudevillians call a deadpan.

T. O. Woody, an old time Matador cowboy who until his retirement worked for Clarence Scharbauer, Jr., tells about a cowboy who had stood night watch and was trying to snatch sleep under the chuck wagon the next day. Flies swarmed about. In his half sleep he unconsciously brushed them off. Suddenly a bumble bee flew under the wagon and the cowboys came to watch as it buzzed close to their dozing companion. It settled on his hip and dug in its stinger. The cowboy grunted, brushed it off and turned sleepily on his other side, mumbling, "Well, there's got to be one smart aleck in every crowd, I guess."

The cowboy hates the caricature of himself found in the dime novels and most movies. Nothing irritates him more than to see a cowboy behave in the manner of his caricature — to be loud, blustery, overbearing, to carry guns and to get tanked in saloons or to make a spectacle of himself. Woody tells a story of a former Texas cowboy who retired to become a bartender in a small New Mexico town.

A swaggering cowboy, wearing guns, and about half-drunk, came into the bar.

"Give me a drink — I'm a low-down dog from Texas!" he bellowed.

The elderly bartender feigned an amiable smile and replied heartily, "Yes sir! I knew you was a low-down dog, but I didn't know what state you was from."

Of the contrived incidents none was more popular in its day than the badger game practiced throughout Texas in the 1880's and 1890's.

During winter months in town, with little to do except talk cows and "spread the bull," a group of men organized the Midland Badger Club. Uncle John Scharbauer was President. Taylor Brown, George Elliott and Jim Flannagan held lesser offices. This club under the imaginative leadership of Uncle John was reputed to be the most successful in existence. Every newcomer in town was a prospective victim. He may have seen badger fights in kind, but the Midland affair was so well organized and made such a lavish display of money that he would believe it to be a real fight between the dog and the badger.

> When word went around that a badger fight was to be staged, storekeepers and clerks walked away from counters; barkeepers stepped out of their white aprons, leaving an open bottle of whiskey on the bar; bank tellers walked off without locking their cash tills, and the gambler left his chips piled on the table — all because Uncle John Scharbauer, the President of the Club, happened to stroll along and hint that a badger account was about to take place.[12]

These gatherings took place at the rear of C. D. McCormick's livery stable. There the boys formed a ring, laughing, betting and joking. Among those who were always present was Henry Rohlfing, a good-natured German who ran the local confectionery store. His robust laughter and "by chimeney crackey" never failed to add to the merriment.[13]

[12] Oden, *op. cit.*
[13] *Ibid.*

One of the best sports ever to be victimized by the game was Charlie Watson, who came to Midland from Arkansas to begin publishing the local newspaper, *The Midland Livestock Reporter*.

In the first issue of this newspaper, young Watson announced that he had come to West Texas to make a permanent home, and was anxious to cooperate in every way with his good neighbors.

Uncle John Scharbauer read the young editor's message. He hurried to the editorial office and announced that one of his cowboys had just caught an unusually fine, vigorous yellow badger out on the WLS Ranch and that he was betting a hundred dollars the badger could whip any dog in town. He told Watson the fight would be held the following day at three o'clock.

Scharbauer thought it would be a nice gesture if the young editor reported the fight. The following afternoon, with the women excluded, a large crowd gathered. With money in their hands, they passed back and forth apparently betting lavishly. The hour approached for the fight to begin. Attention turned to the barrel under which the badger was supposedly imprisoned. Pat Murphy furnished the fighting dog, which was trained to growl and lunge against its chain.

Uncle John, mounted on the tongue of a wagon above the crowd, called to several well-known citizens, requesting each in turn to "pull the badger."

Each refused, giving as his reason that he had bet money on either the dog or the badger. Charlie Watson, it soon became known, was the only man present who had not bet on the fight. As the only impartial spectator it was decided Watson should draw the badger from his box. Uncle John gave him his last minute instructions.

"Sir, you have been elected to play this important role in the contest because it is clear that you are a man of exemplary habits, as is attested by the fact that you have not wagered a penny on the fight about to take place. Only a man of high ideals — a gentleman in every sense of the word — would be so restrained under existing circumstances. As a token then of local esteem, we invite you to pull the badger from his box." [14]

Confused but with good will, Charlie accepted. They handed him a rope which disappeared under the barrel.

[14] *Ibid.*

Uncle John continued in his most oratorical manner:

"However, with all your fine integrity of character, you are but a newcomer among us and so it will be necessary to instruct you how you should conduct this contest in order to guarantee fair play to both contestants. It is understood that the badger must be drawn from his refuge by exactly three jerks, and no more. First, there must be a hard tug. Second, another tug as easy as possible. And third, a jerk of medium strength, but delicately calculated to place the animal face to face with its opponent." [15]

The deadpan prevailed. Young Watson concentrated on the instructions. Then Uncle John gently suggested that the young man mount the wagon where he would be out of danger of a possible attack from the badger. This was done so the crowd could get a better view of him.

Henry Rohlfing shouted out his "by chimeney crackey," and added "De poy understands. Let de fight pegin." [16]

The crowd roared "Pull!" Excited by the shouting, the young editor jerked the rope with all his strength and the "badger" in the form of a chamber pot rolled completely beneath the wagon on which he stood.

Watson took it good-naturedly. As was the custom, he bought drinks for the crowd.

After each such session, Uncle John Scharbauer, consistent in his role of impresario, would hurry over to the Western Union office to wire his "connections" that the Midland Badger Club had had a very successful fight, "and your honorable representative pulled the bell cord." [17]

The following day Charlie Watson included in the columns of his *Midland Livestock Reporter* an article stating that undoubtedly now the editor was a "full-fledged West Texan," as on the previous day he had been initiated into the mystic shrine of the Midland Badger Club.

Again Uncle John Scharbauer saw the writeup and his fertile imagination took hold.

He dropped into the office of the *Livestock Reporter* and casu-

[15] *Ibid.*
[16] *Ibid.*
[17] *Ibid.*

ally announced that "the boys" had found another victim for the badger game and would Charlie kindly hold the dog. Charlie, flattered to be considered one of the initiated, gladly consented.

The next day, when the crowd had once again gathered and were putting on the show for the supposed new victim, this latter turned wide-eyed to Charlie and asked him if he had a good hold on the dog.

"Sure, I've got him," Charlie said encouragingly.

"Then keep him," replied the other, tossing aside the badger rope. "Keep him 'til suppertime."

Once again Watson heard the explosive "By chimeney crackey" and realized he had been duped a second time. And again he bought drinks for the crowd.[18]

In the next issue of his paper, Watson wrote: "If there is a third part to this badger game, somebody please tell me ahead of time, as my funds are running low."

The victims of this game were not always as sporting as Watson however, to the general delight of all assembled; for if a man were a poor sport, the ragging continued in one form or another.

One man, educated but with a poor sense of horseplay, went into a blue rage and shouted, "To think that I finished my education in Europe, and then had to come to Texas to be made a fool of by a lot of damned ignorant cowboys." [19]

Humor was involved in most aspects of living and the man who could turn an ordinary situation into one with humorous overtones had adopted the ways of the West. Frank Tolbert tells the story of wealthy rancher John Gist's first visit to his new sister-in-law. He showed up at the ranch poorly dressed and assumed a beggar's mien to ask for a handout. Not suspecting, the bride invited the wretch in and fed him. Not until her husband arrived and found "Uncle John" sitting in the kitchen drinking coffee did the lady realize she had been spoofed.

The condition of the Westerner has changed, and therefore his humor has changed. It has, in fact, become less necessary and is certainly less an art.

The old cow campshack is now frequently a fine home with all

18 *Ibid.*
19 *Ibid.*

conveniences. The cowboy of today is often married and may live in town and commute to his work in a car. With radio, TV and newspapers he no longer needs to create his own entertainment. Today's cowboy retains all the traditions of yesterday's except the cultivation of humor, which is no longer necessary or greatly valued.

THE LOVE LETTERS
OF BESSIE LOVE

⸺⸺⸺⸺⸺⸺⸺⸺⸺⸺⸺⸺⸺→

In winter, when the dusk came early over the barren, wind-swept plains, the cowboys had little to do except huddle around the sheet-iron stove in their isolated bunk houses.

The monotony of these long evenings frequently led men to speculate on the most complex hoaxes imaginable, and to work them out with the greatest finesse of detail.

One such incident was born under these circumstances. Bill Oden, a pioneer Midland cowboy, recalls that dark winter day when one of the cowboys returned from a distant town with a matrimonial newspaper in his hip pocket.

Reading material of any kind was scarce on the range, and that evening the paper was passed around.

Before long, the men had spread the newspaper out on the pine table. From its columns they selected a man who was to figure as the hero of one of the tenderest romances of the plains. The advertiser they chose had the unlikely name of Josh Bantz. He appeared to be fortyish and gave an address in East Texas — far enough away for the cowboys to feel safe.

J. W. Johnson, who had the best penmanship of anyone in the group, was chosen to write the letters. In an atmosphere of grave hilarity, the group turned the full play of their fertile imaginations to the task of providing an answer to Mr. Josh Bantz's loneliness. Rough, unshaven cowboys with plugs of tobacco in their jaws gathered around the kerosene lamp and created certainly one of the most exquisite creatures in the West — "Bessie Love, fairest flower of the cattle country."

The letter began coyly, as was customary from a proper young lady:

Dear Mr. Bantz:
Or perhaps I am too forward in calling you *dear* since I only know

you through your advertisement in the *Do Not Be A Lonely Heart Register*.

Bessie went on to say that she feared she was "Born to blush unseen, and waste her fragrance on the desert air."

Bessie Love came to life that freezing night in a shabby wooden bunk house far out on the plains. The lamp burned late. To her correspondent, however, she described her way of life and her home in plaintive terms indeed.

> Our home, [she said] is large and spacious. Dark-skinned Mexican servants tread the halls with silent feet. My father wears boots though. Outside my window nestling in the mesquite, a nightingale pours its heart out in liquid sweetness to the moon. Or maybe it's a parakeet. I can't tell the difference from where I am seated at the beautiful ancestral mahogany desk on which I write. Beyond the nightingale or parakeet, lie the lonely hills — "cattle and horses on a thousand hills" — all my father's ranch. But not a single man anywhere. Can you blame me for being lonesome? Me, an only child, with nothing but immense wealth to look forward to and not a single person to whom I can unburden my heart, who will love me until death.
>
> With love and best wishes,
BESSIE LOVE

Certainly the elegances of this letter and the skill of the cowboys in composing it are self-evident. They mailed it out as soon as they could send someone the considerable distance into town. And then they discussed it endlessly, wondering if, despite Bessie Love's reticences, it were not still too forward to be convincing, wondering in a word if Mr. Josh Bantz would swallow the bait.

A few days later the cowboys heard a shout in the distance. They looked up to see Pat McCullum riding in under snow-heavy skies. He waved a white envelope back and forth over his head. Josh Bantz had answered by return mail.

The men crowded around the table in the bunk house once again. In a crude but careful script on cheap notebook paper Josh Bantz had written the way he must have talked:

> I allow I understand the heart of any gal. Listening to nightingales and them skeets is about as lonesome as having to sit in a boiler

room with nothing but screech owls for company. That's what
I do, and I surely do sympathize with you. A man's voice — that
is some other man besides your father — ought to be a downright
comfort to you under such circumstances.

Bantz then explained that he had a job tending engines in a lumber camp. He concluded:

One thing is sure if I was around, you wouldn't have to waste your
time listening to no bird talk, because I got a feeling although I
never had the pleasure of setting eyes on your face, that you sure
are the little gal I love.
  Please write me soon, I'll be looking to see if the mail carrier is
going to stop.

> Respt. and truly yours
> JOSH BANTZ

The windows darkened and the men looked out to see snow falling heavily. The weather meant extra chores that afternoon, but
the men fell to them with a new spirit in anticipation of the evening
when they would compose another letter from Bessie Love to her
admirer. A group of half-starved yearlings were rounded in for
special feeding. They tossed hay to cattle that would not be able
to forage through the freezing ground cover of snow. They rode
through the flanking snow to break ice at the various cattle waterings.
  But always they would be back in the bunk house by nightfall.
They warmed their cold-reddened hands and lifted their feet close
to the stove to dry out their soggy boots. With the fall of darkness,
the snow drifted down thickly, enclosing them in the lamp-lit room
against the night and the open spaces and the occasional muffled
bawling of an uncomfortable cow.
  Once again Johnson seated himself at the pine table and waited
for suggestions. "What will little Bessie say tonight?" he asked.
  In this letter, Bessie Love told Mr. Bantz that his letter had deeply
impressed her, but she feared he might not really love her since he
had never seen her photograph. She informed him that her father
owned all the cattle west of the Pecos, and shipped them by the
double trainloads.
  In the answer, which Bantz sent back by return mail, he assured
her of his undying love, and suggested it might be "real handy for

your Pa to have an extra man around to help load them cattle." He signed it "Dvt. yours forever," and added a column of x's.

The correspondence continued with rapid exchanges between Bessie and Josh. As the boiler tender became more ardent, Bessie became more coy, more doubtful, more maidenly. She was afraid he might not really love her as she needed to be loved; or that loving her for a time, his affections might languish and he wouldn't love her "forever and forever and forever and ever and ever." This would break her heart.

Josh answered reassuring her that his love would flow just as long as the old Red River.

Bessie told him she remembered reading where during a dry spell the year before the Red River had dried up enough to permit a wagon and team to be driven across it. This made her fearful.

One of the cowboys produced a photo of a pretty girl from his suitcase, and they sent this along to Bantz with a note:

Enclosed is a portrait you must study carefully, for the man I choose will have to promise to enshrine my likeness in his heart forever and forever and forever and ever and ever.

Josh, in his turn, at Bessie's request, sent her a faded brown picture of himself of the type so popular in that early day. Bessie wrote immediately telling him of her disappointment. How, she asked, could he torment her with such a small, indistinct portrait? How could she give a definite answer to his urgings unless she obtained a larger, clearer photo? — one large enough to reveal the lines of character in his countenance. She explained she must be terribly sure before she confided her fate into the hands of any man. Certainly, she had no doubt that he could measure up to all of her ideals of manhood, so he must not feel too bad, the only thing necessary was to send a larger, clearer photo.

Mr. Bantz sent the larger photo as quickly as possible. On the back he wrote:

To the one and only girl in the world for me.
YOUR JOSHUA

Bessie was still not satisfied. This was a better picture of course, but it was not enough. She wrote:

Darling, I want a life-sized portrait of your dear self so that before I say the final word, I may have a more perfect idea of your size and person. I never wanted to marry a skinny man, nor one that is too fat.

Within a few days, Bill Oden drove in with an enormous package in the wagonbed behind him.

Oden hurriedly unwrapped the photo and gazed upon Josh life-size. The hefty lover had been artfully posed in what was supposed to be an attitude of manly ease, leaning far forward and prevented from falling on his face only by the elegance of an umbrella which he held in both hands, the tip of which formed a triangle away from his slanted body. He stared full-faced into the camera, and had been caught in an unfortunate moment, since his face bore a look of both horror and dullness, as he apparently tried to look like the responsible, serious, sincere person he undoubtedly was.

Oden hurriedly placed the photograph in the center of the pine table, standing it against an empty pickle jar where the cowboys could not fail to see it as they entered the bunk house. He highlighted it by placing a glowing kerosene lamp nearby.

Pat McCullum had been grouchy all day with a severe toothache. When he entered the room and saw the picture, he forgot his troubles. He gazed fixedly at it for a moment and then turned and ran out to the corral. In a moment he went back with a handful of dried alfalfa.

"A bouquet for the groom," he shouted and stuffed the hay into the empty pickle jar.

The reaction of the others is indicated by the fact they could not write a letter that night. Johnson said he had been laughing so hard, his handwriting would look as though he had been "took down with St. Vitus Dance."

The cattlemen's convention was scheduled to be held in El Paso that spring. Since most of the men were going for a day or two, they decided to take Bessie along with them. Then, as Johnson suggested, "Maybe she'd have something to talk about besides just repeating 'Love me forever and forever and forever and ever and ever.'"

So Johnson wrote that she and her dad would be going to the

convention and that they would have rooms at the Sheldon Hotel.

Pat McCullum dictated: "Tell him her curly locks will be done in 'rats and pompadours.' She'll wear a long skirt and bustles for the first time to the Cattlemen's Ball, and her only sorrow is that her young, palpitating heart will keep repeating: 'Oh, for the touch of a vanished hand and the sound of a voice that is still.' — meaning she wishes Josh was along."

Josh's reply threw new problems in the cowboys' laps. Johnson picked the letter up and spread it around camp. It read:

> You can shore count on me being in El Paso to see you. I've been working steady all winter feeding this old boiler and so I'll have plenty of money to show my honey gal a mighty good time.

A joke was a joke but now it had to be stopped. They could not let the man spend his hard-earned money on a fruitless trip to El Paso. The romance had to be ended, and quickly. But how?

Before they could come to any decision, Pat McCullum rode in and announced, "It's all over boys, I sent a telegram." He produced and read a copy of the telegram:

> OLD SWEETHEART JUST RETURNED FROM SOUTH AMERICA. WE WERE MARRIED TODAY, BUT I'LL NEVER FORGET YOU.
>
> BESSIE LOVE

The final letter from East Texas was not in Josh's handwriting. For a moment it gave the cowboys a scare, since they thought immediately that Bantz had probably committed suicide. The letter read:

> Miss Love —
> What does any girl mean by treating Josh Bantz the way you did? If you don't love him what about the things he sent you? The pictures, I mean?
> Poor Josh! It would crush the heart of a mill-wheel to see him. He had his grip all packed to start to El Paso when your telegram came in. He never told me what you said, but he hasn't written since.
>
> Josh Bantz best friend
> WHITTIER GREEN
>
> P.S. Please don't forget to send the pictures.

Relieved at the undertone of the letter, they returned the pictures by boring a hole in the corner of each photograph, tying a six-inch cord through this and attaching a tag labeled:

From:

    Bessie Adams nee Love

    ——————, Texas

To:

    Mr. Josh Bantz

    ———, Texas

The cowboys assuaged their consciences by observing that perhaps they had done Bantz a favor after all. At least this would teach him not to advertise in the newspaper for a love interest. Yes, they had undoubtedly saved him from the clutches of one who might be less the pure maiden than Bessie Love, with all her faults, had certainly been.

PART VI

The Salt

Notes by the Editor
Journal Entries
Photographs

"One feature of the devil's banquet
is a complete absence of salt."

—Heinrich Heine
Doktor Faust: A Dance Poem

BECAUSE OF HIS CLOSE FRIENDSHIP

TO MANY OF THE PEOPLE SHOWN ON

THESE PAGES, *The Salt* IS DEDICATED,

WITH GRATITUDE AND AFFECTION,

TO

JACQUES MARITAIN

Notes

SOME YEARS ago, Maxwell Geismar, writing about John Howard Griffin's novels in *The Nation*, remarked that Griffin wrote as though literary canons simply did not exist.

The same might be said about Griffin's work in photography. Although photography has been one of the great passions of Griffin's life, he has pursued it in a solitary way, apart from the general mainstream.

His journals are filled with allusions to photographic problems over the past twenty-five years:

> It is another attempt, the same as writing, to penetrate the great welter of accidents that surround all objects and to get to the essences. I have no interest in the dramatic moment, but seek the moment that reveals the essential truths of an object or individual. This is not simple. It is a matter of struggling to perceive what might be, what is there to be discovered, of seeking, seeking always to get what is there. And it is a matter of accepting, too, the fact that one works with optics which see without partiality, sometimes cruelly what the eye, tied in with the whole affective nature, often sees differently. There are no Dorian Grays where fine lenses are concerned, and since I will never retouch, I destroy too-revealing negatives, ones that clearly reveal recesses for which the eye might compensate. To dredge men's recesses is not interesting. What is interesting is to find truths in them that can never be simulated — which means finally to find what is authentically human in the human visage.

This search has led Griffin to photograph many world-renowned figures, not because they are world-renowned but because so many people with the kinds of faces he seeks — artists, philosophers, saints, scholars — happen to have achieved some renown.

Griffin's interest in photography was born in the France of the thirties.

In those days, Eugène Atget had been forgotten, though his work was being preserved by that remarkable Berenice Abbott, but others were working experimentally. I loved painting, and through this love I discovered that artists themselves were becoming excited about photography. I had occasion to see the portraits by men like Nadar and David Octavius Hill and was overwhelmed by them. There was no question of imitating painting, or even of comparing the two arts. I began to work, and I scarcely stopped except for the lengthy period of my blindness. I took it up again as soon as my sight was restored.

Griffin's photographic excellence has been appropriately honored. He holds memberships in the American Society of Magazine Photographers (which lists only 600 photographers in the world) and in the Royal Photographic Society of Great Britain.

Technical information about the photographs included in this section: All photographs used available light, without flash or floods; all photographs were made with 35 mm. cameras. The portrait of Pierre Reverdy was made with an early German camera, the make forgotten; all the others with Leica M3's or Alpa 6C's, with Summicron, Elmar and Alpa lenses.

Journal Entries

———————————————————————————→

Finally it boils down to this. Today, for the first time in my life, I am sure I met God in the form of one of His saints — Jean Hussar's brother, André, who has been with the Trappists but was released to do what he could for his country now that France is at war. He came to my room here at Mlle. Augis' where the two brothers were to have their reunion. He came here as a living legend, known before his Trappist experience for his heroic work among the poor in Paris. We sat and talked for hours, the three of us, before a small fire in the hearth of this room. And in every attitude, every gesture and expression from those eyes, I was aware that I was seeing him as though looking through the viewfinder of my camera; even though it was in its case and I did not have the courage to take it out and make the photographs I longed to make. But I could not escape the impression that I was viewing him through the camera finder, studying the light on his tonsured head, the steam from the tea that boiled on the hearth and rose up past the red poppies on the wallpaper to haze his face.

But how to photograph the odors of this room, the odors of this encounter? By what art to suggest . . . But none of this really says what I want to say. I mean it is this: if I had photographed that face, I would have been photographing an aspect of sanctity — the sacred reality that is man — that was clearly visible where it is less visible in most; but usually there, somewhere, to be discovered with one's lenses, one's optics. And that, for me, is the fascination of photographing, the only fascination for me: to focus, to wait until this thing flickers into view in a face, a scene, and then shoot. That is the one truly revealing moment in man, and I find that it almost never occurs in action, but in the depths of self-forgetfulness, serenity — which is why my portraits seldom show what one calls action, dynamism, vitality.

You photograph in the light of day what you sense walking along the Loire banks on a spring night when the air is magical with the fragrance of lime blossoms. Somehow, there must be a way to do that. I fear it can be done better in words or in musical sounds — and how sick that admission makes me. It can be done in sounds better than images. No, there must be a way to break through and do it in images, too. But how can one hope to recognize it in its subtlety when the very subtlety of it is so far removed from one's own experience? Must not an artist know it from his own experience in order to search it out in his subjects, recognize its wrinkles and configurations in order to paint them, photograph them, compose them in music? How much of what appears really comes from one's own conscious percipience? I think a great deal. For example, I believe that what one is, how one feels, one's affective nature somehow actually transforms the image captured by one's lens — or at least selects this image in a far deeper way than merely choosing the moment to click the shutter. This week I made portraits of three people. Those of Jean and Louis Légé, my classmate, came out magnificently — they were what I knew them to be. Every shot looked into their souls, and since they are souls for which I have the profoundest reverence, all of it was there in the negatives.

But those I did of Judge . . . Ah, they were different. He is a brilliant man, a dedicated scholar quite aside from his gifts as an attorney. I felt a vague awareness while I photographed him as he talked, recited the poetry of Reverdy, discussed his archeological work, that he was hiding from me, wearing a mask to prevent my lens (my eyes?) from seeing him. Did he do this purposely?

In any event, though I had some misgivings, I was so flattered to be in his home and he was so brilliant, I felt sure the photos would be at least that much, also.

Late in the evening, though, as he walked me home through the streets of Tours, under the flying buttresses of the Cathedral that loomed over us like the skeletons of some primordial beast, the Judge took my arm and asked me about my work in psychiatry at the *École de Médecine* with Dr. Pierre Fromenty. In a voice full of connivance, as one "adult to another," he told me "adult" and intimate things about himself, his *faiblesse*. What it was is of no significance, except I was not that adult to be hardened to it, and I felt myself shrink with shame for him. And I was filled with shame at myself for feeling this awful shame for him, for he was suddenly there defenseless and I could not even speak to ease his pain. I lay awake, hating myself for my revulsion of this poor man. Finally I got up in the middle of the night, closed the door into Louis' quarters, and developed the negatives.

Now, although they were taken before I knew, I think I would still have known after I had seen them even if he had never talked to me about his problems. They were unspeakably obscene. My lens had penetrated his mask without mercy, revealing the man I had not seen through my viewfinder, but the man as he is. What could I do? I could not show such revealing documents to a man of his sensitivity. I let them dry and then put them in the fireplace and burned them. When he asked me about them, I told him I had foolishly miscalculated my light and got only negatives too faint to print. When I told him this, I watched him closely. Again, my eyes could perceive nothing of his secret from his face. His mask was perfect. Why then had I, without knowing it, snapped him at moments when every wrinkle and line of his face was stamped by evil? Not a single negative failed to catch this . . .

(Postscript — August 13, 1965)

Now, twenty-five years later, I still do not know the answer, but it seems to me that the above childish observations have some fundamental validity, because the same things occur — and this is something more profound than the old saw about the lens not flattering. Certainly, we do know that the eye often compensates, sees what it wants to see in many people whose charm and manners effectively hide what they really might be, and that the lens does not cooperate in this delusion which may be why our negatives reveal too often aspects of men that our eyes have never seen. This remains, I suspect, a profoundly painful experience for almost all photographers who deal with the human face, and who have enough respect for the medium not to alter the lens's truth with massive retouching, à la funeral-parlor artist.

Wednesday, July 18, 1962

Last 24 hours terribly preoccupied with Max Geismar's surgery, pain for him, and made worse by the fact that his father died of this same operation. Have been moved by his attitude of dread and fear, openly expressed, and his request that I help him through it by writing him and by sending prints of the photos I made of him in New York.

I had also jokingly told him that I had tried to find a Patron Saint for his condition, but had been unable to locate one. He wrote back telling me to set up something with *some* saint, anyway. He called his forthcoming surgery his "nightmare."

As yesterday evening approached and I knew he was undergoing the surgery, I asked Gregory[1] to help me pray to some saints. We hit on St. Louis, St. Thomas Aquinas, and St. Alphonse Liguori as being men who would appreciate and commiserate with the kind of troubles Max was having.

In the darkroom, in that weird light of the OA amber safelight, Gregory and I and the three patrons we had chosen for Max all crowded in to work on the photographs. Gregory and I engaged in a wordless dialogue as we brought Max's photographic image to life again and again in the developer — we felt it a symbolic battle to counter the forces of destruction working in Max's body. We would expose carefully under the enlarger, then put the photographic paper into the developer and watch the whiteness dissolve slowly as details of the face appeared. Gregory would whisper, each time, with a tone of intense relief in his voice: "He's coming up. He's okay. Another good one of that great man." We spent the night triumphing over death through this creation of the life image. We worked and watched through the night, surrounded by the strong odor of hypo, the warm-metal odor of the enlarger as it heated, surrounded by the dilute amber glow until dawn turned the light gray and forced us to quit. We had not failed. We had not messed up a single print. Gregory, exhausted by three A.M., said he would go lie down just one moment, and for me to call him. The child went sound asleep, worn from the tensions of his responsibilities to help keep Max alive in the chemicals for me. He aroused

[1] Griffin's youngest son.

himself later in the morning when I was washing the 20 or so prints, and helped me to squeegee and dry them.

Thursday, July 19, 1962

Word today that Max survived the surgery very well indeed and is all right. A great relief. I told Gregory, who takes *all* of the credit for pulling Max through, as though the surgeons and hospital attendants had nothing whatsoever to do with it.

It is odd how one connects life with the image of life. When they discovered my negatives of Reverdy at the *Figaro Litteraire* in Paris a few weeks ago, we asked them to airmail them to us. A few hours ago I made large prints, and felt the extraordinary confusion of realizing that this wonderful head that came up in the developer was taken in life — but that Reverdy is now dead.

Gregory's five-year-old mind solved the dilemma. As the images developed, he assured me excitedly: "He's all right. The great poet is coming up."

I mentioned to Gregory that Reverdy was dead. The child dropped his hands in surprise. "He *is?*" he asked unbelievingly.

"Yes . . ."

"We didn't get to him in time," he said despondently, and then in a voice quaking with rage: "Why didn't you *hurry?*"

"We couldn't hurry enough," I explained. "He died a year ago."

"Anyway, we *did* save the great critic, didn't we?" he asked uncertainly.

"Yes," I reassured him. "With the help of some doctors and nurses."

March 29, 1965

Talpa, New Mexico. Now, late at night, rain continues to fall. The mountain air is fragrant with *piñon* from thousands of warming fires. And in here, we cherish these sounds and smells because the rain, in a way, brought us an art masterwork earlier in the day. We are excited in that rare and special way of having acquired something we never really hoped to have. Even the children are caught up in our jubilance.

We have coveted above all the works of three artists in America — Abraham Rattner, Robert Ellis and Andrew Dasburg. Robert

Ellis, who is our *compadre* in that we are godparents of his daughter, Erendira, has given us many of his works. We have never been able to afford the Rattners and Dasburgs that we love.

Over the years, when we have gone to visit our friends, Mary, Hannah and Sallie Gillespie in Talpa, we have met and become friends with Andrew Dasburg. I have photographed him, but never satisfactorily since he is a most difficult subject to capture. Today, I asked to photograph him again. He consented, inviting Robert Ellis and me to come to his studio where he was working on a new painting.

After breakfast with the Gillespies, who own a number of fine Benrimos, Dasburgs, Bomars and Ellises, Robert drove me to Andrew's studio, a splendid adobe building on the rim of the Llano Quemada with a spectacular view of the valley. This morning, black storm clouds turned the blues and greens of the mountains almost luminous.

Andrew hurried us inside, insisting that a storm would soon open up the skies.

In his studio, we admired the work on the easel. Other works lay on the sofa and chair. Andrew told Bob not to pay any attention to drawings on the furniture. "They are discards. The roof leaks sometimes. I just put them there to protect the furniture." Robert and I grimaced. The "discarded" drawings, one in black and white and another in color, were among the finest Dasburgs we had seen.

"Andrew," I groaned. "You can't be serious. These are magnificent drawings. You're not going to let the rain spot them?"

"I'm not satisfied with them. I set them aside some time ago intending to throw them away."

"Andrew — you can't discard such work," Bob said.

"You like the drawings?" Andrew frowned.

We assured him that it would be a crime to use such works to protect furniture. Andrew shrugged and told us he had intended them for the wastebasket, but that if we liked them we could take them. He gave Bob the color drawing and me the even more beautiful black and white.

Then, Andrew brought out a rare 1935 work, a sepia drawing based on *Uncle Tom's Cabin* which he thought might "amuse" my wife. "It's an old drawing. It has some significance now and especially for your wife since you've been involved in problems of racism," he said.

I told him we could not accept a valuable work like that. He told me, with a small amount of heat, that he wasn't giving it to me, but just asking me to take it to my wife and he was sure I had no right to refuse a gift to her.

As we gathered up these works and prepared to leave, Andrew suggested we might like for him to sign the two "discards." Almost immediately I began to suspect something. Andrew is too thoroughly honest and too independent-minded to sign any work with which he is not satisfied. He would not sign a real "discard." It occurred to me that he had staged this, knowing I could never afford his work, as a graceful means of giving me some of his drawings. Almost in a sweat of shock, I had completely forgotten to photograph him. I remedied this — but hastily, since the storm was almost on us and Andrew was urging us to hurry before the rain began to fall too heavily.

After shooting a couple of rolls of film, we left and went directly to a frame shop to have our drawings mounted and framed. The man at the shop quizzed us discreetly about the Dasburgs. "Works like these must have cost you a fortune," he said. Bob and I were noncommital and gave him only the vaguest answers.

This afternoon we picked the drawings up, mounted and framed, and took them triumphantly to the Gillespies. They were ecstatic.

"And Andrew said they were discards," I said after telling them the story.

"Discards nothing," Hannah said. I shared my suspicions that he had staged this scene as a delicate way of giving us these drawings. "I'm almost sure you're right," Sallie agreed. She explained that the most beautiful of their Dasburgs had been retrieved by Hannah from Andrew's waste bin. It, too, was signed. We were now almost certain that this was Andrew's way of allowing his friends to own his works, especially friends like us who could not afford to buy them.

We became more certain of this when Andrew joined us for supper tonight. After studying the framed drawings, he said to me, "Do you know, I wasn't at all happy with those drawings. But now that I see your enthusiasm for them, and see them properly framed, I'm beginning to believe I was wrong. I think they are better than I realized." And after a moment, he added, "Yes, they are not bad at all."

I almost challenged him about this stratagem of his to get the works in our hands, but decided to leave things as they were. His glow of happiness in our happiness, however, left us no doubt.

Now, we have returned to our rooms. It is late at night and the children are asleep. I have unloaded my cameras and put the exposed negatives away to be developed later. We have turned out all the lights except a lamp on the table where the two Dasburgs stand. We cannot sleep. We listen to the rain pour against our windows and cannot bring ourselves to turn off the lamp.

[*Editor's Note: Griffin was apparently correct in his evaluation of the Dasburg "discards." For almost a year now the drawings given to Griffin, Ellis and the Gillespies have been on loan to various museums throughout the U.S.*]

May 5, 1966

As music demands active cooperation and even participation of the listener, so photography demands them of the viewer. If a viewer does not project himself into a photograph enough to smell the odors, hear the sounds and silences, feel the permeation of atmosphere or mood, then he is not looking correctly. This cannot be done by glancing. It takes time. The viewer must, in a sense, give himself up to the photograph, let it take him where it will. Many viewers look searchingly only at photographs of themselves.

The allusion to music has some validity. Both music and photography are universal languages. Both, if they are worthy, must strike universal resonances in a wide variety of men. Both must be "penetrated." To listen only to the melodic line of a Bach fugal theme and fail to hear the counterpoint and harmony, or perceive the structure, is similar to seeing only what is superficially obvious in a photograph. In his *Daybooks*, Edward Weston said he judged the success of his photographs in accordance with their visual resemblance to Bach fugues.

But all of these evocations must be implicit in the photograph.

This is the photographer's frustration. How to get them onto the negative and then how to make the negatives come to life in the darkroom.

Nell Dorr, in her magnificent photographic study of Teotitlan del Valle, *The Bare Feet,* wrote: "Now I am at home in the quiet of my darkroom. The door to the outside is closed and only my pictures are with me. Once again my old fear returns to haunt me: Will they breathe?"

Will they breathe? Will it all be there when the prints begin to form under an amber safelight in the developing solution? The darkroom is a place of tension at such moments as the photographer studies the emerging print and wonders if he has fulfilled in it the vision he had when he clicked the shutter of his camera. Has he sufficiently emphasized the important areas, obscured the unimportant ones, "got rid of excess ornament," coaxed out a proper gradation of tones?

Marion Palfi's photographic essays communicate these evocations in an almost transforming manner. I think particularly of her geriatrics series, *You Have Never Been Old,* where the viewer is taken so profoundly into the life and problems of the aged.

At Aspen, Colorado, I photographed the Amadeus Quartet playing Schubert. But I failed somehow because the final prints evoked no sound. My photos were an injustice to the performers who appeared to play on silent instruments. In Minneapolis I photographed Zara Nelsova performing a Bach *Partita* for unaccompanied cello. This was better in that something of the music came through in the composition, the tonality and the expression on the artist's face.

These things may well come to life for the photographer in his prints, but he must wonder how many viewers will see, hear, smell and experience fully what is really there.

JACQUES MARITAIN is one of the world's great thinkers, a legendary figure whose work has influenced and changed modern philosophy and theology. Dr. Maritain is the author of *Scholasticism and Politics, Creative Intuition in Art and Poetry, The Degrees of Knowledge, Moral Philosophy* and numerous other works. Griffin photographed Dr. Maritain at Kolbsheim, France, in the summer of 1964.

DON SHOEMAKER is a painter and woodworker. He was photographed at his home in Morelia, Michoacán, Mexico, in 1961.

MAXWELL GEISMAR is one of America's most distinguished literary historians and critics. He is the author of *American Moderns, Henry James and the Jacobites* and *The Novel in America*, a five-volume definitive study of American fiction, 1890 to the present. He also edited the *Portable Thomas Wolfe* and the *Whitman Reader*, in addition to other works. He was photographed at his home in Harrison, New York, in 1964.

ZARA NELSOVA is a world-renowned cellist. Griffin photographed her at Minneapolis, Minnesota, in 1963.

FATHER GEORGES DOMINIQUE PIRE, O.P., received the Nobel Peace Prize in 1958 for his work in behalf of refugees and minority groups. He is the founder of many charitable works, including the University of Peace at Huy, Belgium, where this photograph was made in 1964.

SEAN HAMILTON, a brilliant young actor, was photographed by Griffin at the outset of his career in 1967 while still a drama student at the University of Texas.

FATHER AUGUST THOMPSON is a Roman Catholic priest in the State of Louisiana. Griffin photographed him during a visit to Louisiana in 1963.

SARAH PATTON BOYLE, a leading lecturer in the field of civil rights, is author of *The Desegregated Heart* and *For Human Beings Only*. She was photographed on the campus of Eastern Mennonite College in Harrisonburg, Virginia, in 1964.

ARTHUR LOURIÉ is a world-renowned composer of serious music. He was photographed at Princeton, New Jersey in 1964. Arthur Lourié died at Princeton in October, 1966.

ANDREW DASBURG, one of America's greatest living artists, at left, and ROBERT ELLIS, American artist of international reputation, were photographed in Mr. Dasburg's studio in Taos, New Mexico, in 1965.

GODFREY DIEKMANN, O.S.B., a musician and liturgist, is a member of the Liturgy Commission of the Vatican Council. He is a renowned Patristic scholar, an expert on the writings of the early church. He was photographed by John Griffin at St. Gregory's Abbey, Shawnee, Oklahoma, in the summer of 1965.

Mrs. LEONIA SMITH is the mother of the late Clyde Kennard. She was photographed in 1963 at Hattiesburg, Mississippi, shortly after her son's death.

FATHER JOHN P. MARKOE, S.J., for many years has been an almost legendary figure in civil rights work in the United States. He was photographed at The Creighton University, Omaha, Nebraska, in 1965. Father Markoe died in Nebraska in 1967.

Luis Berbér, orchestral conductor, composer and musical director of the *Niños Cantores de Morelia*, world-renowned Mexican boys choir which has appeared in concerts throughout the world, on records, and in motion pictures, is also conductor of the Texas Boys Choir. He was photographed in Mansfield, Texas, in 1964.

HALDOR LAXNESS (left) and CORNEILLE HEYMANS were photographed at the international meeting of Nobel Prize winners in Huy, Belgium, in December, 1965. Griffin attended the meeting, which studied the problems of world racism and world hunger, as a special guest speaker. Laxness, an Icelandic writer, received the Nobel Prize for Literature; Heymans, a Belgian, was awarded the Nobel Prize in Medicine. Nobel Peace Prize winner Father Georges Dominique Pire, O.P., hosted the event at his University of Peace.

SAUL ALINSKY, criminologist and sociologist, is a leading figure in the civil rights revolution in America. Director of the Industrial Areas Foundation, Mr. Alinsky is the author of several books, including *Reveille for Radicals* and *John L. Lewis: An Unauthorized Biography*. He was photographed in Chicago, Illinois, in 1964.

PADRE ERNESTO TOVAR was rector, until his death in 1965, of the Franciscan Monastery of Solitude at Tzintzuntzan, Mexico, where Griffin photographed him in 1961.

Josh White, the legendary American folksinger, was photographed by Griffin in New York City in 1966 at the time Griffin did an interview with White for the Canadian Broadcasting Company.

P. D. EAST, a native of Mississippi, is the editor of *The Petal Paper*, one of the first Southern newspapers to support the 1954 Supreme Court ruling on school desegregation. A lecturer on race relations, Mr. East is also the author of *The Magnolia Jungle*. He was photographed at John Griffin's farm in Mansfield, Texas, in 1963.

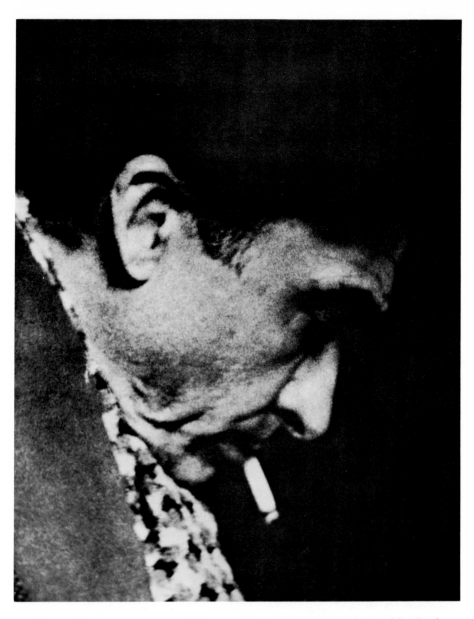

PIERRE REVERDY was a world-famous French poet, an intimate friend of Juan Gris, Braque, Picasso, and others of the period. His many collections of poems included *La liberté des mers*, which was illustrated by Braque. Mr. Reverdy, who died in 1961, was photographed at Solesmes, France, in 1947.

THOMAS MERTON, who is Father Louis, O.C.S.O., of the Cistercian Abbey of Gethsemani in Trappist, Kentucky, is one of the world's most distinguished religious authors. His many books include *The Seven Storey Mountain*, *The Waters of Siloe*, *The Sign of Jonas*, and *Seeds of Destruction*. Father Louis was photographed at Gethsemani in March, 1963.

SISTER FLEURETTE, I.H.M., is engaged in special world-wide projects pertaining to the theater. Much of her work — which chronicles and coordinates the use of dramatic presentations within the framework of Christian communication — has been done in Rome. She was photographed at Menlo Park, California, in 1964.

PATRICK GROMMELYNCK, highly acclaimed young Belgian pianist, was photographed at Huy, Belgium, in the summer of 1964.

TARASCAN FISHERMEN. Photographed in November, 1960, at Janitzio, Michoacán, Mexico, during the Watch of the Dead.

ANNE FREMANTLE is a renowned author and critic. She wrote *This Little Band of Prophets*, *By Grace of Love*, and numerous other books, and is also editor of *The Papal Encyclicals*. She was photographed in New York in 1965.

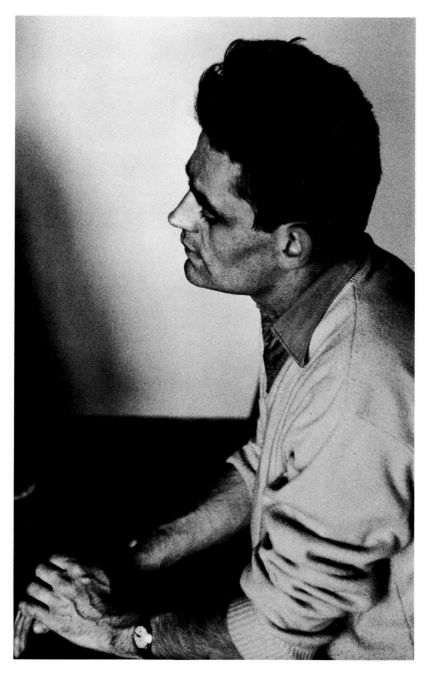

Petit Frère Emmanuel came from France to establish the first Little Brother Foundation in the United States. He was photographed in Detroit, Michigan, in 1964.

ELIZABETH LOURIÉ, noted sculptress, was photographed at Princeton, New Jersey, in 1964.

JOSEPH STANLEY MURPHY, C.S.B., is the Founder and Chairman of the Christian Culture Series of the University of Windsor, Windsor, Ontario, Canada. Father Murphy is also the editor of *Christianity and Culture* and other works. He was photographed at Mansfield, Texas, in July, 1966.

PENN JONES is editor and publisher of the Midlothian, Texas *Mirror*, and the recipient of the 1964 Elijah P. Lovejoy Courage in Journalism Award. Mr. Jones, who authored the best seller, *Forgive My Grief* (A Critical Review of the Warren Commission Report on the Assassination of President John F. Kennedy) was photographed at Midlothian, Texas, in 1964.

JOHN BEECHER, American poet, journalist and custom printer, is a descendent of Henry Ward Beecher and Harriet Beecher Stowe, famous American abolitionists. Mr. Beecher's many books of poems include *Report to the Stockholders* and *In Egypt Land*. He was photographed at Mansfield, Texas, in 1965.

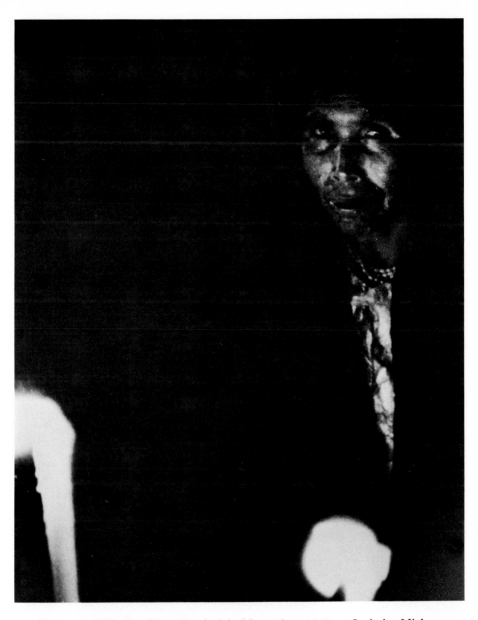

TARASCAN WOMAN. Photographed in November, 1960, at Janitzio, Michoacán, Mexico, during the Watch of the Dead.

BEDE GRIFFITHS, O.S.B., famed Benedictine monk, scholar and a consultant to Pope John XXIII on the Vatican Council, is the author of *The Golden String* and other books. He lives in India in the Benedictine monastery he founded. Griffin photographed him during Father Griffiths' 1963 visit to Santa Fe, New Mexico, to accept the Catholic Arts Association Award.

PART VII

Black Like Me

Notes

—————————————————————————————→

"NIGGER."

From this word, which he as a young boy innocently used in addressing a Negro in the grocery store run by his grandfather, stems John Howard Griffin's first vivid memory of life: a hard slap across his face from his grandfather and the admonition, "They're people — don't you ever let me hear you call them *niggers* again."

Years later Griffin, a teenage student at the *École de Médecine* in Tours, France, questioned the right of a fellow student, a young Negro, to eat in the same restaurant where he and a French classmate were having lunch. The fact that Negroes attended his classes did not disturb him, but he was horrified and indignant — almost to the point of leaving the restaurant — when the Negro sat down at a nearby table. He questioned his companion as to why *they* were allowed to eat in the same room with whites.

The French companion responded with questions that Griffin, a native Southerner and a victim of the double standard of life that comprises the American South's "set of values," could not answer: "Why shouldn't they? Are they not as good as you? Are they not as intelligent as you?"

Griffin realized that his attitude came from the very air that he had breathed in his childhood Texas, from the deeply engrained, prejudiced climate of his Southern heritage. He was ashamed. At that moment, with his classmate pounding question upon question at him, he was ashamed of the fact that he had lived sixteen years without ever once questioning these inherited attitudes.

His mind flashed back to childhood . . . to the slap of his grandfather.

He remembered his Negro "Mammy," whom he and his brothers and sisters thought they loved completely, honestly. He wondered about the validity of love that allowed his family to live in a comfortable home amid pleasant and plentiful surroundings and watch this "beloved" woman return to her sub-human dwelling every night after work.

His attitudes began to change. Years of intense study brought the unquestionable realization that the American "race" problem was nonexistent — that it was the problem of "racism," not of "race." Just as the "Jewish problem" that Hitler espoused was in reality only a matter of "racism."

Griffin saw the terror of the Nazis. He learned firsthand what happens when reason gives way to hatred, truth to fallacy. He was in France when the Nazis invaded, and he became involved in the smuggling of Jewish people out of the country. He saw people whom he loved and treasured as great and valuable human beings transported to Germany to be gassed and cremated — because they were born of Jewish parents. While working with German Jewish refugee families, Griffin recalled a statement by Edmund Burke he had learned in his youth in the South: "I know of no way of drawing up an indictment against a whole people." Was this not a key to the fallacy of racism? The Nazis had drawn up an indictment against the entire Jewish community, and once the indictment was drawn, the atrocities followed.

Returning to the United States after being blinded by an enemy shell while serving in active combat in the South Pacific, he began to hear terms that were frighteningly similar to those he had heard in Nazi-occupied France — the "Negro problem," the "Jewish problem," the "race problem," "inferior," "unequal."

All of this was totally unreal to him . . . because his attitudes had undergone a complete change, because of his academic training in Europe, and because, blinded as he was, the color and appearances of a man meant nothing to him. He could judge only by what each man was, by his character and individual merit as a person.

In 1957 Griffin's sight was restored. At this time he was doing special investigatory studies on the growing Negro suicide rate in the South. These studies were yielding highly contradictory answers. Each completed questionnaire seemed wholly in conflict with its predecessor. Moreover, Negroes refused to answer his questions out of fear that he might use the answers against them, that their names would be discovered and reprisals would be made against them and their families. And, again and again, they hurled the challenge at him: "The only way you can *know* what it is like is to wake up in my skin."

Questions that had plagued him for years came back, day after day, with increasing urgency: *What is it like to be a Negro in the Deep South? What is a second-class citizen? What is the lot of the Negro, of any scorned minority?*

He decided to find out. He decided to step into another man's shoes, to walk his path, to search out his soul, his existence, his destiny. He went to New Orleans. There, within three weeks, through medical treatment and sunlamp exposures, he converted himself. He became a Negro.

As he underwent the medical treatment to transform himself into a more densely pigmented man, Griffin clarified the criteria for his experiment. Were we involved in the same kind of racism as the Nazis — but with a different victim group? We protested that our situation was altogether different, but was it? We denied the practice of racism. To test this, Griffin decided to change nothing except his pigment. He would retain his name, his papers, his background, his speech patterns and he would answer all questions truthfully. If we were not involved in racism, it would mean that men would judge him simply as a human individual, and since he was the same human individual, his life as a colored John Griffin would not differ considerably from his life as a white man. If, on the other hand, we were involved in racism, in the error of "drawing up an indictment against a whole people," then men would judge him by pigment alone and his life as a Negro would differ drastically from his life as a white.

Then he began. For almost two months, in late 1959, he traveled through the Deep South — riding buses, walking, hitchhiking. He was the same person — John Howard Griffin, a man in his late thirties, a citizen, a scholar and novelist, a husband, the father of three young children. The very same person. Only now it was different. He was a Negro. A Negro first, last and above all other things. He was a "nigger" — before he was an American, he learned; a "nigger" before a Catholic; a "nigger" before even a man.

He discovered that he was hated for the mere fact that he was a

Negro; he found that when a person, any person, is rejected or hated or the victim of discrimination, for whatever reason, the rejection is always inflicted on a real and personal level. He realized this rejection was a violation of the human spirit, and that it contained the poisonous seeds of the destruction of the soul. He saw that racism is an irrational state arrived at by irrational judgment and means. Knowing that hatred breeds hatred, he recognized the Southern "System" for the double killer that it is: killer of both the oppressed and the oppressor.

Black Like Me bypasses the usual academic studies of racism; it tells the bewildering and dehumanizing story of his travels into hell — a mile for every mile, a shame for every crossroad. It is not a pretty story. Not a scenic route. But, instead, the rubble-strewn path of man's rank injustice to his fellow man.

This is the South. True. The American South. But, if you listen carefully in the pages of this book, you can hear the echoes of the frenzied goosestep calling its count, you can hear the piercing heartbreak of Dachau and Auschwitz and Belsen crying out through the silent swamps of tradition and prejudice. And you know that if the goosestep isn't stopped in time . . . if the camps aren't stomped out . . . that the ovens *could easily* burn again some day.

Although Griffin meant the work primarily as a source of interest for sociologists, *Black Like Me* propelled him into further work in the field of racism. He has devoted the ensuing years in a concentrated campaign (through articles, heavy lecture schedules both in this country and abroad, and many investigating trips into the South) to alert people to the evils of racism, to urge them to help prevent its spread. Jacques Maritain called *Black Like Me* and Griffin's work against racism "a magnificent expression of love."

The journal passages cover the period prior to Griffin's departure into the Deep South, the period after his return, and contain hitherto unpublished material.

The text of the selections is that of *Black Like Me* (Boston: Houghton Mifflin, 1961). "November 7" is from pages 11–18 of that edition; "November 14" is from pages 62–74; "November 24" is from pages 113–120 and 122–123; "November 28 and 29" is from pages 129–132.

Journal Entries

———————————————————————→

Pruned the trees and calked all of the house openings in preparation for winter.

Strange hours. Next Tuesday I am to leave here, go to New Orleans and have my body darkened; and then I am to travel and live as a Negro in the Deep South. I am to study what discrimination and segregation based on color accomplish in their effects on a man's body and spirit.

This idea, which has so long preoccupied me, is now to be explored. But as the time to leave draws near, many things reveal themselves. The intellectual, scientific fascination remains, but the emotional dread increases to a point of sickness.

I seek to evade the reasons, but I must face them. The dread springs from concern over my family life. What will this do to my parents, my wife and children, not only in the unpleasantness that we anticipate from racist neighbors and friends, but in some deeper realm of our existence? We are, after all, Southerners, living in a land where our lives have been formed by the tainted atmosphere of white superiority. We bear those wounds so deeply within us. We have engrained reactions to Negroes, conceiving them according to stereotypes. Intellectually we know better and intellectually we have liberated ourselves from these base concepts. We are on the side of perfect justice. But can one ever root out these mysterious, spontaneous deeper reactions of the viscera? Are we not still subverted by the clichés that form our concept of Negroes? Yes, and do I not loathe the prospect of becoming a Negro — and I must be clear here — not because of the reprisals, not because of the alienation of my family from neighbors and friends, but precisely because there is the deeper taint within my very bones, a disease uncured and therefore a part of my very chemistry as a man.

If I could face it, would I not know that my profoundest fear comes from the suspicion that becoming a Negro will do some irreparable damage to my humanity. And still more terribly, perhaps forever alter my intimate relationships with my family, my wife especially (who is thoroughly in agreement with this project) and, God forbid, later my children. Yet we do this precisely because of the children, in the hope that what we discover may help us preserve them from being formed by a prejudice that distorts man's view of man; in the hope that they may grow true, without these terrible wounds that merely growing up in a prejudiced society imposes on minds and emotions.

The truth of it is that we have come to the terrible, unspoken fear that I will end up not being merely a white man disguised as a Negro, but that I will be, in effect, merely a human, densely pigmented — which is a Negro. And God knows how this ramifies in the deepest recesses of our beings. We cannot foretell how it will be after my return.

I am still not saying it.

Today, when I talked of this with my mother, I saw the look of abject fear on her face — not because of disapproval of what I am to do, but because of some deeper intuition that I will never again escape the marks of "Negro-ness."

All of this indicates that although we are perfectly clear intellectually, the waters are still muddied at the emotional levels. We are unable to see clear there, unable to harmonize what we believe intellectually and morally with what we feel emotionally.

I, who thought I had long ago ferreted out the last ounce of prejudice, find myself falling into gloom. I think this experiment will reveal many terrible things about us and our convictions. Why do I find this project so offensive now that I must face the reality of it? It has something to do with identity. Perhaps I feel that the physical change will drag along with it a transformation of identity, even interior identity. My family suspects this. It is precisely, I think, their fear that their husband, son and brother, even though theoretically he will change only pigment, will in truth be changed more fundamentally. The eye is more powerful than the intellect in such things. If they should encounter me, they would have to remind themselves that I was *not* a Negro stranger — the *stranger* part is the important one, not the Negro, for we have no thought about a friend's "Negro-ness."

What terrible moments, and how we cling to one another. In the evening, after writing the above, I went home to my wife and children. The tensions were almost unbearable. Though we talk otherwise, our attitude is that this is the end of something, almost as though I were not going on a brief trip of change, but were condemned to be torn from what we now know forever. We intuitively feel that our relationship may never be quite the same again.

After we put the children to bed, this uncertainty overwhelmed us. I felt it at two levels. First, the wholly emotional need for reassurance. Second, the detached and objective need to decipher the truth in its effects on our relationship, to bring it out in the open and clarify it. So when my wife and I went to bed, I turned on the phonograph with a recording of Clara Haskill's performance of Schumann's *Waldscenen*. We lay there in the dark, remembering this music because it was the composition that I taught my wife long ago when she came to me as a young student when I was blind. It was this music that revealed her to me for the kind of person she was, this music that helped us fall in love with one another. Only as we listened to it in this new context did I realize the cruelty of what I had done in playing it.

But we had to know these things. The music helped us overcome the dread that lay like a barrier of ice between us. I felt us make the effort to destroy that barrier, but it remained like a first timidity; and I felt us sink into despair to sense these constraints impose themselves on our affections.

I rolled on my back and spoke to the darkness, slowly, telling my wife that we both knew something was wrong and asking her to help me to understand precisely what it was. "You must tell me the truth, even if you think it will hurt me," I said. "No one's ever done this thing before. We owe it to the truth to try to understand what it is doing to us. Try to tell me what's the matter."

"I don't know."

"I don't either," I groaned. "But we both know something is not right between us about this. If we can't solve it, then I can't go. I can't risk damaging our marriage. Is it repulsive to you to think of me as a Negro?"

"No," she said firmly. "I'm sure it's not."

"Do you think things will be all right for us — I mean for our marriage — when I come back?"

"Oh, yes . . ."

"No, don't just say that. Think about it. Do you have any doubts? Will you look on me as an ex-Negro rather than the man you have known?"

"It's not the ex-Negro — not that . . . it's that something will have happened to you, that you may not be the same. That I won't have any part in even your identity for a while . . . I think we can work it out."

"But you're not sure?" I said, and when she began to protest protectively, I added, "No, it's all right. I'm not sure either. I know we'll always love one another, but I'm not sure there won't be some involuntary movement of revulsion in you. Southern girls are taught to have such a horror of intimacy with Negro men . . . the damned fear of rape . . . Will that connection ever fly into your consciousness when I come back to you? That's what I meant by the ex-Negro question. No, of course, you mustn't answer that. You can't possibly know, can you? But if you even think it might happen that way, then I mustn't go."

"I'm sure it won't," she said. "I haven't got that kind of poison in me as much as some have."

"Does it bother you to talk about it?"

"No," she said. "I think we need to."

I got up and turned the recording over, to a performance of the *Kinderscenen*, switched on the lamp and lighted cigarettes for us. We lay propped up on pillows, side by side, our shoulders touching.

"I need to know one other thing," I said. "In the next weeks when I'm gone, to all the world I'll simply be a bald-headed Negro. I'll probably be staying in a rooming house or hotel room, writing up my notes on a Sunday afternoon. If you think of me, how will you visualize me — as the man you've always known or as a Negro in that room?"

"As a Negro," she said. "I can't help it. I know that's how it'll be."

That was the death sentence to me — how can I explain it? I told her, "Damn . . . damn . . . if you don't visualize me as the white John Howard Griffin, then what happens to that man? That's what scares me. Does he just cease to exist?"

I began to perceive something about the need to *exist* at least in a concept held by someone else. If a man is not known, not even to himself (and I feared that as a Negro I would lose my own existence) the only way to maintain that existence was to have the one person nearest me preserve it by retaining the image of me as she has known me, and as I have known myself.

"I don't think I should go," I said miserably when I had turned out the lamp.

"You'd never forgive yourself if you turned back now," she said.

The constraints had largely vanished between us, but long after she slept, I stared into the darkness.

Finally, an hour ago, I slipped out of bed, dressed and made myself some coffee. I checked all of the children's beds to see that they were properly covered, for the air is chilled. Then I drove here to work in my office at the barn on my parents' farm. The sky is now gray outside. Predawn light falls over the trees and fields. I think of people getting up all over this land, preparing breakfast, beginning the day.

I pour through Maritain's *Scholasticism and Politics*, to find the passages that guide me. In effect, I am acting his philosophy, making it live in action, better than I could act my own.

"The general paganization of civilization has resulted in man's placing his hope in force alone and in the efficacy of hate, whereas in the eyes of an integral humanism, a political ideal of brotherly love alone can direct the work of authentic social regeneration; and it follows that to prepare a new age of the world, martyrs to the love of neighbour may first be necessary. And this also shows how everything depends on a profound renewal of the interior energies of conscience . . ." And, ". . . the primacy of the spiritual cannot be affirmed by denying itself."

I have read this many times with my wife. We realize that the words, "martyrs to the love of neighbour may first be necessary" have a tone of prophecy for us, but that is the least of it. The real danger lies in a man's accepting in conscience a task he is ill qualified to undertake.

November 1, Sunday morning

"Regnum veritatis et vitae, regnum sanctitatis et gratiae, regnum *justitiae, amoris* et pacis."

Nothing else matters. Nothing else is interesting. Once again it is necessary to throw off (by an act of the will) the great dung-burden of self-fears. But this passage now represents the contradiction within me: regnum justitiae, amoris et pacis. But which justice? — the justice that man owes a marriage, the justice that he owes his neighbor? And in this instance I feel the conflict between this latter justice and the reality of a suspension of amoris; for I will not be loved as myself while I am gone: how can I actually be held in love when even my wife will think of me as a Negro stranger — thus the love that holds man in existence will cease for the time that his existence as himself ceases.

We went to early Mass this morning — there, in that context, the conflicts between justice and love were dissolved.

Then, since I was dead from no sleep, I went to bed for a nap. I listened to the noises of my wife and children having their after-Mass breakfast — heard that pleasant noise as I drifted to sleep.

At noon we went to my parents for a large country Sunday dinner. My wife was at ease and happy. The large meal made me drowsy again. I came down here to the barn office to take another nap. I lighted the gas stove. Though it is warm outside, this stone building holds the chill. I stripped off my clothes to sleep.

My wife came down to see if I had an extra pack of cigarettes. She sat beside me on the bed.

"Are you all right?" she asked.

"Yes . . ."

The sun poured through the window. She opened the glass to a strange fragrance of autumn. In my fatigue, it entered as a jubilance as though nature commanded energy from my entrails.

We heard the children approaching the barn. My wife threw a cover over me and went to intercept them. "Be quiet," I heard her whisper. "Your daddy's taking a nap."

Later — night

A deep excitement fills us, a deep pleasure to hear night settle silently over the country, to smell the smoke of wood-burning fires;

the children's baths. All of this lifts me out of the doldrums of twilight, the way in France, at Solesmes, we countered the loneliness of dusk with magnificently chanted Vespers, so beautiful it dilated our hearts. Now, the sounds and smells of autumn in the country, the magical Lipatti recording of the first Bach *Partita*, the splashing of children are our Vespers. I turn on all the lights, flood the place with light.

We realize again, for the thousandth time, some of the implications of what Maritain calls *the sanctity of the intellect*, and the glory of it is that we can realize it on such an evening, such a chill and marvelous evening, when the spirit imposes itself on the body in a glow of health, the smell of bread, the sense of wheat; for we have that tonight — even though in another 36 hours I will be gone to walk into the swamps of Negro life.

Piedy calls me away from the typewriter to tell me that the boys are working in the darkroom (or playing at it) and want me to come and help them develop some pictures. Gregory asked her to tell me that he had already mixed the chemicals, had diluted the "hydrophobia" (meaning hypo) with water.

Monday, November 2

A magnificent morning of work, autumn sunlight and Bach — how I feast on this music, aware that I shall not be hearing it for a long time to come. A fugal morning in the most jubilant sense, giving hints of the whole *ordo universali*, the harmonies of heaven and earth.

Then a moment ago I looked out the window to see Mother at the back screen door gazing toward this barn. Gazing, gazing, surrounded by the loneliness of fields and woods. And I felt suddenly what she must be feeling — the mother's fear (her terror, perhaps) to think of her son's living in the poverty and squalor of the ghettos; being insulted, deprived, God-knows-what. She remained at the door a long time, gazing toward this studio. When she went back to the kitchen, I decided to go up and have a cup of coffee with her.

When I entered, I found her at the sink, her eyes red with tears, working hard at the washing. I felt that mute communication of tenderness that could not express itself in words. We had coffee and talked of the new dachshund. She said nothing about her fears, as I knew she would not, for her discretion, like my Father's, is perfect in such things.

Now, back in the office, the world closes out and I hear what she tells me better than any words could say it. As though born of the sunlit country silence, I hear the piano from the house. She plays Beethoven, the Opus 110 Sonata — and there is imposed on me the certainty that this is her incomparable gift. She plays a work that I love above almost every other. And how marvelously she plays it, full of itself, not introvert, but contemplative, with sanity and health. On the morning air, it carries clear and clean into my windows. The crusts dissolve inside me. Everything enters again into the harmony of daylight and belly and the health of the Aquinas texts on justice that lie on my desk in a square of sunlight. It turns everything right somehow. Now, it is Schubert, the *Impromptus*.

Later

Early afternoon, and I feel the undercurrent of excitement as my departure draws near. I feel it in a dozen ways, but mostly I feel it in my body, in the nights I shall sleep alone God-knows-where. And also in the intellectual affections — I shall miss this narrow, white-washed room. I glance around and notice the books — the Latin scholars, Voltaire, the Aquinas studies, Pascal, Berenson, Barzun, de Wulf, Aristotle, Mauriac — and hundreds more. Here beside me the Trappist calendar from The Abbey of Gethsemani in Kentucky, not yet turned to November. I turn the page, see a photo — a gray and barren sky, leafless winter trees, monks walking under a cloister porch. The photo is permeated with their silence, and to look at it, I seem to hear, as I heard at the monastery of Solesmes, the distant bawling of a calf from somewhere around the farms.

I do not allow myself to think of the coming weeks. The full view of life is too much. I pull back and seek these more amiable diversions, all in remembering Pascal's statement: "Diversion amuses us and leads us unconsciously to death."

But the diversions must be — a sort of repose from the tension of facing the reality of what I am entering. Nothing is more difficult than to face this, than deciding to look squarely at profound convictions and to act upon them, even when doing so goes contrary to all our desires; deciding to abandon ourselves deliberately and completely to that which is so beautiful, justice, and to that which is so terrible, the reprisals, the disesteem of men. Yes, it must be done. We know it, perhaps we have even done it, made the act, the *fiat*, said the yes, but we wait, seek the diversions. In our case, we have the impression, never voiced, that the diversions amuse us (perhaps) and lead us *consciously* to death . . . or at least a sort of death, like the year of immense sadness Lillian Smith spoke of when she had finished thinking out her book, *Killers of the Dream;* like the soul-destroying repercussions that have wrecked P. D. East after he spoke up for justice in a land that does not love white men who speak against "traditions."

Later

Piedy and the children have been here and spent a few moments and then gone away. It is as though the carnival had come and gone in some little farm community. I see the debris of a moment of delight: Gregory's paper-envelope hat lies on the end of my cot where he forgot it.

The diversions. Pascal had no Gregory or he would have qualified his epigram. These diversions sustain a man in life.

At base, it is perhaps another of the Pascal *Pensées* that drives me to do this:

"Why do you kill me?"

"What? Do you not live on the other side of the river?" (Are you not different?)

I go to live on the other side of the river, hoping to find that it is no different from this side, and that we can no longer justify dehumanizing man for such false reasons.

BLACK LIKE ME

———————————————————————————➤

November 7

. . . I fixed myself a bite of supper and drank many cups of coffee, putting off the moment when I would shave my head, grind in the stain and walk out into the New Orleans night as a Negro.

I telephoned home, but no one answered. My nerves simmered with dread. Finally I began to cut my hair and shave my head. It took hours and many razor blades before my pate felt smooth to my hand. The house settled into silence around me. Occasionally, I heard the trolley car rattle past as the night grew late. I applied coat after coat of stain, wiping each coat off. Then I showered to wash off all the excess. I did not look into the mirror until I finished dressing and had packed my duffel bags.

Turning off all the lights, I went into the bathroom and closed the door. I stood in the darkness before the mirror, my hand on the light switch. I forced myself to flick it on.

In the flood of light against white tile, the face and shoulders of a stranger — a fierce, bald, very dark Negro — glared at me from the glass. He in no way resembled me.

The transformation was total and shocking. I had expected to see myself disguised, but this was something else. I was imprisoned in the flesh of an utter stranger, an unsympathetic one with whom I felt no kinship. All traces of the John Griffin I had been were wiped from existence. Even the senses underwent a change so profound it filled me with distress. I looked into the mirror and saw reflected nothing of the white John Griffin's past. No, the reflections led back to Africa, back to the shanty and the ghetto, back to the fruitless struggles against the mark of blackness. Suddenly, almost with no mental preparation, no advance hint, it became clear and it permeated my whole being. My inclination was to fight against it. I had gone too far. I knew now that there is no such thing as a disguised white man, when the black won't rub off. The black man is wholly a Negro, regardless of what he once may have been. I was a newly created Negro who must go out that door and live in a world unfamiliar to me.

The completeness of this transformation appalled me. It was unlike anything I had imagined. I became two men, the observing one and the one who panicked, who felt Negroid even into the depths of his entrails.

I felt the beginnings of great loneliness, not because I was a Negro but because the man I had been, the self I knew, was hidden in the flesh of another. If I returned home to my wife and children they would not know me. They would open the door and stare blankly at me. My children would want to know who is this large, bald Negro. If I walked up to friends, I knew I would see no flicker of recognition in their eyes.

I had tampered with the mystery of existence and I had lost the sense of my own being. This is what devastated me. The Griffin that was had become invisible.

The worst of it was that I could feel no companionship with this new person. I did not like the way he looked. Perhaps, I thought, this was only the shock of a first reaction. But the thing was done and there was no possibility of turning back. For a few weeks I must be this aging, bald Negro; I must walk through a land hostile to my color, hostile to my skin.

How did one start? The night lay out there waiting. A thousand questions presented themselves. The strangeness of my situation struck me anew — I was a man born old at midnight into a new life. How does such a man act? Where does he go to find food, water, a bed?

The phone rang and I felt my nerves convulse. I answered and told the caller my host was out for the evening. Again the strangeness, the secret awareness that the person on the other end did not know he talked with a Negro. Downstairs, I heard the soft chiming of the old clock. I knew it was midnight though I did not count. It was time to go.

*

With enormous self-consciousness I stepped from the house into the darkness. No one was in sight. I walked to the corner and stood under a street lamp, waiting for the trolley.

I heard footsteps. From the shadows, the figure of a white man emerged. He came and stood beside me. It was all new. Should I nod and say "Good evening," or simply ignore him? He stared intently at me. I stood like a statue, wondering if he would speak, would question me.

Though the night was cold, sweat dampened my body. This also was new. It was the first time this adult Negro had ever perspired. I thought it vaguely illuminating that the Negro Griffin's sweat felt exactly the same to his body as the white Griffin's. As I had suspected they would be, my discoveries were naïve ones, like those of a child.

The streetcar, with pale light pouring from its windows, rumbled to a stop. I remembered to let the white man on first. He paid his fare and walked to an empty seat, ignoring me. I felt my first triumph. He had not questioned me. The ticket-taker on the streetcar nodded affably when I paid my fare. Though streetcars are not segregated in New Orleans, I took a seat near the back. Negroes there glanced at me without the slightest suspicion or interest. I began to feel more confident. I asked one of them where I could find a good hotel. He said the Butler on Rampart Street was as good as any, and told me what bus to take from downtown.

I got off and began walking along Canal Street in the heart of town, carrying one small duffel bag in each hand. I passed the same taverns and amusement places where the hawkers had solicited me on previous evenings. They were busy, urging white men to come in and see the girls. The same smells of smoke and liquor and dampness poured out through half-open doors. Tonight they did not solicit me. Tonight they looked at me but did not see me.

I went into a drugstore that I had patronized every day since my arrival. I walked to the cigarette counter where the same girl I had talked with every day waited on me.

"Package of Picayunes, please," I said in response to her blank look.

She handed them to me, took my bill and gave me change with no sign of recognition, none of the banter of previous days.

Again my reaction was that of a child. I was aware that the street smells, and the drugstore odors of perfume and arnica, were exactly the same to the Negro as they had been to the white. Only this time I could not go to the soda fountain and order a limeade or ask for a glass of water.

I caught the bus to South Rampart Street. Except for the taverns, the street was deserted when I arrived at the Butler Hotel. A man behind the counter was making a barbecue sandwich for a woman customer. He said he'd find me a room as soon as he finished. I took a seat at one of the tables and waited.

A large, pleasant-faced Negro walked in and sat at the counter. He grinned at me and said: "Man, you really got your top shaved, didn't you?"

"Yeah, doesn't it look all right?"

"Man, it's slick. Makes you look real good." He said he understood the gals were really going for bald-headed men. "They say that's a sure sign of being high-sexed." I let him think I'd shaved my head for that reason. We talked easily. I asked him if this were the best hotel in the area. He said the Sunset Hotel down the street might be a little better.

I picked up my bags and walked toward the door.

"See you around, Slick," he called after me.

An orange neon sign guided me to the Sunset Hotel, which is located next to a bar. The drab little lobby was empty. I waited a moment at the desk and then rang a call bell. A man, obviously awakened from sleep, came down the hall in his undershirt, buttoning on trousers. He said I would have to pay in advance and that he didn't allow men to take girls up to the rooms. I paid the $2.85 and he led me up narrow, creaking stairs to the second floor. I stood behind him as he opened the door to my room and saw over his shoulder the desolate, windowless cubicle. I almost backed out, but realized I could probably find nothing better.

We entered and I saw that the room was clean.

"The bathroom's down the hall," he said. I locked the door after him and sat down on the bed to the loud twang of springs. A deep gloom spread through me, heightened by noise of talk, laughter and juke-box jazz from the bar downstairs. My room was scarcely larger than the double bed. An open transom above the door into

the hall provided the only ventilation. The air, mingled with that
of other rooms, was not fresh. In addition to the bed, I had a tiny
gas stove and a broken-down bed stand. On it were two thin hand
towels, a half bar of Ivory soap.

It was past one now. The light was so feeble I could hardly see
to write. With no windows I felt boxed in, suffocating.

I turned off my light and tried to sleep, but the noise was too
much. Light through the open transom fell on the ceiling fan, casting distorted shadows of the four motionless blades against the opposite wall.

A dog barked nearby and his bark grew louder as another tune
from the juke box blasted up through my linoleum floor. I could
not shake the almost desperate sadness all this evoked, and I marveled that sounds could so degrade the spirit.

I slipped into my pants and walked barefoot down the narrow,
dim-lit hall to the door with a crudely lettered sign reading MEN.
When I stepped in, the hollow roar of water beating against the
wall of a metal shower filled the room, along with an odor of cold
sweat and soap. One man was in the shower. Another, a large, black-
skinned man, sat naked on the floor awaiting his turn at the shower.
He leaned back against the wall with his legs stretched out in front
of him. Despite his state of undress, he had an air of dignity. Our
eyes met and he nodded his polite greeting.

"It's getting cold, isn't it?" he said.

"It sure is."

"You talking to me?" the man in the shower called out above the
thrumming.

"No — there's another gentleman here."

"I won't be much longer."

"Take your time — he don't want to shower."

I noted the bathroom was clean, though the fixtures were antique
and rust-stained.

"Have you got a stove in your room?" the man on the floor
asked. We looked at one another and there was kindness in his
search for conversation.

"Yes, but I haven't turned it on."

"You *didn't* want to take a shower, did you?" he asked.

"No — it's too cold. You must be freezing on that bare floor, with no clothes on."

His brown eyes lost some of their gravity. "It's been so hot here recently. It feels kind of good to be cold."

I stepped over to the corner washbasin to rinse my hands.

"You can't use that," he said quickly. "That water'll run out on the floor." I looked beneath, as he indicated, and saw it had no drainpipe.

He reached beside him and flicked back the wet canvas shower curtain. "Hey, how about stepping back and letting this gentleman wash his hands?"

"That's all right, I can wait," I said.

"Go ahead," he nodded.

"Sure — come on," the man in the shower said. He turned the water down to a dribble. In the shower's obscurity, all I could see was a black shadow and gleaming white teeth. I stepped over the other's outstretched legs and washed quickly, using the soap the man in the shower thrust into my hands. When I had finished, I thanked him.

"That's all right. Glad to do it," he said, turning the water on full strength again.

The man on the floor handed up his towel for me to dry my hands. Under the dim light in the tiny room without windows, I realized I was having my first prolonged contact as a Negro with other Negroes. Its drama lay in its lack of drama, in its quietness, in the courtesies we felt impelled to extend to one another. I wondered if the world outside were so bad for us that we had to counter it among ourselves by salving one another with kindness.

"Do you want a cigarette?" I asked.

"Please sir — I believe I will." He leaned his heavy body forward to accept one. His black flesh picked up dull highlights from the bare globe overhead. I fished in my pants pocket for matches, and lighted our cigarettes. We talked local politics. I told him I was new in town and knew nothing about them. He refrained from asking questions, but explained that Mayor Morrison had a good reputation for fairness and the Negroes were hoping he would get elected governor. I sensed the conversation made little difference, that for a few moments we were safe from the world and we were loath to break the communication and go back to our rooms. It gave us warmth and pleasure, though we talked formally and showed one another great respect. Not once did he ask my name or where I came from.

When the man in the shower finished and stepped out dripping, the larger man hoisted himself up from the floor, tossed his cigarette into the toilet bowl and got into the shower. I told them good night and returned to my room, less lonely, and warmed by the brief contact with others like me who felt the need to be reassured that an eye could show something besides suspicion or hate.

Griffin remained in New Orleans where his bewilderment increased daily at the deepening horror of life in the Negro community. His profoundest shock came with the realization that he as a white Southerner had never had the slightest concept of the destructive effects of segregation and racial suppression on all aspects of human living.

"Merely taking on a denser pigment changed everything about my life," he says. "And in ways we whites never dream."

He sought employment in New Orleans, and later throughout the South, by telephoning in answer to employment-wanted ads in the newspapers. In every instance except one his qualifications interested employers enough to get him invitations for interviews. When he appeared for the interviews and it was seen that he was colored, he was made to understand there was no question of his getting the jobs.

> *I had to face this: [Griffin says] there was no doubt that the white John Griffin could have had a good proportion of these jobs. But this same man, with the same name, with precisely the same qualifications could not get these jobs the moment employers saw the color of my skin. And I had to ask myself always that key question: was I being judged by my qualities as a human individual or were men merely looking at me, seeing this visual tab of pigment and including me in an indictment against a whole people. Toward the end, I found myself silently begging just one employer to ask me at least one question before he rejected me — not to reject me merely on the basis of the color of my flesh. Not one*

*did. Finally, I stopped telephoning, stopped seeking. What was
the use? So long as men persisted in judging you by your pigment
rather than by your qualities as a man, you had no chance. The
maddening thing about being a victim of racism is that you spend
your life standing in front of doors that are open to man, that are
necessary for any man to enter in order to become a fully-functioning human, but that are closed to you. I stood constantly in
front of doors that would have unhesitatingly opened to me when
I was white, but that were closed to this same human now that I
was colored.*

*One morning, news swept through the Negro community that
the Pearl River County Grand Jury of Mississippi had refused to
consider the FBI investigative dossier concerning the killers of
Charles Mack Parker. A wave of embittered anguish spread
through the Negro population. Negroes viewed it as new proof
that justice was rigged on the white man's side, that the white man
could do anything he wanted to a Negro and never get punished
for it.*

*Against the advice of his Negro companions, Griffin decided to
move into Mississippi and experience life as a Negro there. He
caught a bus out of New Orleans for Hattiesburg. His seat companion, a young Negro whom he calls "Bill," and some of the other
Negroes at the back of the bus, learning that Griffin had never been
to Mississippi before, carefully explained the "techniques of living,"
the local taboos and how he must act to avoid trouble with the white
man.*

November 14

. . . It was late dusk when the bus pulled into some little town for
a stop. "We get about ten minutes here," Bill said. "Let's get off
and stretch our legs. They've got a men's room here if you need to
go."

The driver stood up and faced the passengers. "Ten-minute rest
stop," he announced.

The whites rose and ambled off. Bill and I led the Negroes toward the door. As soon as he saw us, the driver blocked our way. Bill slipped under his arm and walked toward the dim-lit shed building.

"Hey, boy, where you going?" the driver shouted to Bill while he stretched his arms across the opening to prevent my stepping down. "Hey, you, boy, I'm talking to you." Bill's footsteps crunched unhurriedly across the gravel.

I stood on the bottom step, waiting. The driver turned back to me.

"Where do you think you're going?" he asked, his heavy cheeks quivering with each word.

"I'd like to go to the rest room." I smiled and moved to step down.

He tightened his grip on the door facings and shouldered in close to block me. "Does your ticket say for you to get off here?" he asked.

"No sir, but the others ——"

"Then you get your ass back in your seat and don't you move till we get to Hattiesburg," he commanded.

"You mean I can't go to the ——"

"I mean get your ass back there like I told you," he said, his voice rising. "I can't be bothered rounding up all you people when we get ready to go."

"You announced a rest stop. The whites all got off," I said, unable to believe he really meant to deprive us of rest room privileges.

He stood on his toes and put his face up close to mine. His nose flared. Footlights caught silver glints from the hairs that curled out of his nostrils. He spoke slowly, threateningly: "Are you arguing with me?"

"No sir . . ." I sighed.

"Then you do like I say."

We turned like a small herd of cattle and drifted back to our seats. The others grumbled about how unfair it was. A large woman was apologetic, as though it embarrassed her for a stranger to see Mississippi's dirty linen.

"There's no call for him to act like that," she said. "They usually let us off."

I sat in the monochrome gloom of dusk, scarcely believing that in this year of freedom any man could deprive another of anything so basic as the need to quench thirst or use the rest room. There was nothing of the feel of America here. It was rather some strange country suspended in ugliness. Tension hung in the air, a continual threat, even though you could not put your finger on it.

"Well," I heard a man behind me say softly but firmly, "if I can't go in there, then I'm going in here. I'm not going to sit here and bust."

I glanced back and saw a poorly dressed man who walked in a half crouch to a place behind the last seat, where he urinated loudly on the floor. Indistinguishable sounds of approval rose around me — quiet laughter, clearing throats, whispers.

"Let's all do it," a man said.

"Yeah, flood this bus and end all this damned foolishness."

Bitterness dissolved in our delight to give the bus driver and the bus as good as they deserved.

The move was on, but it was quelled by another voice: "No, let's don't. It'll just give them something else to hold against us," an older man said. A woman agreed. All of us could see the picture. The whites would start claiming that we were unfit, that Negroes did not even know enough to go to the rest room — they just did it in the back of the bus; never mentioning, of course, that the driver would not let us off.

The driver's bullish voice attracted our attention.

"Didn't you hear me call you?" he asked as Bill climbed the steps.

"I sure didn't," Bill said pleasantly.

"You deaf?"

"No sir."

"You mean to stand there and say you didn't hear me call you?"

"Oh, were you calling me?" Bill asked innocently. "I heard you yelling 'Boy,' but that's not my name, so I didn't know you meant me."

Bill returned and sat beside me, surrounded by the approval of his people. In the immense tug-of-war, such an act of defiance turned him into a hero.

As we drove more deeply into Mississippi, I noted that the Negro comforted and sought comfort from his own. Whereas in New Orleans he paid little attention to his brother, in Mississippi everyone who boarded the bus at the various little towns had a smile and a greeting for everyone else. We felt strongly the need to establish friendship as a buffer against the invisible threat. Like shipwrecked people, we huddled together in a warmth and courtesy that was pure and pathetic.

The threat grew as we penetrated deeper toward the center of the state. The distance between the whites and the blacks grew tangibly greater, even though we saw only the backs of their heads and shoulders, their hats and the cigarette smoke rising from them as night fell and bus lights switched on. They said nothing, did not look back, but hostility emanated from them in an unmistakable manner.

We tried to counter it by being warm and kind to one another, far more than strangers usually are. Women discussed where they lived and promised to visit one another, though all knew that such visits would never take place.

As we neared Poplarville, agitation swept through the bus. Everyone's mind was on the Parker youth's lynching and the jury's refusal to consider the FBI evidence against his lynchers.

"Do you know about Poplarville?" Bill whispered.

"Yes."

Some of the whites looked back. Animated Negro faces turned stony.

Bill pointed out places in a quiet, expressionless voice. "That's the jail where they snatched him. They went up to his cell — the bastards — and grabbed his feet and dragged him down so his head bumped against each stairstep. They found blood on them, and blood at the bottom landing. He must've known what they were going to do to him. He must've been scared shitless."

The bus circled through the streets of a small Southern town, a gracious town in appearance. I looked about me. It was too real for my companions, too vivid. Their faces were pinched, their expressions indrawn as though they felt themselves being dragged down the jail stairway, felt their own heads bumping against the steps, experiencing the terror . . .

Bill's voice cut through, sourly: "That's the courthouse where they made that decision." He looked at me to see if I understood what decision he meant. I nodded.

"That's where they as much as told the whites, 'You go ahead and lynch those niggers, we'll see you don't get in any trouble.' "

I wondered what the whites in front were thinking. The lynching and the callous decision of the Pearl River County Grand Jury were surely on all their minds. Perhaps the injustice was as nightmarish to them as it was to those surrounding me.

We drove through wooded countryside into the night. Bill dozed beside me, his snores adjusted to the hum of the tires. No one talked. After a while Bill roused himself and pointed out the window. "That's where they fished his body out of the creek," he said. I cupped my hands to the window but could see only black masses of foliage against a dark sky.

We arrived at Hattiesburg around eight-thirty. Most of the Negroes hurried to the rest rooms. Bill gave me instructions with such solicitude that I was alarmed. Why, unless there was real danger, would he be so careful to help me avoid it? I wondered. He told me where I should go first, and whom I should request to see.

"What's the best way to get there?" I asked.

"Have you got some money?"

"Yes."

"Take a cab."

"Where do I catch one?"

"Any of those cabs out there," he said pointing to a string of parked cabs driven by white men.

"You mean a white driver'll take a Negro passenger?" I asked.

"Yeah."

"They wouldn't in New Orleans . . . they said they weren't allowed to."

"They're allowed to do anything to get your dime here," he said. We walked to one of the cabs.

"Yessir, where can I take you?" the driver said. I looked through the window to see a pleasant young man who showed no hint of animosity. Bill told him the address where he should deliver me.

"Wait just a second, will you?" Bill told the driver. He grabbed my arm and walked away.

"I'll find out where you're staying. I'll come around about noon tomorrow and check on you to see you're all right."

Again I was overwhelmed that strangers should go to such trouble for me.

I thanked him. He hesitated, as though uncertain and then said,

"I'm not buttin' into your business, but if you're planning on getting a girl — you don't want to get one that'll burn you."

"I sure don't." I thought of La Fontaine's *Les deux amis*, where the friend offers to help rid the hero of his sadness, even to procuring a girl for him. I detected no hint of lasciviousness in Bill's voice or manner, certainly no element of pimping; no, he was simply trying to protect me.

"If you do plan on getting one, you better let me help you find a clean one."

"I'm worn out, Bill," I said. "I guess I'll by-pass it tonight."

"That's fine . . . I just didn't want you to go getting yourself messed up."

"I appreciate it."

The cab driver delivered me to an address on Mobile Street, the main street of the Negro quarter. It was narrow, cluttered, lined by stores, cafés, bars. He was completely civil, and in such an authentic way, I felt it was his real nature and not just a veneer to please the customer — the way I had seen it in the stores in New Orleans.

"Looks awful wild down here," I said as I paid him. I had to speak loudly to make him hear me above the shouts and the amplified wails of juke-box rock-and-roll music.

"If you don't know the quarter, you'd better get inside somewhere as soon as you can," he said.

My contact inside referred me to another person in the quarter. As I walked down Mobile Street, a car full of white men and boys sped past. They yelled obscenities at me. A satsuma (tangerine) flew past my head and broke against a building. The street was loud and raw, with tension as thick as fog.

I felt the insane terror of it. When I entered the store of my second contact, we talked in low voices, though he made no effort to be guarded or cautious in expressing his contempt for the brutes who made forays into the area.

"The sonsabitches beat one boy to a pulp. He was alone on a stretch of walk. They jumped out of the car, tore him up and were gone before anyone knew what was happening," he said. "They framed another on a trumped-up charge of carrying whiskey in his car. He's one of the finest boys in town. Never drinks."

His bitterness was so great I knew I would be thought a spy for the whites if I divulged my identity.

Another car roared down the street, and the street was suddenly deserted, but the Negroes appeared again shortly. I sought refuge in a Negro drugstore and drank milkshakes as an excuse to stay there.

A well-dressed man approached me and asked if I were Mr. Griffin. I told him I was. He said there was a room for me and I could go to it whenever I got ready.

I walked through the street again, through the darkness that was alive with lights and humanity. Blues boomed from a tavern across the street. It was a sort of infernal circus, smelling of barbecue and kerosene.

My room was upstairs in a wooden shanty structure that had never known paint. It was decrepit, but the Negro leaders assured me it was safe and that they would keep a close watch on me. Without turning on my light, I went over and sat on the bed. Lights from the street cast a yellowish glow over the room.

From the tavern below a man improvised a ballad about "poor Mack Parker . . . overcome with passion . . . his body in the creek."

"Oh Lord," a woman said in the quiet that followed, her voice full of sadness and awe.

"Lordy . . . Lordy . . ." a man said in a hushed voice, as though there were nothing more he could say.

Canned jazz blared through the street with a monstrous high-strutting rhythm that pulled at the viscera. The board floor squeaked under my footsteps. I switched on the light and looked into a cracked piece of mirror bradded with bent nails to the wall. The bald Negro stared back at me from its mottled sheen. I knew I was in hell. Hell could be no more lonely or hopeless, no more agonizingly estranged from the world of order and harmony.

I heard my voice, as though it belonged to someone else, hollow in the empty room, detached, say: "Nigger, what you standing up there crying for?"

I saw tears slick on his cheeks in the yellow light.

Then I heard myself say what I have heard them say so many times. "It's not right. It's just not right."

Then the onrush of revulsion, the momentary flash of blind hatred against the whites who were somehow responsible for all of
this, the old bewilderment of wondering, "Why do they do it?
Why do they keep us like this? What are they gaining? What
evil has taken them?" (The Negroes say, "What sickness has taken
them?") My revulsion turned to grief that my own people could
give the hate stare, could shrivel men's souls, could deprive humans
of rights they unhesitatingly accord their livestock.

I turned away from the mirror. A burned-out light globe lay on
the plank floor in the corner. Its unfrosted glass held the reflection
of the overhead bulb, a speck of brightness. A half-dozen film negatives curled up around it like dead leaves. I picked them up and
held them before the light with strange excitement, curious to see
the image that some prior occupant of this room had photographed.

Each negative was blank.

I imagined him going to the drugstore to pick up the package of
photos and hurrying to this squalid room to warm himself with the
view of his wife, his children, his parents, his girl friend — who
knows? He had sat here holding blank negatives, masterpieces of
human ingenuity wasted.

I flicked the negatives, as he must have done, toward the corner,
heard them scratch dryly against the wall and flap to the floor.
One struck the dead globe, causing it to sing its strange filamental
music of the spheres, fragile and high-pitched above the outside
noises.

Music from the juke box, a grinding rhythm, ricocheted down the
street.

                    hangity
          hangity   *hangity*   *oomp*
    Harangity   *oomp*   *oomp*

The aroma of barbecue tormented my empty insides, but I did
not want to leave the room to go back into the mainstream of hell.

I took out my notebook, lay across the bed on my stomach and
attempted to write — anything to escape the death dance out there
in the Mississippi night. But the intimate contentment would not
come. I tried to write my wife — I needed to write to her, to give

her my news — but I found I could tell her nothing. No words would come. She had nothing to do with this life, nothing to do with the room in Hattiesburg or with its Negro inhabitant. It was maddening. All my instincts struggled against the estrangement. I began to understand Lionel Trilling's remark that culture — learned behavior patterns so deeply engrained they produce unconscious, involuntary reactions — is a prison. My conditioning as a Negro, and the immense sexual implications with which the racists in our culture bombard us, cut me off, even in my most intimate self, from any connection with my wife.

I stared at the letter and saw written: *Hattiesburg, November 14. My darling,* followed by a blank page.

The visual barrier imposed itself. The observing self saw the Negro, surrounded by the sounds and smells of the ghetto, write "Darling" to a white woman. The chains of my blackness would not allow me to go on. Though I understood and could analyze what was happening, I could not break through.

Never look at a white woman — look down or the other way.

What do you mean, calling a white woman "darling" like that, boy?

I went out to find some barbecue, down the outside steps, my hand on the cool weathered railing, past a man leaning forward with his head cushioned on his arm against a wall, leaking into the shadows; and on into a door somewhere. There were dim lights and signs: NO OBSENETY ALLOWED and HOT LINKS 25¢.

A roundfaced woman, her cheeks slicked yellow with sweat, handed me a barbecued beef sandwich. My black hands took it from her black hands. The imprint of her thumb remained in the bread's soft pores. Standing so close, odors of her body rose up to me from her white uniform, a mingling of hickory-smoked flesh, gardenia talcum and sweat. The expression on her full face cut into me. Her eyes said with unmistakable clarity, "God . . . isn't it awful?" She took the money and stepped back into the open kitchen. I watched her lift the giant lid of the pit and fork out a great chunk of meat. White smoke billowed up, hazing her face to gray.

The meat warmed through the bread in my hand. I carried the sandwich outside and sat on the back steps leading up to my room to eat it. A streak of light from the front flowed past me, illuminating dusty weeds, debris and outbuildings some distance to the rear. The night, the hoots and shouts surrounded me even in this semi-hiding place.

hangity
hangity   hangity
Harangity   . . .

The music consumed in its blatant rhythm all other rhythms, even that of the heartbeat. I wondered how all of this would look to the casual observer, or to the whites in their homes. "The niggers are whooping it up over on Mobile Street tonight," they might say. "They're happy." Or, as one scholar put it, "Despite their lowly status, they are capable of living jubilantly." Would they see the immense melancholy that hung over the quarter, so oppressive that men had to dull their sensibilities in noise or wine or sex or gluttony in order to escape it? The laughter had to be gross or it would turn to sobs, and to sob would be to realize, and to realize would be to despair. So the noise poured forth like a jazzed-up fugue, louder and louder to cover the whisper in every man's soul, "You are black. You are condemned." This is what the white man mistook for "jubilant living" and called "whooping it up." This is how the white man can say, "They live like dogs," never realizing why they must, to save themselves, shout, get drunk, shake the hip, pour pleasures into bellies deprived of happiness. Otherwise, the sounds from the quarter would lose order and rhythm and become wails.

I felt disaster. Somewhere in the night's future the tensions would explode into violence. The white boys would race through too fast. They would see a man or a boy or a woman alone somewhere along the street and the lust to beat or to kill would flood into them. Some frightful thing had to climax this accelerating madness.

Words of the state song hummed through my memory:

> *Way down South in Mississippi, Cotton blossoms*
> *white in the sun,*
> *We all love our Mississippi, Here we'll stay where*
> *livin' is fun.*

The evening stars shine brighter, And glad is every
dewy morn,
For way down South in Mississippi, Folks are happy they
have been born.

Scenes from books and movies came back — the laces, the shaded white-columned veranda with mint juleps served by an elegantly uniformed "darky," the honor, the magnolia fragrance, the cotton fields where "darkies, happy and contented," labored in the day and then gathered at the manse to serenade their beloved white folks with spirituals in the evening after supper . . . until the time when they could escape to freedom.

Here, tonight, it was the wood plank beneath my seat, the barbecue grease on my lips, the need to hide from white eyes degenerate with contempt . . . even in the land "where livin' is fun."

And God is loved in Mississippi, Home and
church her people hold dear.

Griffin was helped out of Hattiesburg by his friend, the noted Mississippi newspaper editor, P. D. East. Continuing his journey through Mississippi and Alabama, Griffin learned the wearying techniques of rejection and survival.

"You never knew when you would get it," Griffin says. "You could not tell by their appearance which men or women would humiliate or degrade you. You learned to expect it always, and always it came."

He learned to play deaf and keep moving when whites called him "Boy" or "Uncle" or "Nigger" or "Jig."

Since there were few public accommodations, he stayed often in the homes of Negro families. Whenever he tried to tell his hosts that he was not really a Negro, but a white man, they looked on him with sorrow and distress, as though he were obviously demented.

In these homes, we talked incessantly. [Griffin says] During the day we had to do our grinning and our yessing, because if we did not we were considered "bad niggers" — "uppity" — and we got our punishment. But at night we talked about every indignity we had suffered during the day. And always we asked ourselves the same three questions: Why? What sense does it make? and What good does it do them to keep it like this for us? We never found an answer.

The irony was that we were constantly being exhorted to educate ourselves, to better ourselves, to lift ourselves up by the bootstraps. The whole white world told us that. But our lives proved every day that that would change nothing for us. What every Negro knows is that when men judge you by pigment, it makes no difference how distinguished you are. The whites never ask your background before they suppress you. Indignities are heaped upon you whether you are a college president or an illiterate. A Negro Ph.D. can not enter libraries or churches that are open to the most degraded white-skinned man.

Griffin realized that the truths of racism were almost completely obscured under the Southern myths. He had been brought up to believe that only the "trash" were involved in cruelties to fellow human beings.

But to close all the doors that lead a man to any kind of human fulfilment is the greatest cruelty of all. And in this, it was our educators, our ministers, our attorneys and doctors who maintained the system. I learned that where racism goes unrepudiated, it finally ends up tainting even our highest institutions. I was driven away from churches, from libraries, even though I dressed well and have some basic education at least. If I wanted medical treatment I would have to enter a separate waiting room at the doctor's; I might very well be rejected by hospitals. The "trash" may do the physical lynching, but all of us, no matter how distinguished, who go along with the system are involved in that more tragic lynching of men at the spiritual, emotional, intellectual levels; we kill men's spirit even before they have an opportunity to become men.

It was staying in the homes of Negro families where there were children that most devastated Griffin. He stayed in many such homes, but describes one in particular in the following passage from Black Like Me. The incident occurred one night when Griffin hitchhiked through the swamp country of Alabama.

*

November 24

. . . A distant hum behind me caught my attention. I turned to see a yellow glow on the road's horizon. It grew stronger and head-lights appeared. Though I dreaded riding with another white man, I dreaded more staying on the road all night. Stepping out into full view, I waved my arms. An ancient car braked to a halt and I hur-ried to it. To my great relief, the reflections from the dash lights showed me the face of a young Negro man.

We discussed my problem. He said he lived back in the woods, but had six kids and only two rooms. He wouldn't even have a bed to offer me. I asked him about some other house in the area where I might rent a bed. He said there were none any better than what he had to offer.

However, we could find no other solution.

"You can't stand out here all night. If you don't mind sleeping on the floor, you're welcome to come with me," he said finally.

"I don't mind sleeping on the floor," I said. "I just wouldn't want to put you to any trouble."

As we drove several miles down a lane into the forest, he told me he was a sawmill worker and never made quite enough to get out from under his debts. Always, when he took his check to the store, he owed a little more than the check could cover. He said it was the same for everyone else; and indeed I have seen the pattern throughout my travels. Part of the Southern white's strategy is to get the Negro in debt and keep him there.

"It makes it hard, doesn't it?" I said.

"Yeah, but you can't stop," he answered quickly. "That's what I tell the men at the mill. Some of them are willing just to sit there. I told them, 'Okay, so you're going to give up just because you get no butter with your bread. That's no way to act. Go ahead and eat the bread — but work, and maybe someday we'll have butter to go with it.' I tell them we sure ain't going to get it any other way."

I asked him if he could not get together with some of the others and strike for better wages. He laughed with real amusement.

"Do you know how long we'd last, doing something like that?"

"Well, if you stuck together, they sure couldn't kill you all."

"They could damn sure try," he snorted. "Anyway, how long could I feed my kids? There's only a couple of stores in twenty miles. They'd cut off credit and refuse to sell to us. Without money coming in, none of us could live."

He turned off the lane into a rutted path that led through dense underbrush up to a knoll. The headlights fell on a shanty of unpainted wood, patched at the bottom with a rusting Dr. Pepper sign. Except for the voices of children, a deep silence hung over the place. The man's wife came to the door and stood silhouetted against the pale light of a kerosene lamp. He introduced us. Though she appeared embarrassed, she asked me in.

The subdued babble of children mounted to excited shouts of welcome. They ranged in age from nine years to four months. They were overjoyed to have company. It must be a party. We decided it was.

Supper was on the makeshift table. It consisted entirely of large yellow beans cooked in water. The mother prepared mashed beans and canned milk for the infant. I remembered the bread and candy I had bought earlier and offered it as my contribution to the meal. Neither parent apologized for the meagerness of the food. We served ourselves on plastic dishes from the table and sat where we could find places, the children on the floor with a spread-out newspaper for a tablecloth.

I congratulated them on such a fine family. The mother told me they had been truly blessed. "Ours are all in good health. When you think of so many people with crippled or blind or not-right children, you just have to thank God." I praised the children until the father's tired face animated with pride. He looked at the children the way another looks at some rare painting or treasured gem.

Closed into the two rooms, with only the soft light of two kerosene lamps, the atmosphere changed. The outside world, outside standards disappeared. They were somewhere beyond in the vast darkness. In here, we had all we needed for gaiety. We had shelter, some food in our bellies, the bodies and eyes and affections of children who were not yet aware of how things were. And we had treats. We cut the Milky Way bars into thin slices for dessert. In a framework of nothing, slices of Milky Way become a great gift. With almost rabid delight, the children consumed them. One of the smaller girls salivated so heavily the chocolate dribbled syrup-like from the corner of her mouth. Her mother wiped it off with her fingertip and unconsciously (from what yearning?) put it in her own mouth.

After supper, I went outside with my host to help him carry water from a makeshift boarded well. A near full moon shone above the trees and chill penetrated as though brilliance strengthened it. We picked our way carefully through fear of snakes down a faint footpath to the edge of the trees to urinate. The moon-speckled landscape exhaled its night rustlings, its truffle-odor of swamps. Distantly the baby cried. I listened to the muffled rattle of our waters against damp leaf loam. A fragment of memory returned — recollection of myself as a youngster reading Lillian Smith's *Strange Fruit*, her description of the Negro boy stopping along a lonely path to urinate. Now, years later, I was there in a role foreign to my youth's wildest imaginings. I felt more profoundly than ever before the totality of my Negro-ness, the immensity of its isolating effects. The transition was complete from the white boy reading a book about Negroes in the safety of his white living room to an old Negro man in the Alabama swamps, his existence nullified by men but reaffirmed by nature, in his functions, in his affection.

"Okay?" my friend said as we turned back. Moonlight caught his protruding cheekbones and cast the hollows beneath into shadow.

"Okay," I said.

The house stood above us, rickety, a faint light at the windows. I could hear the whites say, "Look at that shanty. They live like animals. If they wanted to do better they could. And they expect us just to accept them? They *like* to live this way. It would make them just as miserable to demand a higher standard of living as it would make us miserable to put us down to that standard."

I mentioned this to my host. "But we can't do any better," he said. "We work just for that . . . to have something a little better for the kids and us."

"Your wife doesn't seem to get down in the dumps," I remarked.

"No — she's good all the way through. I'll tell you — if we don't have meat to cook with the beans, why she just goes ahead and cooks the beans anyhow." He said this last with a flourish that indicated the grandness of her attitude.

We placed buckets of water on the cast-iron wood stove in the kitchen so we could have warm water for washing and shaving. Then we returned outside to fill the wood-box.

"Are there really a lot of alligators in these swamps?" I asked.

"Oh God yes, the place is alive with them."

"Why don't you kill some of them? The tails make good meat. I could show you how. We learned in jungle training when I was in the army."

"Oh, we can't do that," he said. "They stick a hundred-dollar fine on you for killing a gator. I'm telling you," he laughed sourly, "they got all the loopholes plugged. There ain't a way you can win in this state."

"But what about the children?" I asked. "Aren't you afraid the gators might eat one of them?"

"No . . ." he said forlornly, "the gators like turtles better than they do us."

"They must be part white," I heard myself say.

His laughter sounded flat in the cold air. "As long as they keep their bellies full with turtles, they're no danger to us. Anyway, we keep the kids close to the house." [1]

The cheerful and fretful noises of children being readied for bed drifted to us as we returned to the kitchen. Physical modesty in such cramped quarters was impossible, indeed in such a context it would have been ridiculous. The mother sponge-bathed the children while the husband and I shaved. Each of the children went to the toilet, a zinc bucket in the corner, since it was too cold for them to go outside.

Their courtesy to me was exquisite. While we spread tow sacks on the floor and then feed sacks over them, the children asked questions about my own children. Did they go to school? No, they were too young. How old were they then? Why, today is my

[1] The fine for killing alligators appears to be a conservation measure and means of controlling turtles, not a punitive action against the Negroes, though few Negroes realize this.

daughter's fifth birthday. Would she have a party? Yes, she'd certainly had a party. Excitement. Like we had here, with the candy and everything? Yes, something like that.

But it was time to go to bed, time to stop asking questions. The magic remained for them, almost unbearable to me — the magic of children thrilled to know my daughter had a party. The parents brought in patchwork quilts from under the bed in the other room and spread them over the pallets. The children kissed their parents and then wanted to kiss Mr. Griffin. I sat down on a straight-back kitchen chair and held out my arms. One by one they came, smelling of soap and childhood. One by one they put their arms around my neck and touched their lips to mine. One by one they said and giggled soberly, "Good night, Mr. Griffin."

I stepped over them to go to my pallet near the kitchen door and lay down fully dressed. Warning the children he did not want to hear another word from them, the father picked up the kerosene lamp and carried it into the bedroom. Through the doorless opening I saw light flicker on the walls. Neither of them spoke. I heard the sounds of undressing. The lamp was blown out and a moment later their bedspring creaked.

Fatigue spread through me, making me grateful for the tow-sack bed. I fought back glimpses of my daughter's birthday party in its cruel contrasts to our party here tonight.

"If you need anything, Mr. Griffin, just holler," the man said.

"Thank you. I will. Good night."

"Good night," the children said, their voices locating them in the darkness.

"Good night," again.

"Good night, Mr. Griffin."

"That's enough," the father called out warningly to them.

I lay there watching moonlight pour through the crack of the ill-fitting door as everyone drifted to sleep. Mosquitoes droned loudly until the room was a great hum. I wondered that they should be out on such a cold night. The children jerked in their sleep and I knew they had been bitten. The stove cooled gradually with almost imperceptible interior pops and puffings. Odors of the night and autumn and the swamp entered to mingle with the inside odors of children, kerosene, cold beans, urine and the dead incense of pine ashes. The rots and the freshness combined into a strange fragrance — the smell of poverty. For a moment I knew the intimate and subtle joys of misery.

And yet misery was the burden, the pervading, killing burden. I understood why they had so many children. These moments of night when the swamp and darkness surrounded them evoked an immense loneliness, a dread, a sense of exile from the rest of humanity. When the awareness of it strikes, a man either suffocates with despair or he turns to cling to his woman, to console and seek consolation. Their union is momentary escape from the swamp night, from utter hopelessness of its ever getting better for them. It is an ultimately tragic act wherein the hopeless seek hope.

Thinking about these things, the bravery of these people attempting to bring up a family decently, their gratitude that none of their children were blind or maimed, their willingness to share their food and shelter with a stranger — the whole thing overwhelmed me. I got up from bed, half-frozen anyway, and stepped outside.

A thin fog blurred the moon. Trees rose as ghostly masses in the diffused light. I sat on an inverted washtub and trembled as its metallic coldness seeped through my pants.

I thought of my daughter, Susie, and of her fifth birthday today, the candles, the cake and party dress; and of my sons in their best suits. They slept now in clean beds in a warm house while their father, a bald-headed old Negro, sat in the swamps and wept, holding it in so he would not awaken the Negro children.

I felt again the Negro children's lips soft against mine, so like the feel of my own children's good-night kisses. I saw again their large eyes, guileless, not yet aware that doors into wonderlands of security, opportunity and hope were closed to them.

It was thrown in my face. I saw it not as a white man and not as a Negro, but as a human parent. Their children resembled mine in all ways except the superficial one of skin color, as indeed they resembled all children of all humans. Yet this accident, this least important of all qualities, the skin pigment, marked them for inferior status. It became fully terrifying when I realized that if my skin were permanently black, they would unhesitatingly consign my own children to this bean future . . .

I searched for some other answer and found none. I had spent a day without food and water for no other reason than that my skin was black. I was sitting on a tub in the swamp for no other reason.

I went back into the shanty. The air was slightly warmer and smelled of kerosene, tow sacks and humanity. I lay down in the darkness, in the midst of snores.

"Mr. Griffin . . . Mr. Griffin."

I heard the man's soft voice above my shouts. I awakened to see the kerosene lamp and beyond it my host's troubled face.

"Are you all right?" he asked. In the surrounding darkness I sensed the tension. They lay silent, not snoring.

"I'm sorry," I said. "I was having a nightmare."

He stood upright. From my position flat on the floor his head appeared to touch the ceiling beams far above. "Are you all right now?"

"Yes, thank you for waking me up."

He stepped carefully over the children and returned to the other room.

It was the same nightmare I had been having recently. White men and women, their faces stern and heartless, closed in on me. The hate stare burned through me. I pressed back against a wall. I could expect no pity, no mercy. They approached slowly and I could not escape them. Twice before, I had awakened myself screaming.

I listened for the family to settle back into sleep. The mosquitoes swarmed. I lighted a cigarette, hoping its smoke would drive them out.

The nightmare worried me. I had begun this experiment in a spirit of scientific detachment. I wanted to keep my feelings out of it, to be objective in my observations. But it was becoming such a profound personal experience, it haunted even my dreams.

My host called me again at dawn. His wife stood in lamplight at the stove, pouring coffee. I washed my face in a bowl of water she had heated for me. We spoke by nods and smiles to avoid waking the children sprawled on the floor.

After breakfast of coffee and a slice of bread, we were ready to leave. I shook hands with her at the door and thanked her. Reaching for my wallet, I told her I wanted to pay her for putting me up.

She refused, saying that I had brought more than I had taken. "If you gave us a penny, we'd owe you change."

I left money with her as a gift for the children, and the husband drove me back to the highway.

Shortly after the above, Griffin stopped taking the daily medication that helped him retain his pigment. He disappeared into a boardinghouse in the Negro ghetto of Montgomery, Alabama, and remained in hiding until he lost enough of the pigment to risk passing back into the white community once again. Late one night he left the room, for which he had paid in advance, and walked through the streets toward the white world from which he had come almost two months before.

November 28

I decided to try to pass back into white society. I scrubbed myself almost raw until my brown skin had a pink rather than black undertone. Yes, looking into the mirror, I felt I could pass. I put on a white shirt, but by contrast it made my face and hands appear too dark. I changed to a brown sports shirt which made my skin appear lighter.

This shift was nerve-racking. As a white man I could not be seen leaving a Negro home at midnight. If I checked into a white hotel and then got too much sun, it would, in combination with the medication still in my system, turn me too dark and I would not be able to return to the hotel.

I waited until the streets were quiet outside and I was sure everyone in the house slept. Then, taking my bags, I walked to the door and out into the night.

It was important to get out of the neighborhood and into the white sector as quickly and inconspicuously as possible. I watched for police cars. Only one appeared in the distance and I dodged down a side street.

At the next intersection a Negro teenager strode by. I stepped out and walked behind him. He glanced at me and then kept his eyes to the front. Obviously thinking I might harass him, he pulled something from his jacket and I heard a click. Though I could not see what he held in his hand, I have no doubt it was a switch-blade knife. To him I was nothing more than a white stranger, a potential source of harm against whom he must protect himself.

He stopped at the corner of a wide street and waited to cross. I came up beside him.

"It's getting cold, isn't it?" I said, seeking to reassure him that I had no unfriendly intentions.

He stood like a statue, unresponsive.

We crossed the street into a brighter downtown section. A policeman strolled toward us and the boy quickly dropped his weapon into his jacket pocket.

The policeman nodded affably to me and I knew then that I had successfully passed back into white society, that I was once more a first-class citizen, that all doors into cafés, rest rooms, libraries, movies, concerts, schools and churches were suddenly open to me. After so long I could not adjust to it. A sense of exultant liberation flooded through me. I crossed over to a restaurant and entered. I took a seat beside white men at the counter and the waitress smiled at me. It was a miracle. I ordered food and was served, and it was a miracle. I went to the rest room and was not molested. No one paid me the slightest attention. No one said, "What're you doing in here, nigger?"

Out there in the night I knew that men who were exactly as I had been these past weeks roamed the streets and not one of them could go into a place and buy a cup of coffee at this time of the night. Instead of opening the door into rest rooms, they looked for alleys.

To them as to me, these simple privileges would be a miracle. But though I felt it all, I felt no joy in it. I saw smiles, benign faces, courtesies — a side of the white man I had not seen in weeks, but I remembered too well the other side. The miracle was sour.

I ate the white meal, drank the white water, received the white smiles and wondered how it could all be. What sense could a man make of it?

I left the café and walked to the elegant Whitney Hotel. A Negro rushed to take my knapsacks. He gave me the smiles, the "yes, sir — yes, sir."

I felt like saying, "You're not fooling me," but now I was back on the other side of the wall. There was no longer communication between us, no longer the glance that said everything.

The white clerks registered me, surrounded me with smiles, sent me to my comfortable room accompanied by a Negro who carried my bags. I gave him his tip, received his bow and realized that already he was far from me, distant as the Negro is distant from the white. I locked the door, sat on the bed and smoked a cigarette. I was the same man who could not possibly have bought his way into this room a week ago. My inclination was to marvel at the feel of the carpet beneath my feet, to catalogue the banal miracle of every stick of furniture, every lamp, the telephone, to go and wash myself in the tile shower — or again to go out into the street simply to experience what it was like to walk into all the doors, all the joints and movies and restaurants, to talk to white men in the lobby without servility, to look at women and see them smile courteously.

November 29

Montgomery looked different that morning. The face of humanity smiled — good smiles, full of warmth; irresistible smiles that confirmed my impression that these people were simply unaware of the situation with the Negroes who passed them on the street — that there was not even the communication of intelligent awareness between them. I talked with some — casual conversations here and there. They said they knew the Negroes, they had had long talks with the Negroes. They did not know that the Negro long ago learned he must tell them what they want to hear, not what is. I heard the old things: the Negro is this or that or the other. You have to go slow. You can't expect the South to sit back and let the damned communist North dictate to it, especially when no outsider can really "understand." I listened and kept my tongue from giving answer. This was the time to listen, not to talk, but it was difficult. I looked into their eyes and saw sincerity and wanted to say: "Don't you know you are prattling the racist poison?"

Montgomery, the city I had detested, was beautiful that day; at least it was until I walked into a Negro section where I had not been before. I was a lone white man in a Negro neighborhood. I, the white man, got from the Negro the same shriveling treatment I, the Negro, had got from the white man. I thought, "Why me? I have been one of you." Then I realized it was the same stupidity I had encountered at the New Orleans bus station. It was nothing I had done, it was not me, but the color of my skin. Their looks said: "You white bastard, you ofay sonofabitch, what are you doing walking these streets?" just as the whites' looks had said a few days before: "You black bastard, you nigger sonofabitch, what are you doing walking these streets?"

Was it worth going on? Was it worth trying to show the one race what went on behind the mask of the other?

Journal Entries

---→

I take only a moment to run here to the office, while my wife and children visit with my parents in the house, to make these notes while the return home is fresh in memory.

I sat in the jet this afternoon, flying home from New Orleans, and looked out the window to patterns of a December countryside. I felt the deepest dread for the task that now lay before me, the task of telling truths that will make me and my family the target of all the hate groups.

But even more, the nervousness over this reunion. I knew I looked different, but still myself, white once again. Still, my wife would be meeting a man who has been thoroughly a Negro for many weeks. Would seeing me now in the present be able to obliterate all of the mysterious background resonances that **are** at the heart of anyone brought up in this region?

We talked on the phone last night, and I heard the immeasurable tone of relief in her voice when I told her it was all over and she said, "Thank God . . ." She sounded all right, as though there were no trace of revulsion for me as an ex-Negro. But by the time the plane landed at Love Field in Dallas, I was in a cold sweat of shock. I hurried to collect my bags and walked out front. The car soon arrived with children waving and shouting. I hardly had looked at them before I felt their arms around my neck, their hugs and the marvelous jubilation of reunion. I glimpsed only a beaming expression of pleasure on my wife's face.

In the midst of this, the blackness of the prejudice and bigotry from which I had just come flashed into my mind and I heard myself mutter, "My God, how can men do it when there are things like this in the world?" The faces of my wife and mother spoke relief after strain — a strain I will probably never fully comprehend, for they will never share it with me.

We came directly here to my parents' farm, to leave Mother at home. We sat in the dining room for a time while my father fixed coffee, smiling all over himself.

My mother asked: "Was it as horrible as I think it was?"

"Yes," I said. "Worse, I expect."

Nothing more was said. It was time to forget for a while, time to visit with the children who fought for places in my lap, time to talk of nothing, time for the pleasure of normalcy again.

After a time, I got up and said that I was going to wash some of the grime from my hands. I walked through the bedroom and into the bathroom. I heard the children run out into the front yard. My parents' voices followed them out. Then, my wife's footsteps approached the bathroom door.

A hint of panic spread through me. She opened the door, stepped in and closed it after her. We stared at one another, completely defenseless.

"Is it all right?" I asked, hearing my voice full of strain.

"Yes . . . oh, yes . . ."

We embraced. "I'm so glad," I said.

"I am too." I felt her sobbing with relief.

She quickly controlled herself. "What would you like for supper?" It was such a natural question, asked with such naturalness, there was genius in it at that moment. I dried my hands while she stood beside me. Some steaks, yes, cooked with real butter. By the time we walked out, it was almost back to normal with us, the way I had hoped against hope it might be but feared it would not. There were no recesses in her, then, no "southern-nigger-rape" recesses in her as there are with so many white women, or if there had been, she had somehow got rid of them while I was gone.

Following Griffin's return to Mansfield, Texas, while he was preparing Black Like Me, *his experiment became known. It created a furor, even before the author's findings had been published. He and his parents became victims of an almost relentless hostility.*

"I expected the reprisals for myself," Griffin says, "but I did not expect people to aim them at my parents. My parents were overwhelmed by the viciousness of the calls and the general hostility.

Finally, unable to bear it, they sold their home and moved to Mexico."

During the first tense weeks, Griffin was hanged in effigy on the main street of his home town, was forced to take his family into hiding and had to be on guard against violence. He learned later that during this time his home was being guarded by Negro men from his community who spent each night in the woods overlooking his house.

By August of 1960, fearing the effects of the tensions on their young children, the Griffins decided to move to Mexico.

"I had been warned that my time was up," Griffin recalled, "that I would be castrated and the date had been set first for June 15, then for July 15 — and now it was set for August 15. We decided I would wait until after that date, so that they could not say they had frightened me away."

August 9, 1960

We prepare to leave for Mexico. I have spent the day clearing out this barn office at my parents' deserted farm. Decherd Turner and Penn Jones, two friends who have remained rock firm in their support, have been out to help me.

I sorted books and papers gathered here over the past 13 years of my life. Strange to go back over them, to dig them out and decide what to give, what to store, what to keep. The sun scorches the countryside and overpowers the best efforts of an old, old fan that once cooled my grandfather's store in South Dallas.

From the highway café where all the racists hang out, the frightful blare of jukebox cowboy blues floats clearly to me over the countryside.

I sit here, surrounded by things that have nourished me through the years. They range from magnificent volumes like the *Paleographie Musicale* from Solesmes to our little two-franc school volumes of Molière and Hugo studied in dusty classrooms at the Lycée Descartes in Tours. Each was once new, once held with incomparable excitement.

I find an old and worn copy of Louÿs' *Pages Choisies*. It brings back incidents long forgotten — the visits to the cluttered little second-hand bookshop near the Cathedral in Tours; the purchase for little or nothing; the excitement of hurrying to my room up darkened steps and finally sitting in a chair near the dormer window and opening the world.

The music — *Beethoven Concerto for Piano in C minor*, so tattered it is unmanageable, with Jeannette Tillett's marked instructions for my practice, and that same square handwriting on scores of Brahms *Intermezzi*, Mozart sonatas, Bach concerti, Scarlatti sonatas, joined in some of the scores by later markings put there by later teachers — Casadesus, Batalla, Boulanger. I bring them to my nose to see if they smell of France, or of the lavender water Miss Tillett always wore — they smell only of age-musted paper.

The experience of taking out and examining these things — in a way saying good-bye to them — becomes unbearable; the evocations are fresh again, but stripped to their essences; and the essences were good, for all of it was discovery, marvel, delight.

All is packed. I sit here and stare at these whitewashed stone walls and hear the incredibly dolorous music from the highway. I sense the emptiness of my parents' former home a few yards away. And I cannot bear to remain here any longer.

August 16, 1960

They did not come to mutilate me last night. My car is packed to leave. My wife and children will join me at the home of noted American artist Robert Ellis in Cuautla, since they are to fly to Mexico City. How difficult it is to leave a place one loves, but how impossible to remain. Not one person has called to tell us good-bye or wish us luck.

Later

When I drove through town, slowly in a car packed to the maximum with our things, men simply looked. No one waved. Nothing.

For thirteen years this has been my home, and it has been my wife's all of her life. I drove away from it and no one made the slightest sign.

If my experiment proved anything, it proved that we are involved in racism — in judging a man not by his qualities as a human individual, but rather by his pigment, and that all of us, every citizen of this land pays for the folly of our racism. The proof lies in this. I, as the white John Griffin in the U.S.A., can move toward my goals and I am on velvet. But the moment this same man, with the same goals and the same potential for fulfilling them became a Negro in appearance, I was no longer on velvet; I was walking neck-deep in the stenchiest swamp imaginable; and it was too difficult. I gave up.

I suggest that it is folly in a land like ours, where daily we pledge allegiance, ending with the terms "with liberty and justice for all," to maintain a system that not only gives lie to that oath, but that prevents any citizen from becoming a fully-developed, fully-functioning and fully-contributing member of our society. In every instance of racism, regardless of whether the victim is a Negro, a citizen of Latin American extraction, an American Indian or whatever, we fall into precisely the same error of doing what Burke said was impossible: drawing up an indictment against a whole people.

PART VIII

Racism

FOR LILLIAN SMITH

AND THOMAS MERTON

Notes

⎯⎯⎯⎯⎯⎯⎯⎯⎯⎯⎯⎯⎯⎯⎯⎯⎯⎯⎯⎯⎯⎯⎯⎯⎯⎯⎯⎯→

GRIFFIN'S WORK on racism continues to this day. Each year he leaves his home and family and fulfills an extensive, near-exhausting schedule of public lectures in all parts of this country. In the summers he participates in European conferences on racism and teaches at the University of Peace in Huy, Belgium, a school founded by Father Georges Dominique Pire, O.P., recipient of the 1958 Nobel Peace Prize. In addition, he maintains a heavy writing schedule of articles for various national and international publications. He currently has several projects dealing with racism in progress, one a book-length biographical account of Clyde Kennard, a young Mississippi Negro martyred in 1963.

His journals are crammed with observations and research material; dozens of cases involving racism have been investigated and recorded. The following extracts were chosen from journal entries written between 1959 and 1966.

*

(1959)

What is the prevailing feeling among self-respecting whites in the South who listen to and observe the cheap antics of the segregationists and know that they are being associated with such? It is the feeling of shame and humiliation to be numbered even geographically among them.

*

(1959)

The segregationist regards himself as a responsible citizen with an almost holy mission. He looks on Negro shanties and says: "We were doing all right down here until the North stuck its big nose in our business." Presumably, then, the U. S. Supreme Court is a "Northern" outfit.

*

(1960)
It is strange that the white-supremacy man screams against this Supreme Court decision because it takes away his rights. What rights? The right to make another sit at the back of a bus? The right to keep another from eating in the same room or attending the same school? The right of the white man to deny the Negro his?

*

(1960)
Take the teaching of logic out of a civilization and reason is reduced to the squalor of prejudice. All of the classic fallacies of logic then become a sort of weird virtue and man seeks by loudness, fear and violence to win causes that could not be won by rational persuasion. This is the segregationist. He uses noise, religion, bombast and diversionary considerations — such as states rights and mongrelization — to cloud an issue that would be seen as absurd if stripped of these trappings. His credo would seem to be: If the truth makes you uncomfortable, don't change yourself but simply alter truth to conform to your comfort.

*

(1961)
Man is technically defined as a rational animal. This admits of no degrees of superiority or inferiority except on the basis of individual virtue or accomplishment. The man who judges a *whole race* to be anything less than this definition is obviously not measuring up to it himself, for this is prejudice rather than rationality.

*

(1961)
We speak of rights, but they are inseparable from obligations. If man has a true right, then others have the obligation to respect that right and cannot deprive him of it unjustly. Rights may be either natural or positive. Natural rights are those due man simply because

he is man, and the laws based on those rights are as unchangeable as human nature itself. The first of those rights is that of self-preservation, both *social* and physical. The second is man's right to pursue his goals insofar as that pursuit does not impinge upon the same pursuit in his fellow man. These rights are obviously not subject to change, as are human positive rights, by vote. They concern the very nature of man, and man is not white or black, not Christian or Jew, not Democrat or Republican. Man is man. It is therefore impossible to demand that another be under obligation to respect your natural rights as man, and to find any logic that will allow you to escape the obligation to respect his natural rights as man.

*

(*1962*)

Although they speak of the good of *both* races, the segregationists — make no mistake about it — base their entire behavior on the conviction that the Negro is an inferior being.

They contend that integration is a *law* made by the Supreme Court, contend that it is illegal since the courts cannot make laws, but only enforce them, and warn that "Once the Supreme Court overthrows Congress and takes over the making of our laws, we will have dictatorship, etc. . . ."

They preach that popular will alone makes the law and they confuse popular will with unchangeable guaranteed Constitutional rights to a point of actually accusing the Supreme Court of "perverting" the Constitution because it is not in agreement with the popular will of this group!

*

(*1962*)

A law is just if: (a) It is directed to the common good; (b) it does not exceed the power of the lawmaker; (c) it distributes its goods and burdens among the citizens with proportionate equality.

The old segregation laws were transparently not directed to the common good; they did exceed the power of the lawmakers, since man cannot change human natural laws but only human positive laws; they did not distribute their goods and burdens among the citizens with proportionate equality. Therefore, let it be clear that the Supreme Court's decision corrects a fallacy of justice rather than renders one.

*

(1962)

Mongrelization — an effective word, a question-begging epithet that has a remarkable way of impressing itself on the unreflecting mind when repeated often enough and with enough emphasis. Mongrelization is a problem subsidiary to the issue. It is not the issue. Denouncing integration because it might hypothetically lead to mongrelization is like denouncing marriage because it might hypothetically lead to divorce. The fear of mongrelization is based on the false premise that the Negro is an inferior being. In Nazi Germany this fear was based on the false premise that the Jew was inferior to the Gentile. In the South we segregate the Negro from the white to prevent mongrelization. In Nazi Germany the inferiors were massacred to prevent mongrelization. The core of the matter is the same in both cases since both "solutions" proceed from the same false premise of racial superiority; and yet those who called Hitler's logic that of a madman, permit themselves to embrace, in this instance, one that is identical in essence.

*

(1963)

Segregationists often naïvely use the animal kingdom to illustrate the validity of segregation among humans. They will tell you that white piglets will not mingle with black ones in the same pen. This is not true, but even conceding that it were, it is certain that they show no such fastidiousness about breeding together. This makes for an interesting conclusion among humans. Are we to deduce from this that we should not socialize with the Negro race, but that it is perfectly natural and proper to breed with it?

*

(1964)

What does the Negro ask? He does not ask for the right to force himself on the white man; he does not ask to breed with the white man. He asks for a most basic and profoundly necessary thing —

the right *not to be rejected* because of his color. It is to our great discredit that any man in this land should have to ask for such a right; that it not be freely accorded him. If we suspect him of more than this, then our suspicions reflect our own potential culpability rather than his and are a sour admission indeed.

*

(*1964*)

We speak of being "practical" about this thing. This shows the moral and intellectual tenor of the segregationists. Always when you hear someone say: "Well, we've got to be practical about this thing," you can be sure he feels the compromise of conscience and is trying to rationalize away a principle that he finds uncomfortable or inconvenient. Otherwise, would he not say simply: "Well, we've got to do what's right about this thing."

*

(*1964*)

For the blind man, the whole issue of segregation on the basis of inferiority according to color or race is solved axiomatically. He can see only the heart and intelligence of a man, and nothing in these things indicates in the slightest whether the man is white or black, but only whether he is good or bad, wise or foolish. This indicates the enormous superficiality of segregationist judgments which are based on mere physical sight rather than perception. Is not this gift of sight then being abused since it leads men to judge an object by the accident of its color rather than by its real substance — is a red table any more of a table than a green one? But the most astonishing abuse is that physical sight blinds them to perception to a point that allows them to do what Burke contended to be impossible: — to draw up an indictment against a whole race.

*

(*1964*)

In matters of justice the rule conforms always to the object of the action and admits of no modification by the subject who must give everyone his due. If I owe you two dollars, justice demands that I pay you exactly that amount, not that I pay you what I think you deserve. If I pay more, it is no longer justice but liberality; if I pay less it is injustice no matter what I may think about it or how I may rationalize your inferiority. Commutative justice is both material and spiritual. It demands the restitution of what has been taken from someone else. It demands that the thief who has stolen money restore it. It equally demands that the thief who has stolen someone's rights restore them.

*

(1965)

One human freak makes more headlines than a thousand ordinary men and one bellowing fanatic makes more noise than a thousand quiet men. The rest of the world should at least understand that these whited-sepulchres, these belchers of hatred, these orators of mob will, neither represent nor lead the South's respected citizenry — they are only the noisy herders of a noisy group with as little respect for the privacy of conscience of the whites as for that of the Negroes. The whites, themselves, of this there can be no doubt, the thinking ones and the sincere ones — and there are many more than the extremists would lead us to believe — are stymied by fear and dread of being themselves subjected to the very condition imposed on the Negro by segregation — social rejection. How many say: "I know what I think, but if you open your mouth you're called a 'nigger-lover' and threatened." Or, in other words you are rejected by a portion of human society, and any normal man, white or black, is devastated before such an obscene injustice that deprives him of human dignity, of a consciousness of personal value and exposes him to aversion. Another reason for the silence is that most of them feel they are being dragged into the mud to have even the contaminating contact of opposing such low-grade opponents.

*

(1966)

There is a strange and ironic tie-in between the two old Southern terms *nigger-lover* and *poor white trash*. Whereas they once had something in common, they are now quite opposites. Certainly it is among those who used to be considered *poor white trash* (many of whom may now more accurately be called *rich white trash*) that the most extreme hue and cry against integration is raised, and it is they who now call those who favor Constitutional Law *nigger-lovers*. Despite the former stinging connotations of the term, it should be considered an accolade rather than an injury in these days, for a *nigger-lover* comes more and more to mean one who can no longer rationalize himself into thinking that the accident of his skin pigmentation carries with it some special right to deprive men otherwise pigmented of any of their rights; or that white is the color of divine approbation and black that of divine condemnation.

*

The selections on racism that follow were published between 1963 and 1966. "Racist Sins of Christians" first appeared in *Sign* magazine in August, 1963; "Dialogue with Father August Thompson" was carried in the 1963 Christmas issue of *Ramparts* magazine and subsequently appeared in the anthology, *Black, White and Gray: 21 Points of View on the Race Question* (Edited by Bradford Daniel, Sheed & Ward, New York, 1964); "Preface to Gabriel Cousin's *L'Opéra Noir*" was published in *Théâtre I.* (Gabriel Cousin, Gallimard, Paris, 1963); "The Tip-Off" appeared in "Mississippi Eyewitness," a special issue of *Ramparts* magazine in 1964; "The Intrinsic *Other*" appeared as a chapter in Father Georges Dominique Pire's *Building Peace* (The Marabou Press, Belgium, 1966.)

RACIST SINS OF CHRISTIANS

Two groups of American citizens are hurtling toward one another in a conflict that can result in the worst bloodshed since the Indian wars. I have toured the entire country this year — with an additional two survey trips through the Deep South — and I am convinced that a Negro-white clash is inevitable. While the North and South have wasted time bickering about which is worse, Negroes, particularly young Negroes, have lost their illusions about "good whites." They have seen us equivocate endlessly and finally grow silent in times of crisis, when issues were clear and words of protest or sanity would have sounded with clarion clarity.

Racism — discrimination based on skin color — has grown strong, hard, and bitter throughout the length and breadth of America. Racists who claim to be anti-Communists are doing the Communists' work magnificently well by showing the world our racist abuses and thereby turning the world from us in disgust.

Recent murders of William Moore in Alabama and Medgar Evers in Jackson, Mississippi; the hideous martyrdom of Clyde Kennard; the terrible revelations of James Baldwin and Martin Luther King, Jr., have shocked Americans. We are now a deeply concerned people, but we are not well informed.

White Americans and Negro Americans, communicating at only the most superficial level, tend to see the same event in entirely different lights. Whites view the growing Negro militancy with fear. Negroes view it as the only solution, because they can see little hope that whites will voluntarily grant them their rights — and they can no longer live without these rights. Negroes grow more determined as they grow more disillusioned by the cheating, the continued harassments, the obstructionism that is openly practiced all over America against any move to exercise their civil rights.

Negroes are well informed, through their own news media, of

the constant racist depredations. Since newspapers seldom carry controversial material, the non-Negro public is only vaguely informed. I have seen the same brutality in New York City that I have seen in Mississippi. I have seen the same lack of communication between Negro and white citizens in Cleveland, Detroit, Los Angeles, Rochester, and Buffalo that I have seen in Alabama.

Uninformed, the national conscience cannot manifest itself. We remain two groups of citizens with two different sets of information who do not trust one another and who cannot discuss our problems at a sufficiently profound depth.

*

My information about and attitude toward the crisis today are deeply influenced by an experience three years ago when I had a dermatologist darken my skin, and I lived as a Negro in the Deep South. Behind this sociological experiment there lay the profound conviction that America's most corrosive problem was not a racial problem but a problem of racism and that unless this problem of racism were understood, it could destroy us.

In my teens, as a medical student in France, I had seen the extremes to which racism could lead when I helped smuggle German and Austrian Jews from the Nazi "final solution." I had seen men and women of great quality destroyed because they were born of Jewish parents. Later, in America, I had made studies of crisis community patterns in areas where racial prejudice subverted justice. These studies showed appalling parallels to the growth of racism I had witnessed in Germany. Mental attitudes were similar. In Germany, a man was condemned, not by his qualities as a human being, but because he was Jewish. In America, skin pigmentation was enough to condemn a man to second-class citizenship.

Listening one evening to the Beethoven *Opus 132 Quartet*, one of the sublimest utterances in all music, I realized that if Beethoven lived in the South today, he would be considered a Negro, a second-class human. I, as a white man in the South, could not sit down at a restaurant table with Martin of Porres or Benedict the Moor, though I could eat there with the most derelict white.

I decided that the only way to demonstrate what racism does to a human being was to become a Negro and experience it from the side that no white man can really know. I had a deep concern for the Negro as a victim of racism, but I had an equally deep concern for the white who, whether he realized it or not, was also a victim of racism. Obviously, the situation that warps and handicaps the Negro child must — perhaps even more terribly — warp and handicap the white child.

On a chilly November night in New Orleans, after extensive treatments by a dermatologist, I was ready to enter the world as a Negro. I was evenly dark from head to foot, and I had shaved my head. Otherwise, I was the same. I retained my name, my credentials, my speech pattern. I decided that if I were questioned I would answer truthfully. In the next seven weeks, no white man asked my name; no one questioned my identity as a Negro.

But if I remained essentially the same man, everything about my life was drastically altered. Doors of dignity and self-respect that had been opened to me as a white man were closed to me as a Negro.

The full impact of it hit me that first night when I was directed to the best hotel accommodations for Negroes. It was a wretched little place in the ghetto area. I asked for the best room and paid in advance. The proprietor led me up rickety stairs to the second floor. My "best room" was a cubicle scarcely larger than a double bed. It had no windows. I locked the door and began to undress. Noises of talk, laughter, and juke-box jazz from a nearby tavern drifted through the thin clapboard walls. I turned out the light and crawled into bed. A dog yowled somewhere in the distance. I lay awake in the oppressive closeness and felt desolation spread through me. For the first time, a statement came from my lips that I have heard Negroes utter countless times since: "It doesn't make any sense."

What sense did it make? Here I was, the same John Griffin who had often been an honored guest in New Orleans. I had been there on concert tours with the French pianist Robert Casadesus. I had been received in the finest homes, the finest hotels, the finest restaurants. I was that same man, with the same characteristics, even the same wallet and the same money. But because my skin was black, all of those doors were closed to me. No amount of money could buy me better accommodations. I lay in a wretched hole, because I was a Negro. I realized that if my pigmentation were permanently dark, my wife and children would have this sort of accommodations. I would have to see them deprived, because they were of my flesh and blood.

In the next few days, I looked for jobs. I answered some want ads by telephone. My credentials often elicited interest, and I was virtually assured of the job, until I appeared for an interview. Then, when they saw I was a Negro, I was courteously turned away. There is no question but what I could have earned a decent living as a white man. As a Negro, the best jobs I held were shining shoes and unloading trucks. Only in the professions or after a long period of working oneself up could a Negro make a decent living. So I worked hard for my three or four dollars a day.

In this economic bracket, my diet was largely reduced to the sempiternal rice and beans of the area. This was delicious and cheap, but after a week of eating little else, my mind tended to pray, "Give us this day our daily beans . . ."

Many whites are poor, of course, and subsist on inadequate diets. The important difference is that they are not kept poor because of the color of their skin.

And yet, New Orleans was a disarmingly courteous city. Individual whites treated me with great courtesy. But all of the courtesies in the world do not long mask the one massive discourtesy of segregation that inexorably banishes the Negro to humanity's junkheap.

This involves being the victim of what Negroes call the "System." This System is a complex of customs and traditions so deeply engrained in the Southern white that they have all the force of law, plus the actual Jim Crow ordinances. Though it may vary in its details from locality to locality, the System says in effect that American Negroes are indeed citizens and, as such, should pay taxes and defend their country from its enemies but that they should *not* vote or have equal protection under the law or equality of educational or job opportunities and that they should *not* have the use of public parks and beaches (even though their tax dollars help maintain these) or of public eating places, hotels, libraries, concert halls and hospitals. The System contrives, in a thousand subtle ways, to defraud Negroes of constitutional rights, to kill their incentive to struggle for something better, and to deprive them of opportunities for developing their full human potential, thereby depriving this country of their full contribution as citizens.

The System plunges a whole group of citizens into intimate misery. As a Negro, I soon felt this misery. It consisted in facing daily the mountain of rebuffs that struck me from the very core of the System.

These rebuffs are unknown to the white man. As a white, I had always been free to walk into a nearby door whenever hunger, thirst, or rest room needs made themselves felt. As a Negro, I quickly learned what it meant not to be free to walk into such doors. It can be a humiliating frustration to need rest room facilities and to discover that you must go halfway across town to find a place that will accommodate men of your color. Getting a drink of water was no longer simple. It meant searching, asking questions, locating places.

I began to see WHITE ONLY signs in a new way — as a cruel rebuff to nature and humanity. This is not a matter of mere physical inconvenience. It goes far deeper. Life turns somber when a man is never for a moment free from this grinding concern over the purely animal aspects of his existence. The white hand kept my mind crammed down into my viscera, and I grew to hate the senseless degradation of it. All Negroes do. Life seldom rises above a mood of smoldering resentment over such indignities. The fact that Negroes often hide this resentment in order to survive does not mean that they become inured to it. The "Problem" is the obsession at all levels of society in the Negro community.

Like all other Negroes, I soon found myself imprisoned in the stereotype. And yet I never encountered a Negro who fitted this stereotype which white men have contrived in order to justify racist injustice and salve their consciences.

My soul shriveled to sit with a group of Negroes, sensitive human beings, and listen to what the radio told us of our plight. A white woman with a marvelously patronizing voice spoke of our "earning" our rights to full citizenship — this in a country where every American is born with those rights and where Negroes have fought in wars to defend them for all. One night, we sat in the ghetto squalor and heard a politician warn the public that any move toward racial justice that might give us the hope of human dignity was "playing into the Communists' hands." And he concluded that the System was "for the Negro's own good."

We stared at our dark hands and wondered if he had any idea what a massive crime he was committing. The deepest irony for us was to see white racists act always under the guise of patriotism and Christianity.

Many whites came to our shoe-shine stand on a skid row street in New Orleans. Many wanted us to help them find immoral pleasures — girls, gambling, obscene photographs. We learned to spot them, for they treated us with a conniving friendliness and "equality." I mentioned this to my partner, an elderly veteran who had lost a leg in World War I.

"Oh, yes," he remarked astutely. "The whites are much more democratic in their sinning than in their worship."

I did not immediately realize the profound scandal involved in his words, and certainly I did not connect it with the Catholic Church. What struck me was that the racist, who spoke so often of the lower morals of Negroes, appeared to live on a much lower moral level than I found among Negroes. His concern for "racial purity" did not extend to the colored race, as any Negro soon learns.

That afternoon, as we prepared to quit work, I asked my shine partner where I could find the nearest Catholic church.

"I guess the closest *colored* Catholic church would be way over on Dryades Street," he said.

"There's no such thing as a colored Catholic church," I replied quickly.

He looked up at me in astonishment. "You don't really believe that, do you?"

I assured him I did. "I know some churches practice segregation," I said. "But the Archbishop right here in New Orleans has declared segregation a grave moral sin."

"You're black now, John," my companion said in a gentle voice. "And this is the South. You're going to find that a lot of white Catholics look on you as a nigger first and a Catholic second, no matter what the Archbishop says. And a nigger Catholic's got to stay in his place, just like any other nigger."

*

On Dryades Street, in the Negro section, I mounted the steps of St. John the Baptist Catholic Church and opened one of the heavy doors. Street noises were muffled with its closing. Soft light filtered through magnificent stained-glass windows in this oldest of New Orleans' churches — once a church for Catholics, now a church for Negro Catholics.

I sat in a pew, dwarfed in the vast structure, and leaned forward with my head against the bench in front. Glancing down at my hands, I saw each black wrinkle, each dark pore. This blackness condemned me out in the world, but the blessed illusion of sanctuary within the church was so intense that I could not believe it condemned me here. I was home. I belonged here as much as any man. I felt superbly safe from that incessant threat of humiliation which daily accompanies the American Negro. I knew the Church's teaching allowed for no racial distinction between members of the human family. It regarded man as a *res sacra*, a sacred reality. God created all men with equal rights and equal dignity. The color of skin did not matter. What mattered was the quality of soul. I recalled a statement made by Father J. Stanley Murphy, C.S.B.: "Whenever any man permits himself to regard any other man, in any condition, as anything less than a *res sacra*, then the potentiality for evil becomes almost limitless." Remembering this in the skin of a Negro, I saw that it summed up the racist fallacy and its effects on us.

Later, as I made my way slowly through the more deprived areas of the South, I learned some of those burningly shameful contradictions that Negro Catholics have to face. If it is painful to see that your country does not practice what it preaches, it is infinitely more painful to see that your Church does not. Though we deny that segregation exists in the Catholic church, it does in effect exist.

I learned the humiliating protocol. In areas where there was a Negro Catholic church, it was made clear to me that I had better attend that one and no other. In areas where no such provision existed, I attended a "white" church. But I was instructed by other Negro Catholics I was to sit to one side. If I wanted to receive Christ, I waited until the last white person had received Him and had returned to his seat before I approached the altar rail. Otherwise, I was warned, I would risk being passed at the altar rail. Negroes are constantly affronted by this. It either drives them deeper into the faith or it drives them away.

How can the Catholic Church be God-centered and yet practice this sort of segregation which it denounces as a "grave sin"? The point was clear. The Church did not practice this sort of segregation — this was the practice of bad Catholics, pure and simple. They persisted in a sin which their religion abominated. Knowing this, however, was strangely poor consolation. In such areas, the blessed illusion of sanctuary within the Church was shattered. We were hurt there in our deepest selves. We were, in effect, second-class Catholics, as we were second-class everything else. It was the same for all other Christian religions, of course, but that did not help either. And when we Negroes heard priests and bishops quietly explain their hesitancy to repudiate such attitudes "for fear of alienating souls," we knew they were referring to the souls of prejudiced white Catholics. And we wondered why they appeared to have so little "fear" of alienating the souls of Negroes.

How did otherwise decent white Christians justify such things? They said: "Why Negroes are more comfortable in their place. They like it that way. It's a kindness really." I never heard a Negro say such a thing or in any way act as though he "liked it that way." One of our greatest problems was the white's willingness to solve our problems according to his comforts. This is true in the North, South, East and West.

In the many rural areas and small towns, the "wonderfully harmonious relations" whites claimed to enjoy with Negroes resembled those one might enjoy with an animal beaten into utter submission. Here we knew that if we did not grin and say "Yes, yes, yes" to everything the white man wanted, we would be taught a lesson. We "accommodated," but when we went home in the evenings, we wept and said how could the white man twist his mind enough to think this death of our manhood, our hopes, and our dignity — this slavery — was for our own good.

As a stranger in their midst, I was taken in by Negroes and treated with the sort of protective tenderness that comes only from those who have suffered to the point of despair.

One night, I watched a mother feed mashed yellow beans in Carnation milk to bright-eyed youngsters who did not yet know that doors into wonderlands of education and justice and employment opportunity were barred to them. They reminded me of my own white children who could enter all of those doors. And I wondered how any human parent could tolerate a System that arbitrarily marked my children for privilege and these children for deprivation. I said to myself: "We are not that evil. It's because we don't know, don't understand what a killing thing it would be to look into your children's eyes and know they didn't have a chance." I told myself that we would shout our outrage if anyone advocated that we physically maim these children. Yet we daily implicated ourselves in the vaster crime that saw them spiritually maimed.

At that moment, I saw the lamplit wretchedness in sharp focus, saw my hosts' faces flattened of all expression, dulled of hope or enthusiasm. I saw my black hands clenched in my lap and was torn to remember that I was once white. And I realized, with sickening horror, that we whites have permitted ourselves to allow fellow human beings to be turned into the burnt-out shells who sat with me in that shanty. And I asked myself what great thing have we gained that was worth making them pay this kind of price.

These were people of quality. With education, the incentives of fair employment, a chance at human dignity, all of this would have been different. But we had condoned the System that deprived them of any chance to fulfill themselves. And then, unbearable irony, we had attributed their nonfulfillment to racial defect.

I could not understand how Negroes resisted the temptation to hate. They have a remarkable record for resisting subversion, for manifesting a deep love of country. But this is a love of what the country is supposed to be, the American Dream — not what it is where racism is practiced. No, even in despair, Negroes could resist the temptation to hate whites, and this for two reasons.

First, Negroes understood clearly what whites are only beginning to understand — that whites are as helplessly entrapped by the "System" as Negroes are and are as handicapped by it.

Second, Negroes believed that their misery came from the "white trash" and that the trash, though powerful and unscrupulous, were a minority as oppressive and painful to the "good whites" as to the Negroes. We Negroes seldom met these good whites, but we were sure they were there and could be counted on to behave correctly and to call for justice when the time came. A handful of them had stood up and been counted. Lillian Smith, that great and brave Georgia woman of prophetic vision, had warned that those who embraced the strangely shallow dream of white supremacy were killers of the American Dream of a society based on freedom, equality, and justice, and she had been slashed to bits by racist reprisals. P. D. East, in Mississippi, had spoken and suffered. Sarah Patton Boyle, in Virginia, had spoken and been devastated.

But since I returned to white society, all of this has changed, is now changing. The changes are so drastic that those who knew something about the South ten years ago, or even two years ago, are misinformed if they rely on that information today.

*

Can the wounds be cured? Is death to be the only effective educator? We go on speaking of gradualism, but in the skin of a Negro and through his eyes, it has become obvious that gradualism can stretch on to eternity. We go on speaking of Negro crime, when Negroes know that these are not the crimes of Negroes but the crimes of men, the crimes of the ghetto where we have so long forced Negroes to remain. We go on in the euphoric illusion of progress, while the Negro cries, "It looks like all Africa is going to be free before we can get a lousy cup of coffee in America." Can we draw love out of this cauldron of growing hatred, before it dehumanizes all of us? These are the questions that lead to the core of the problem. It is a moral problem, and unless we attack it at this level, we have no chance of evading the nationwide explosion that must occur.

If Negroes have been embittered by the "white man's Christianity," they have been made deeply cynical by the "white man's politics." Demagogues have ridden to political power through appeals to popular prejudice and racist vilification. National political leaders have talked timidly about justice and acted even more timidly to implement it. White men have consistently decided what Negroes want, what is good for them, and how their problems should be solved — but always according to the white man's lights. Even in intergroup councils, Negroes seldom choose their own representatives. The whites choose those Negroes whom they want on the councils. As one Negro minister put it: "They always talk for us and to us but never *with* us."

In the early days of the Kennedy Administration, despite some implementation that appeared catastrophically radical to segregationists, Negroes viewed the Administration's refusal to "go all the way" as merely more tokenism. There lingered the suspicion that the late President's civil rights stance was a matter of political maneuver rather than statesmanship. After so many disappointments with past presidents, few dared hope that Kennedy's affirmations of right would stand the acid tests that would prove them true principles. When the showdown came, would he relax into the safety of nonaction or would he act as a man of principle?

The showdown clearly came during the Alabama crisis. For the first time in history, a President of the United States spoke on the matter of civil rights without equivocation, without those fatal "if's, and's, and but's," and he followed through with a civil rights bill that had the ring of authentic statesmanship.

> We face [he said] a moral crisis as a country and a people. It cannot be met by repressive police action. It cannot be left to increased demonstrations in the streets. It cannot be quieted by token moves or talks. It is time to act in the Congress, in your state and local legislative body, and, above all, in our daily lives.

The late President did not speak of Negroes as Negroes but as men, as citizens. He made no mention of the "Negro Problem" but spoke clearly of America's problem and of the problems of every individual American. "A great change is at hand," he said, "and our task, our obligation, is to make that revolution, the change, peaceful and constructive for all."

The late President was giving leadership, and he was asking for leadership at the regional, the sectional, the local and the individual level. The issues were clear, and they had been clearly stated. Then as now, we must choose to embrace the sanity of justice, or we will perish as a nation in the insanity of violence. Negroes and most whites, surely, realize that we hang in the balance now. Yet the late President's words have been obstreperously repudiated by the Southern bloc, with a veritable orgy of question-begging epithets that any unprejudiced twelve-year-old of normal intelligence could recognize as such.

Religion, in the eyes of many, has been a failure. When asked what he thought of the contributions of Christian ministers to the solution of our racist problems in the South, P. D. East replied, "Very damn little. I always thought ministers of God were supposed to be leaders, not followers."

Many religious leaders have remained silent out of fear of precipitating violence. Others, ministers of the Protestant faiths, have often remained silent because they knew they would be put out by their congregations, which would demand ministers with the "right kind of religion." The growing new sentiment, however, suggests that the time is so critical that ministers must speak up in an attempt to clear the consciences of their congregations and let the chips fall where they may. In Mississippi, twenty-eight Methodist ministers spoke up. All have been fired. Presbyterians, Episcopalians, Quakers and many others have spoken up and have suffered the consequences. Among Catholics, the archbishops of New Orleans and Atlanta have been notable exceptions to a dreary picture. The National Catholic Conference for Interracial Justice reports that twenty Catholic dioceses of the twenty-five stretching from West Virginia to Texas have announced a school-integration policy.

In other areas, the scandal of silence prevails in most churches, Catholic and non-Catholic. Where tensions are extreme, the encyclicals *Mater et Magistra* and *Pacem in Terris* appear to be ignored.

There are many reasons for this silence. The bishops are in a difficult position where almost any overt movement could create chaos. However, we must face the painful fact that to the Negro Catholic and to many white Catholics, these reasons are obscure and they suffer the bitter disillusion of seeing that Holy Mother Church does not speak up for her children and that she appears prudent to the point of paralysis and overly patient with injustice. This is an agony for many priests. Individual Catholics, and also groups like The Grail and Caritas, are throwing their lives into this shallow reservoir of charity in a desperate attempt to stem the tide of conflict. Often they ask in anguish, "Why doesn't the Church here speak *now?*"

This year, I have had close contact with some of the best-informed people in the world: Jacques Maritain, Thomas Merton, Louis Lomax, Lillian Smith, P. D. East, Sarah Patton Boyle, Professor Dwight L. Dumond. All have said the same thing. Time is running out in America. We are being subverted by expediency and compromise faster than we are being converted to ethical principles and wisdom. All agree that we are faced with two basic alternatives.

We can look beyond the accident of skin color and view one another simply as humans and as citizens and join together in repudiating every injustice suffered by every citizen. Or we can deny the humanity that lies beneath our skins and set about the insane business of killing one another.

DIALOGUE WITH FATHER AUGUST
THOMPSON

⟶

Father Thompson, since you are a priest who happens also to be a Negro, we might begin talking of the effects of racism on religion in the U.S. The Church has, of course, been strongly outspoken on this subject.

Yes, I have in my hand *Pacem in Terris*, which means so much to me because here is the Pope speaking, and we can't evade the fact that once the Holy Father speaks, we must listen. Pope John XXIII's death was a grievous loss to us, but I am happy to see that Pope Paul VI is moving ahead in the same spirit.

There is one part here in *Pacem in Terris* where His Holiness speaks specifically about racism. "But truth requires the elimination of every trace of racism," Pope John says in paragraph 86. Racism is our major problem in the world today. If we face this truth, we must get rid of racism. I'd like to concentrate on this — to air some of these truths even where they hurt, even where they are likely to cause strong disagreement.

We needn't beat around the bush, Father. We are going to discuss one of the greatest incongruities in our times — the racism that exists quite openly in some areas of the South and other areas of the country as practiced by Catholics. Didn't your own sister have to leave the South in order to become a registered nurse?

Yes, my sister Margarette. She had to leave the South for her studies because no Catholic hospital in the South would take her for training. This was about 1951, I believe, but even today in the so-called Deep South I do not think that any Negro girl could get into a Catholic hospital for her nurse's training . . . Now, with Archbishop Hallinan's courageous stand, it might be possible in Atlanta.

Father, to clear the air, let's talk about racists' claims that Negroes are morally inferior by nature; that there are more Negro crimes; a looser sexual morality . . .

I'd like to make two points here. Much of this kind of talk comes from the need to justify injustices. Only by believing that Negroes are intrinsically inferior can non-Negroes tolerate in conscience the system that defrauds us of our civil and human rights. We hear talk about "Negro crime," but do Negroes commit any crimes that men of other complexions do not commit? No, these are not Negro crimes, but the crimes of men. If statistically Negroes commit more crimes in America than non-Negroes, the cause lies not in our "Negro-ness" but in the very ghetto life that we are forced to lead under a system of rigid segregation, in the formation we receive. This system, with all its injustices, deprives men of any sense of dignity or personal value — and no man can live without that. If you kept a significant number of white men in such a degrading environment, systematically deprived them of dignity and hope, closed most doors to self-fulfillment and left open only the door to despair, the white crime rate would soar. Also, since Negroes see that law enforcement generally means abuse for us, we grow up with less respect for the law than we should have. In the South, where so many of the police belong to the Klans or other racist groups, no example is set that might give Negroes any true respect for the law.

Here again, I would like to refer to the Holy Father's *Pacem in Terris*. He says: "It is not true that some human beings are by nature superior and others inferior. All men are equal in their natural dignity. . . ."

And yet, Father, we hear constantly the cant that Negroes must "change," must earn the rights we unhesitatingly accord even the most degraded non-Negro. We hear it also among Catholics, don't we?

Yes, and here the truth is going to be painful. I realize that white Catholic Southerners are the products of their environment — the prisoners of their Southern segregated culture just as we Negroes are. From their point of view, changes in their attitudes are difficult — and in fact they are not even aware that such changes might be indicated. I sympathize deeply with the agony that comes when the need for such changes of attitude is perceived — and more and more are perceiving it.

But let me speak from the Negro's point of view. We have our own dilemmas. They expect us to "change" and yet they give little help to bring about change. This is particularly true and troublesome in the area of religion. In some Southern dioceses, for example, Negroes cannot attend retreats or days of recollection. I have had parishioners come up and ask me what a retreat is. They have only heard about them. But we cannot attend retreats —

Except as a group?

Not even as a group. They just don't want us. In some places our young people cannot attend camps. Too often we cannot join church societies. Yes, it is true that we could form our own little segregated Negro versions of these same societies, but you lose the whole spirit — the very Catholicity — of it when you do that. In such areas, Negro couples cannot attend Cana Conferences. Do you know that I, as a priest, have never attended a Cana Conference? Do you know that white non-Catholics are welcomed into Catholic churches and can attend church functions where I, as a Negro priest, would not be permitted? . . .

Negro writers in particular have spoken out with a kind of slashing bitterness that often shocks the white community. Do these writers mirror resentments felt by most members of the Negro community? What they say certainly disagrees with the oftenheard contention of Southern whites that Negroes were a happy, contented people until outside agitators and the U. S. Supreme Court began stirring them up.

Yes, one doesn't know whether to laugh or cry when our discontent is blamed on outside instigators and the 1954 Supreme Court decision. How false. How false to think that our discontent is anything other than the discontent of men who are not allowed to be whole. . . .

What about claims frequently made by whites that Negroes, never having known anything else in the South, become inured to all of these undignifying things — that they do not really suffer from the lack of rights they have never known?

How can any man ever become accustomed to getting cheated? When the body is never fully fed, it never stops being hungry. It is the same with man's spirit — it hungers, hungers after dignity, freedom and love; and it never stops hungering after these things until it is finally crushed. We Negroes have often referred to our treatment as being like a bone thrown to a dog. You don't ask the dog if it wants this bone, or if it wants another or if it wants a piece of meat. You just throw the bone and tell the dog it must take that. And that's what happens too often to our citizens of color. Negroes are thrown a bone and told: "That is what you want. This is how you want it." The Negro just cannot understand why it is that some persons never think we can grow up enough to know exactly what we want and always have to have others tell us what we want and how we want it. In the past, Negroes who said: "I want more than a bone. I need something more than that for myself and my children," were called "bad niggers" and silenced . . .

What about the role of religion in solving this problem of racism? In your youth and even now, how have religious leaders solved this problem? I do not mean Catholics exclusively, but all religious leaders.

In my youth, it simply wasn't solved. It wasn't solved because everyone was silent. Everyone was afraid.

Afraid of what, Father?

Afraid of the truth. Afraid to face facts. Negroes and some percipient whites have for a long time tried to make these truths known — but they are too painful for most to face. And finally, you get tired of trying to bring forth the truth when no one listens. You are talking to the wall. You are talking to the wind.

Father, this truth about which we speak — this truth as you know it and as I have known it as a Negro Catholic — in many of its aspects, this truth is deeply scandalizing. Many of us have held back telling these things out of our love of the Church. Do you think we were right?

We are never right in suppressing any truth that could help to bring about right.

Let's pursue this. We very often hold back for fear of offering scandal, particularly to non-Catholics; for fear that anti-Catholics might build their case against Catholicism even stronger through over-emphasis on this scandal of truth. And yet I wonder if by doing this — and you can answer this better than I — we have not deepened and in effect perpetrated the scandal. Have we hidden our problems rather than solved them?

This has been a source of the deepest trouble with me. Many believe that we should keep our skeletons in the closet; but I am convinced that we simply cannot afford to have any skeletons — especially skeletons that disillusion souls and drive them from God.

Imagine what happens to a new Negro convert who has been taught only what the Church is, what the Church stands for, and who then encounters the kind of segregation-within-the-faith one finds in many areas of the South. I know that I, in my convert classes, have been guilty of hiding many of these things, not telling the converts what they are likely to find: that in some "non-segregated" but still segregated churches they must sit to one side; that in some Catholic churches they will not even be permitted to worship. And then I have seen them suffer the terrible shock of discovery. In taking account of our silence here, we must not forget these souls that have been sickened and alienated — souls of Negroes, yes, but precious in God's sight. The fault — the ramifications of segregation within some Southern churches — becomes monstrous when seen in this light . . .

Do you, as a priest, feel any direct effects of prejudice within the Church?

Yes, some Catholics will not even call me Father — they dodge around such an endearing term by calling me Reverend or Padre or something like that. Of course, there are many churches and functions which I do not attend . . .

In other areas of activity, prejudice complicates the priestly life at the personal level. I am rarely invited, for example, to do anything with other priests — to go fishing, for example, or make a trip. But this is simply the way things are, and does not indicate prejudice on their part necessarily. In general, priests enjoy such recreation and indeed many nonrecreational pastimes with one another. I am not directly excluded from such activities, I am just never *included* in them . . .

Father, when I lived for a time as a Negro in the Deep South, my greatest shock came with the discovery that if there was a Negro Catholic church in the area, I had better attend that one and that I was not free to go to Mass, for example, in the "white" church, even if that happened to be much nearer. Most Catholics are under the illusion that the Catholic Church has no taint of this kind of segregation — that any Catholic can attend any Catholic Church anywhere in the world. I recall that when a Negro companion first mentioned the "Negro Catholic Church," I told him there was no such thing. But in practice, there is this kind of distinction, isn't there?

I'm afraid there is. When we refer to the Negro church, it means two things: first, it means the church that is located in the Negro neighborhood, where Negroes are expected to attend, as people within any given parish are expected to attend their parish church; second, it means also that all Negroes in the vicinity, even if they happen to live miles away and are located in an area served only by a "white" church, are expected to come to the Negro church. Or, if the distance is inordinate, then Negroes can receive the sacraments at the local "white" church, but usually with a special protocol — they sit in a section reserved for them and they do not go to the communion table until all whites have received and returned to their places.

Let me tell you something else. In an area where there is a Negro church, if we have one Mass or two Masses at the Negro church and a Negro cannot attend either of them for some legitimate reason; then, even though there might be two or three other Masses that he could attend in some "white" church, he has no obligation to attend any of them. I must say here that some churches *have* opened their doors to Negro Catholics. But in many areas this has not happened yet — and so the Negro who has missed Mass in the Negro church is under no obligation to attend Mass if that means going into a white church. I can't see this double standard of morality at all.

How does this happen? I mean by what authority does a Negro feel that if he has missed Mass in his home church he has no obligation to attend Mass elsewhere?

It's tradition and it's also practice. If he went to some white churches, he would simply be put out. This doesn't seem possible, but in practice it's true enough. He would not be accepted. I know of an instance where there was only one Negro Catholic in a town and the parish there paid someone to drive this person every Sunday to the nearest town where there was a Negro Catholic Church — this rather than let the person worship with them. I have people come to my church from as far as seventeen miles away, and some from towns eight or ten miles away . . .

Father, you received much of your seminary training in the South. Were you aware of any discrimination as a seminarian — either within or outside the seminary? Did the fact that you were a seminarian nullify any of the prevailing prejudices?

The fact that I am a priest has not nullified them, so they were certainly not nullified by the fact that I was a seminarian. There were certain churches I could not enter then just as there are churches and church activities — first communions, confirmations, Cana Conferences — where I am not allowed now, where I cannot say a scheduled Mass.

How are you made aware that you should not attend these things, Father? Does someone actually tell you that you should not —?

I have been told, yes. I have been told that I should not attend these functions or say a scheduled Mass.

So you are segregated as a priest also. Is this the same for all Negro priests in the South?

Well, let's say that in some areas, we Negro priests might be called second-class Christs, if that's possible.

We know that we do have the profound scandal of second-class Catholics — I mean this is a thing that is too well-known to hide any longer, but when it is the scandal of a "second-class Christ" it becomes inconceivable. You are really a Negro first and a priest second, then?

The priesthood should take primacy over everything else, of course, but with us it's "a Negro first, a Negro second, and finally a priest."

How do you react to this? This must burn you very, very deeply — not as August Thompson, but as a priest of the Catholic Church, does it not?

As a priest it does, because it degrades the priesthood. And that's why I try to do everything possible to right it. It's not just me — it's others — it's the scandal of it as it affects other Catholics that hurts the deepest.

Have you spoken this frankly to others — to priests and members of the hierarchy?

I think I have done my share of speaking frankly.

How has this been received?

I don't think I succeed in making myself clear. The simplest facts in this sort of problem tend to sound like complaining. It is suggested that I do not appreciate the complexities of the problem. But still, this does not answer the questions, nor, much more importantly, does it give me answers to the questions that others are asking.

Yes, now, you as a priest obviously cannot keep this completely from your parishioners. And eventually the whole Negro community knows about it. How do your parishioners and the potential converts in your community feel about this? Or do you hide it from them?

I do not think such things should be hidden, but I guess I do hide it as much as possible. I hide it because I know this is *not* the Church, but only the sinful acts of other Catholics — we have to make that clear. But nothing can really be hidden. Let me give you an example of how this affects new converts. Last year we went to a Christ the King rally where every parish was supposed to be represented. We went there to give honor to Christ the King of the whole world. At this rally, I was the only Negro in the procession. The Negro families who accompanied me — all of them converts of recent years — watched from the sidelines. They saw that we had only white altar boys and flower girls — no Negro children in that procession. Well, things like that stand up and cry to be seen, and you can be sure that the full impact of it hit every one of my parishioners. And they wanted to know *why* . . .

Do you see any perceptible change for the better? What about Bishop Gerow's recent statement after the murder of Medgar Evers in Mississippi?

I was heartened to see this statement. I have it right here. I was particularly heartened by this. He said: "I am ashamed when I review the events of recent days and weeks. As a loyal son of Mississippi and a man of God, I feel in conscience compelled to speak out in the face of the grave racial situation in which we now find ourselves. This problem is unmistakably a moral one. We need frankly to admit that the guilt for the murder of Mr. Evers and the other instances of violence in our community tragically must be shared by all of us. Responsible leadership in some instances has been singularly lacking." Certainly, he is including himself as part of that leadership and is accepting his part of the guilt. It took a humble man to make such a statement.

Many people seemed to feel that it was very late in the day for Bishop Gerow to speak — that he should have spoken up a long time ago.

I can only say that I am very glad and edified to see that he spoke so well when he did speak.

Father, I would like to get down to this question of religious leadership in the Deep South as it concerns specifically human and civil rights. We have two striking examples of action on the part of Catholic leaders — the work of Archbishop Rommel in New Orleans and of Archbishop Hallinan in Atlanta. What about other Bishops? Are we moving ahead, stagnating or falling back?

There have been many other moves, certainly, made with no fanfare. I myself do not believe in a lot of fanfare in connection with good actions. Out of the twenty-five dioceses in the South, twenty have desegregated schools. But even five dioceses represent a sufficiently large area to cause us grief. Yes, we are moving ahead, but of course in many cases, Negroes think it is a little too slow and that we are perhaps a little too cautious. Many Negroes still use the old "bone" symbol. They feel that white Catholics are throwing us the bone and telling us this is what we want and this is what we should have.

I'm not saying either that Negro Catholics want any kind of special treatment. They feel they are getting special treatment right now, and that is the trouble. All they want is to be treated exactly the same as any other Catholic . . .

Father, on research trips through the Deep South, I have often encountered non-Negro Catholics who are deeply concerned. Almost invariably these people — and these are not Negroes — will ask me: "Why doesn't the Church speak now?" The Church has been "speaking" for a long time, of course. What they mean is why do not the local prelates speak up NOW. This was particularly true in Mississippi before Bishop Gerow issued his recent statement. Do you, as a Negro priest, feel that the silence of some of the Bishops is as loud as we Catholics sometimes seem to hear it?

I fear that the silence in some areas is quite loud. Many people think that this silence is a sign that those in authority agree with the situation as it exists. Whether they do or not, that is not for me to say. It does seem that the splendid statement of the American Bishops on racial justice has not always been implemented — or at least the Negro Catholic in the South can not always see evidence of its having been implemented. I feel that something must be done, and done fast, or the misunderstanding will grow . . .

My impression, and I would like to see if it corresponds with yours, is that in the past few years Negroes — both Catholic and non-Catholic — have become progressively disillusioned with the Catholic Church, and this because of this tacit segregation and all it implies and our slowness to correct it.

That appears to be true, and it is an agonizing admission for me to make. But it is only by practicing what we preach that we can hope to undo this disillusion. I am not exaggerating when I say that this is a deeply disturbing and widespread feeling among Negroes. The apparent gains very often show up to Negroes as merely other aspects of tokenism. Even many of the authentic gains appear in a suspicious light.

Have we lost ground in this area?

We have. There are many Catholics who do not go to church because the pain of this kind of humiliation is simply unbearable. Think of going to church, going to communion, and in order to receive Christ you must wait until every white Catholic has gone to the communion table and returned to his seat — knowing that you might well be skipped if you approached the altar while some white person was still there. Think of that encouraging people to receive communion. Many do, of course, but with a deep sense of sickness, and then resentment that even this great sacrament should be clouded in indignity for them. Many are so affronted by this that they fall away or simply do not enter the church — and think of this tremendous harvest of souls we lose by simply disgusting them away from the Church . . .

What are the answers, Father?

The answers are not simple but the Church has given them. The Church has told us what Man is, a *res sacra* or sacred reality . . . a *res sacra* regardless of color. She has told us that strict justice admits of no modification, and that anything less than strict justice is simply injustice, regardless of what you choose to name it. Let every Catholic, no matter what his color, become a real Catholic, a true Catholic . . .

PREFACE TO GABRIEL COUSIN'S
L'OPÉRA NOIR

———————————————————————————→

Last night I read *L'Opéra Noir*. No, I *lived* it, for the author made me see and hear and smell the scenes with a kind of hallucinant reality. I finished the play at dawn, and then I slept as though I had been bludgeoned (assommé).

At noon, the dazzling Texas sunlight awakened me and I stared out to the countryside around this farm, a countryside that simmered under a hot, intense light. Seated on my bed, I could not hear the music of Bach or Mozart — or the Gregorian *alleluia* — that usually springs to consciousness to accompany me from sleep to wakefulness each morning. No, the vast silence contained another music, heard like some distant carousel that has broken down, gone crazy, producing only a dolorous cacophony — it was the murmur of Negro spirituals, the cries of jazz trumpets, the sobs of *blues*, mingling in counterpoint.

In the disorder of half-awakened senses, I wondered if I had really read this manuscript or if the experiences of *L'Opéra Noir* were not really the extension of old nightmares I had once had when I was a Negro. My Negro nightmares resembled this play, they were brilliant crystallizations of all the elements that made up our misery. This is why I detest jazz, blues — even the most exuberant are nothing but funeral music when one is black. They plunge you into that hell where the whites, all in saying how much they esteem you, have already for many generations plunged you. The music becomes the consoler, yes, but it recalls too vividly the misery of its roots.

I asked myself, who is this Gabriel Cousin who knows in his bones what it is to be a Negro in the Deep South? Few American white people have any intimate knowledge of the problems of Negroes; but this Frenchman creates a work as authentic as any created by an American Negro. I felt that what Mr. Cousin had done was impossible. The view that we white Americans have of our fellow citizens of color is so false that I could not see how a Frenchman's views could be any less false. Yet, it is not false here. It is true in its nuances, in its smells and in the rhythm of its language . . . true, alas, even to the *Christ Blues*. How this *Christ Blues* will shock white Christians. And yet it is precisely because we white Christians have presented such an unholy image of Christ to Negroes that they have developed such contempt for "the white man's Christ." We whites who could call ourselves Christians and at the same time practice the most wounding kind of racism — we wrote this blasphemous piece; Negroes only transcribed it. When I was a Negro, I heard all about the "white man's Jesus." I once saw a Negro youth who had been handed one of those little pious cards where Christ and his Disciples are portrayed as white, white, white. I saw this youth stare at the card for a moment and then hurl it into the dust, muttering that he was sick of the white Jesus. The woman who had given him the card stared at him in horror. Such a blasphemy sickened her. But we Negroes understood and remained silent. He had seen how little the white man practiced Christianity, how little that "white Jesus" was meant for him — he had been too deeply hurt; hurt there in his deepest self.

This is part of the dilemma and the senselessness that accompanies *racism* wherever racism is allowed to grow. To the Southern white segregationist, Jesus Christ was a white, Southern protestant. Negroes know all about white Southern Christians. If they are holy, they rarely show that holiness to Negroes. Recently, after I had lost my color and become a "white man" again, I went into the South, near the Mississippi border, to visit a Negro Catholic priest. In this little town, it was considered the worst kind of offense for a white man and a Negro to spend the night under the same roof. I knew that I could visit this priest only so long as the white community did not know that I was there. The only place we could go to eat was in the homes of Father's Negro parishioners; and on a previous visit, the Negro family who had sheltered me and fed me were threatened by the Ku Klux Klan there. Now, here is the irony and the senselessness. If the whites there had caught me in the home of this Negro priest, where I spent the night, they would have certainly attacked me; but if they had found me, a white man, spending the night with a Negro woman in the same part of town, for immoral purposes, they would have laughed and considered it part of the "charm" of the Southern Way of Life. Strange Christianity. Believe me, these men consider themselves Christians. No wonder, then, that Negroes view the "white man's Jesus" with pain and disillusion.

But we white Americans, though we constantly claim to "know all about our nigras," do not know any of this. It is a strange blindness — a lack of awareness, we have, that must seem unbelievable to people in other countries — unless they remember that our problem in America is not a problem of race, but of racism; not a racial problem, but a racist problem, similar to the racism of Nazi Germany which was directed against the Jews.

Whites here, though we do not realize it, are as much prisoners of our "System" as Negroes are. Future historians will be mystified that generations of us could stand in the midst of this sickness and never see it, never really *feel* how our System distorted and dwarfed human lives because these lives happened to inhabit bodies encased in a darker skin; and how, in cooperating with this System, it distorted and dwarfed our own lives in a subtle and terrible way.

It is part of our cultural formation. We absorb our prejudice from the air that surrounds us, and it goes into us to taint us even when we try to combat it. This is part of our duality. I was born in the South. I grew to adolescence seeing "White" and "Colored" signs above drinking fountains, rest rooms, cafés, and I never realized what these signs *really* meant. Like most Southerners, I suffered the delusion that I had a deep and real love for the Negroes I knew.

We thought we were civilized, kind. If a Negro died, we took the family food. If a Negro became ill, we took him to the doctor and sometimes paid the doctor's bills. We helped them solve their problems, or we *thought* we did, but these were *our* solutions to our concepts of their problems. We were as outraged at a lynching as any member of the Negro community. We were good to them, but with one terrible condition — that they stay in their place. We extended them many courtesies, never seeing that all the courtesies in the world do not nullify the one gigantic discourtesy of defrauding them of human and civil rights which we contend that every person born in America possesses. We felt that as American citizens they should pay taxes and defend this country from its enemies — but we did not want them to vote, for example. If a Negro told us the truth — that he resented paying taxes and not being allowed to vote, we were horrified; we considered him arrogant and did not tolerate his presence in the area. He lost his job. He was beaten or driven away. So few Negroes dared to tell us the truth. They climbed their mountains of "yes, yes, yes," and grinned, but we did not know that at night they went home and wept because our System closed all the doors into areas of learning, growth and human dignity.

When I came to France to attend school, I was in my early adolescence. I was what one might call a "civilized Southerner." Every morning of my life, almost, I had awakened to hear my mother practicing the piano — sonatas of Mozart and Schubert, Bach preludes and fugues. We lived in a world of great music, great books, kindness and religious fervor. If anyone had told us we were prejudiced against Negroes, we would have denied it with vigor. We would have said what white Southerners have always said: "But we love our Negroes [always they were *our* Negroes, the paternalism we loved, but which was such a hideous burden to Negroes]; we are good to our Negroes — you just don't understand."

How could we, as conscious human beings, live in such a climate of euphoria? I do not know, but I do know that I only discovered the amount of damage when I was sent to France to school.

As a white man, though I knew abstractly that segregation (which is only the symptom of racism) created tragic deformations of its victims, I had little precise idea of the totality of this tragedy of injustice until I lived as a Negro. This is part of the despair among American Negroes — the certainty that no white man can know what it *really* is — what it does to children. And the tragedy becomes truly mammoth when one considers all of the broken and distorted lives of the past three hundred years; and it becomes even more mammoth when one considers that these blind whites go on perpetrating the System under the illusion that it is both patriotic and Christian; and that they therefore teach their own children this insanity, go on blinding their children for generations.

I was therefore quite astonished to see that a Frenchman, Gabriel Cousin, could create, through the alchemy of art, an absolutely authentic Negro Opera — that he could somehow get into the skin of an American Negro and there discover all the nuances, even the most obscene ones, that are usually unknown to the whites who nevertheless create the causatory conditions. Even that remarkable courtroom scene, with all of its cynicism, its idiotic counterpoint wherein the white magistrates frame the Negroes, rings painfully true, and is brilliantly realized.

It is the kind of an opera an American Negro might write from the depth of his own experience. It is the tragedy that springs from the soil of our times. Proof of the remarkable truth of this work is that any American Negro would see it as an authentic exposition of the very essence of his experience; while most American whites would see it as a false and insulting piece! — or at best, one that makes them uncomfortable, the way any tragic fairy tale might. They are wrong, of course. Mr. Cousin is right.

THE TIP-OFF

───→

The murder of the three young men in Mississippi follows the same pattern of racist dehumanization we have seen before and since. A group of men, some of them in responsible positions, deliberately planned and coldly executed these murders. They even added the usual sadistic fillip of beating the Negro member of the trio.

Not all of it can be told yet. Much cannot be told, because other men, equally dehumanized by racism, would kill again in reprisal, blindly, senselessly. We are counting human lives now.

Last year in Mississippi alone we had sixty-nine atrocities that we know about. Fifty-five bombings have occurred in Alabama. Now an average of two churches a month are destroyed in Mississippi, and there have been only occasional token arrests.

These killings and burnings are not isolated accidents. They are the products of generations of racism. They flourish in the climate of permissive violence.

In Negroes' homes one hears the talk. Men are shot and coroners call it death by heart failure. Men are found dead beside roads and police call them victims of hit-and-run drivers. Always Negroes are the victims of these gunpowder heart failures and hit-and-run drivers. But just telling it isn't enough. You have to be in these homes, see the faces ravaged with grief, hear the peculiar deadness of voices as when a young lady said, "We couldn't even count the bullet holes in my brother's head — but they called it heart failure."

How many of these killings can be checked out? Who checks them out? Negroes will not talk to strangers. Reprisals come too easily. It has to be someone Negroes know and trust: a James Farmer, a Dick Gregory. You have to run in and work fast because these are police states. The police soon get on your tail and then harass anyone you visit. The police are part of the racist Establishment. It is difficult to present evidence, because someone with a name gave you the evidence. He will be killed if you leave any trace that can lead back to him. Perhaps others bearing his name will be killed. A young doctor in an Alabama hospital warned a new hospital patient: "Gibbs? Are you related to the Gibbs? In this town we kill any nigger that's got that name."

But some of us try to check them out and document them. One or another of us runs into the "bad areas" whenever an atrocity occurs. At best though, we do not cover more than ten percent. We do this because local authorities and newspapers either ignore the events or distort facts beyond recognition.

*

We sat at a side table in a San Francisco night club, the hungri i, where Dick Gregory was fulfilling an engagement. I had just seen him perform, sitting on a stool under the spotlight. Now he leaned across the table in another room, a different man, his eyes softened by the anguish of our subject. I was going into Mississippi to see about the three missing students. Dick Gregory had just come from there. He knew already that the three young men were dead, that they had been killed within twenty-four hours after the police picked them up in Philadelphia, Mississippi. He whispered rapidly, "Take these phone numbers. If you make it to Meridian go to a pay phone and call. When they answer, tell them you want to thank them for sending the camera. That way they'll know you've been with me."

The cavelike odor of the underground room surrounded us as we discussed ways of getting in to Meridian without the usual police harassment. The message needed to be taken. There was at least one witness in hiding. We could not telephone long distance because operators simply listen in and then tell anything of importance. Mr. Gregory told me of the disguises he used to go in. I think few people in this land realize how difficult it is to circulate in a police state.

"At least try to get them the name of the tip-off man," he urged. "He's trusted. He mustn't find out anything more. He's the one who telephoned to Philadelphia and *told* the police the three were on their way and to pick them up."

The picture became clearer as I listened. This killing had been carefully planned. Men in America had met together and decided to take lives — two whites and one Negro this time.

A waiter approached. Mr. Gregory waved him away.

"But how're you going to get in, baby?"

"God knows," I sighed. "The last few times I went in, the police were following me after only a few hours."

"They're checking everybody now. Why don't you go to Memphis — get a car. Wear that black suit you got on. They might figure you for a Justice Department man."

"Yes, but if they should start quizzing me, I'd let the cat out of the bag. I never can think up plausible answers. I've got friends in New Orleans. I think I'll go there. Maybe I can get Jack Sisson to go in. He's got a valid reason for traveling in Mississippi. We'll figure something."

"Well, if you go in from New Orleans, be sure you've got enough gas to get to Meridian. If you stop for gas on the way, the filling station people are likely to start quizzing you. If you can't give good answers, they'll telephone your license to the Highway Patrol. If the police start following you, you might as well give up and get out."

"You're sure they're dead?" I asked, hoping he might have some doubt.

"They were dead by two that first morning," he said.

"Bastards," I groaned.

"Chaney got it worse. They tore him up."

Mr. Gregory's eyes were red-rimmed as though he had not slept. I sensed in him the same burden of disbelief and despair that I have felt so often these last years. I wondered how he could control himself sufficiently to make any attempt at humorous performances so long as he possessed his tragic knowledge.

*

Every trip into Mississippi is filled with tension and fear. But this one approached terror for me. I was certain I would not succeed, filled with the premonition that I would never reach my goal. And yet human lives depended on it. The word had got out that if the police picked up Dick Gregory, he was not to live. The same probably held for anyone else in those days of explosive tension. I was known and loathed in the area, and I had recently on national television called for a federal take-over of police departments in Mississippi, so my face had been seen and I risked being recognized. As I moved through the darkness I felt the same sickness of terror that I had felt in Nazi Germany in 1939 when I worked to smuggle Jewish refugees out. The surrounding evil then and now was too great. It had corrupted too many men's hearts.

*

On Wednesday, I was able to telephone that the word had been carried. The endangered lives of some were temporarily safeguarded. The tip-off man would never again be trusted.

*

(Author's Postscript)
Since writing the above, a great deal has become known about the killings in Philadelphia, Mississippi. The world was scandalized when all of the killers managed to go free, and Nobel Prize winners notified President Johnson and Southern governors and legislators of their distress.

Less well known has been the fate of James Chaney's family. Typically, racists "blame the victim." As soon as the pathologist's report on James Chaney was published, revealing the horrible mutilations young Chaney suffered before he was killed, and as soon as the bodies were definitely identified, the victim's family was made to suffer. Word was passed in Meridian, Mississippi, not to let James Chaney's mother earn a livelihood. With three other children at home to support and school, Mrs. Chaney was left destitute. The bakery where she worked fired her on the pretext that during her period of grief over her son's martyrdom she had missed too many days at work. She was obliged to change residence and the home where she was believed to have moved was bombed.

I gave two lectures about her plight, one in Oxford, Ohio, and another for the Mothers of the Cenacle, in Carmichael, California. These brought enough money to help pay her monthly bills in Meridian for a time. But the harassments continued and she has been unable to find any way to earn a living. Even some of the money that friends sent to her was intercepted, apparently, since it never arrived.

Oddly enough, but understandably, I have received small contributions from members of the white community in Meridian who knew that I could get money to her and who did not dare to go across town and place it in her hands themselves. They presumably feared reprisals for themselves. I am assured that many men in Meridian, who abhor this cruelty, would give her employment if they dared. No one dares, so great is the power of the racists in that area.

THE INTRINSIC *OTHER*

$\longrightarrow$

Lionel Trilling has remarked that culture is a prison unless we know the key that unlocks the door.

And it is a common anthropological truism that the "prisoners" of any given culture tend to regard those of almost any other culture, no matter how authentic that culture, as merely underdeveloped versions of their own imprisoning culture.

The language that men use constantly reveals this attitude. The grasping Jew. The immoral French. The savage Negro. The godless Russians. The snobbish English.

Even when we may be totally unaware that we possess such attitudes of racial or ethnic superiority, our language expresses these judgments in a glaringly clear manner.

"Some of my best friends are Jews," we say. Or, "Personally, I am very fond of Negroes, but I would not want to live next door to one."

One of the characteristics of our expression of such attitudes is that they are often perfectly natural to the speaker and unnatural to the hearer. They reveal in the speaker the falsity of viewing others as intrinsically *Other*, intrinsically different as men. This intrinsic difference always implies some degree of inferiority.

Racist attitudes begin benignly enough from this basic concept of the other as intrinsically *Other*. Once one views others as "different," the stereotype develops. We then speak of the "immoral Latins," the "shifty Orientals," the "ugly Americans," etc.

Implicit in this process is a consent to racism. Edmund Burke gave us the touchstone of this error when he said: "I know of no way of drawing up an indictment against a whole people." Racism begins when we draw up an indictment against a whole people merely by considering them *as a whole* underdeveloped versions of ourselves, by perpetuating the blindness of the stereotype.

The Nazis drew up an indictment against a whole people, the world Jewish community. And once the indictment was drawn, and far more importantly, once mankind consented to the indictment and did not cry *no* — the rest followed: the dehumanization of the total community, Jewish and Nazi.

In America and Africa, we have drawn up an indictment against whole peoples, the dark-skinned peoples. This has led to the dehumanization of all men, white and black. And once the error is accepted, then other victim groups are engulfed. The Klans of America are not only anti-Negro, but anti-Catholic, anti-Jewish, anti- *Other*.

Let me repeat that this is insidious, because it is often done in good faith, is often accomplished with an illusion of benevolence. It leads to master delusion. The delusion lies in the fact that no matter how well we think we know the *Other*, we still judge from within the imprisoning framework of our own limited cultural criteria, we still speak within the cliché of the stereotype. I have known missionaries, splendidly cultivated men, who have spent years in other cultures without ever penetrating the other culture, who go on judging everything by the limited criteria of the educated European or American. In my own life, this error was once thrown into my face.

I was living on a Pacific island doing language studies. I considered, with great affection, my subjects to be "primitives," "unevolved people," "aboriginals." There was no question but what theirs was an "inferior" and mine a "superior" culture. They were *Other*. After many months on the island, however, whenever I went from one village to the other through the jungles, I still had to have a five-year-old lad guide me. I could not find a trail. If I were lost, I would not have known how to survive, what to eat in the jungles. It became obvious to me that within the context of that culture, I was clearly the inferior — an adult man who could not have survived without the guidance of a child. And from the point of view of the local inhabitants — a valid point of view — I was *Other*, inferior, and they were superior.

But such perceptions are difficult because our culture forms us in attitudes at the emotional level very early in our lives. These learned behavior patterns are so profoundly ingrained in us that we tend to call them human nature, which they are not at all. But nevertheless, even when we are intellectually liberated from our prejudices, we often remain emotionally imprisoned by them.

My own experience, living as a Negro in the Deep South, overwhelmingly demonstrated this. Almost the deepest shock I had came the first night that I went out into the New Orleans night as a Negro. I went to a hotel in the Negro ghetto and took the best available room — a tawdry, miserable little cubbyhole. I sat on the bed and glanced at myself in the mirror on the wall. For the first time I was alone as a Negro in the Negro community. That glance in the mirror brought a sickening shock that I tried not to admit, not to recognize, but I could not avoid it. It was the shock of seeing my black face in the mirror and of feeling an involuntary movement of antipathy for that face, because it was pigmented, the face of a Negro. I realized then that although intellectually I had liberated myself from the prejudices which our Southern culture inculcates in us, these prejudices were so profoundly indredged in me that at the emotional level I was in no way liberated. I was filled with despair. Here I had come all this way, had myself transformed chemically into a black man, because of my profound intellectual convictions about racism and prejudice, only to find that my own prejudices, at the emotional level, were hopelessly ingrained in me.

However, within five days, that involuntary movement of antipathy was completely dissipated, because within five days I was living in the homes of Negro families and I was experiencing emotionally what intellectually I had long known — that the *Other* was not other at all; that within the context of home and family life we faced exactly the same problems in the homes of Negroes as those faced in all homes of all men: the universal problems of loving, of suffering, of bringing children to the light, of fulfilling human aspirations, of dying. Therefore, the wounds that I had carried thirty-nine years of my life were healed within five days through the emotional experience of perceiving that the *Other* is not other at all, that the *Other* is me, that at the profound human levels, all men are united; and that the seeming differences are superficial. The illusion of the *Other*, of these superficial differences, is deeply imbedded through this inculcated stereotype we make of the *Other*, which falsifies man's view of man.

Jean Lacroix has said that before one can truly dialogue in depth, one must open oneself to the *Other* (*il faut s'ouvrir à l'autre*). I think this is not enough. I believe that before we can truly dialogue in depth, we must first perceive that there is no *Other*, that the *Other* is self, and that the I-and-thou concept of Martin Buber must finally dissolve itself into the *We* concept.

It seems to me that this and this alone is the key that can unlock that prison of culture. It is also the key that will neutralize the poisons of the stereotype that allow men to go on benevolently justifying their abuses against other men.

PART IX

Works in Progress

Notes

———————————————————→

EDMUND WILSON once wrote of John Steinbeck: "When his curtain goes up, he always puts on a different kind of show."

The same could be said of John Howard Griffin.

By going his own highly individualistic way, he is creating works that differ startlingly and bravely from those being produced by a majority of his contemporaries. Certainly *The Devil Rides Outside* and *Nuni*, which differ vastly from each other, are worlds apart from the fiction now in vogue: worlds apart in value because they both *say something* about the world we live in: about the mess we have made of that world: about what horrors the brotherhood of man has done to the brotherhood of man in the name of love: about the redemptive effort that must be generated in us, both individually and collectively, before we can again turn in the direction of endurance and salvation, or even sanity.

When one ponders *The Devil Rides Outside, Nuni,* and the brilliant new novel *Street of the Seven Angels* (soon to be published), it is hard to disagree with Maxwell Geismar's statement that Griffin is returning the American novel and the American novelist to the great tradition.

Then there is the journalistic Griffin whose articles are concerned with a multitude of interests — the largest number being in the field of human relations, in his one-man crusade against bigotry. This is decisively not a "safe" field on which to do battle: a Southerner in the South taking up the fight against racism. This work both precedes and follows his life as a Negro and the publication of *Black Like Me.*

And sandwiched somehow in between was time for numerous short stories and *Land of the High Sky.* Again a different kind of Griffin, a different view of his personality and interests: this time his role that of an historian, creating a beautiful and haunting love song to the past. Freedom is the keynote of *Land of the High Sky*, and freedom is a recurring major theme in all his work — freedom for a man to set his own direction, unhampered, unconstrained, except by his own heart and own conscience in the rightness of his particular path.

*

Where now for John Howard Griffin? What next?
Many things in many directions.

The first will be *Scattered Shadows*, the initial volume of his autobiography. Like *Street of the Seven Angels*, it is scheduled for publication in the near future. A long book, it is the story of the years of Griffin's blindness: 1946 (when sight was lost) to 1957 (when sight was regained). One amusing story is told by Griffin about the hundreds of congratulatory messages he received from well-wishers after he recovered his sight: "They came from all over the world . . . and were from such personages as Vice-President Richard Nixon, Katharine Cornell, Gene Tunney . . . But perhaps my favorite one at the time was from the then-Senate Majority Leader Lyndon B. Johnson. 'Congratulations,' Johnson's wire read, 'This is one thing that happened in Texas that I can't see any way of taking credit for.' "

Two selections from *Scattered Shadows* are included here. Both take place in France after World War II at the time when Griffin's sight was failing.

Passacaglia, an intricate and massive novel, will appear sometime after *Street* and *Scattered Shadows*. It is impossible to predict any date for *Passacaglia*, as Griffin is still re-writing and re-working the book. It is his most ambitious undertaking to date: already he has labored on it the better part of a decade.

Still to be finished is his cultural history of the Tarascan civilization which he began in Mexico in 1960. "Passion at Tzintzuntzan," a chapter from that book, is an account of Griffin's pilgrimage to that ancient Tarascan city to observe and photograph the activities of Holy Week, 1961. It is published here for the first time.

Through the years he has been investigating the problems of censorship and obscenity, and has written at length on this topic. His current plan is to someday incorporate all these articles into a book-length study. Three of these pieces appear here. "Current Trends in Censorship" was first printed in the Summer, 1962, issue of the *Southwest Review;* "Prude and the Lewd" first appeared in the November 5, 1955, issue of *The Nation;* "Notes on Smut-Hunters" is carried here for the first time.

He is compiling a book on the changing and disappearing methods of agriculture and livestock production around the world. This will give special attention to the American Amish country, the château farms of France and Belgium, and the breeding ranches of Mexico that produce the great fighting bulls.

Also he is preparing a book of reminiscences about some of the people he has known. To be entitled *The Faces of Intelligence,* the work will utilize an exciting combination of text and photography — especially interesting because Griffin has had friendships with some of the world's most acclaimed figures.

Four chapters from *The Faces of Intelligence* are presented here. "The Poulenc Behind the Mask" was first published in the October, 1964, issue of *Ramparts* magazine; "Martin Luther King" was a chapter in the anthology, *Thirteen For Christ* (Edited by Melville Harcourt, Sheed and Ward, New York, 1963); "My Neighbor, Reverdy" appeared in the Spring, 1958, issue of *Southwest Review;* portions of "A Visit to Huy" were carried in the August, 1965, issue of *Ramparts* magazine.

SCATTERED SHADOWS — SELECTION ONE

───→

In the summer of 1946 I returned to France to spend the remaining months of my sighted life. There, in the magnificent surroundings of the Palace of Fontainebleau, nourished by music, the act of seeing became its own drama — private, intimate and personal. And it became very nearly sublime.

I told no one. I felt that losing my sight was a thing I had to do alone. I led two lives — one as a conservatory student; the other as a man looking avidly on things with the peculiar light of knowing he sees them for the last time.

My attempts to hide my condition were not always successful. Toward the end of summer, the celebrated baritone, Pierre Bernac, came to Fontainebleau to give a recital with Gaby Casadesus. The Casadesus family were old and dear friends of mine. Gaby, Bernac and I were alone in the empty concert room of the palace early in the afternoon when they prepared to rehearse. Seeing my reluctance to leave them, Gaby asked Bernac if he minded my staying.

"Of course not," he said. "He can turn the pages for you."

Standing behind Gaby, I saw the music as a white page with blurred gray notes. She played the accompaniment and Bernac sang to rows of empty seats.

The first page ended with a descending scale, which I saw as a streak. I managed to turn it correctly, but on the second page I could make out nothing and I knew I should never be able to bluff my way through.

I kept my gaze fixed on Gaby's head, thinking she might nod at the point where the page should be turned. They halted in mid-phrase. Bernac sighed with disgust — the disgust of a master musician who wondered how another musician could fail to follow such a simple score.

I apologized, muttering, "The light is so poor in here."

They passed it off gently. Perhaps a glance was exchanged. I knew Gaby had long suspected. I wondered in view of the abrupt change in Bernac's manner, if he did not suspect also. He offered me a chair on the empty stage and the two continued without my help.

I had no doubt Bernac had guessed the truth when he began to sing a berceuse, of Gounod, I think; for he turned directly to me. At the point where the mother tells the child to close its eyes, Bernac leaned over me and sang *ferme tes yeux* in a whisper, pleadingly, tenderly, infusing the words with direct meaning. The texture of my flesh changed and I lowered my head, unable to bear the evocation he created.

His voice moved away from me as he continued. Strange understanding was born in the empty hall, unspoken but sung on music and words from the past that communicated all their subtlety to the moment at hand.

And yet no mention was made of it afterward.

*

When they had finished rehearsing, I left them and walked across the street to the Hotel d'Albe. Climbing the narrow wooden steps to the third floor, I asked myself why I had not simply told them. But the answer was clear. I feared myself. I was not able to cope with the temptation to play the tragic figure. My silence was the only guarantee against falling into that trap.

I opened the door to my room. Lighted by one dormer window and sparsely furnished with a bed, writing table and washstand, it gave out its welcome hints of poverty and warmth.

My desk and bed were stacked with scores of Bach, Mozart, Chopin, Stravinsky and Hindemith, and with twenty-franc volumes of paperback classics. During these weeks, with the aid of a large magnifying glass, I buried myself in the works of Heraclitus, Epictetus and Marcus Aurelius. They refreshed the dim certainties within, assuring me that I had a will that was free, and therefore a right to see that tragedy lay not in a given condition, but merely in man's concepts of that condition. My fiercest struggles, I knew, would not be against blindness, but against the pressures of men's opinions about blindness. I hated in advance the assaults of public opinion that would surround me and judge my condition tragic.

I knew that there were truths in this that I had not found, and that I must find them or risk being sucked into the vortex of society's castrating pity. These truths were not in the platitudes:

You must not be bitter.
You must take this thing like a man.

They meant nothing. They were mere etiquette unless founded on a deeper source. My fear of blindness lay not in the handicap, I realized, but in the risk of its forcing me to adopt a role — the "brave blind man" role — that might perhaps edify others even while it corroded me with its falsity.

Alone and unguided I sought attitudes that would legitimately lead me to the kind of acceptance I knew I must have. I asked myself: "If this had not happened to you, another soldier would have been there that night. Would you prefer this happened to you or to another?"

Then I could say, with no mental reservations: "Thank God it happened to me and not to another." That way there was peace. It was a beginning.

I read and analyzed music with my magnifying glass. The jubilant mystery of Mozart — that second innocence or "second naïveté" as Einstein called it, preoccupied me. I sought to analyze from the black notes on white paper, to catch this supreme secret, for it contained the answer to the way I wanted to go . . . not musically but psychologically or spiritually. And when the headaches started I paced the floor and smoked cigarettes and raged with some focusless love. I could make no sense of any of it.

My window gave a view into the flower-filled courtyard below. I looked down on the heads and shoulders of conservatory students who sat on benches doing their lessons in harmony and counterpoint. And I marveled at the sight of hair and flesh and the evidence of intelligence as they worked. A floor below and to my left I saw Bernac and Robert Casadesus look out the window of Bernac's room. All of it registered. All of it was new. Sunlight glistened from Casadesus' balding crown. Lichen grew up the stone wall and touched Bernac's unheeding fingers on the windowsill. It was enough. I saw these things as few others would be privileged to see them — with a sense of astonishment. I stored them, engraved them, not in my mind but in some deeper place of the passions.

I became aware of the guilt of jaded eyes. I had hated not the unbeautiful, as is right, but the unattractive. Now I was given a few months in which to make up for the times when I had walked along streets and had not deigned to look, when I had turned away from good hearts because they were hid behind unattractive physical features.

Faced with nothing, very little became everything. The sight of a pin, a hair, a leaf, a glass of water — these filled me with trembling excitement. The plants in the courtyards, the cobblestones, the lampposts, the faces of strangers — I no longer took them in and bound them up in me — they retained their values, their own identities and essences. I went out to them, immersed myself in them and found them more beautiful than I ever dreamed they could be. They taught, they nourished when one gave oneself to them.

Dusk brought me face to face with the inevitable question. How did a man without sight find love? Was it possible in the human realm to love what one could not see? Was not love a thing of glances and half-gestures?

The question loomed murky when one tried to solve it alone. But the strange light of fascination shone through. It was like the light I sometimes saw in kitchens when I walked outside in the evenings. How often I dreamed of the time when I would belong in such a kitchen, enclosed there from dusk with my wife and children while another walked outside and noticed the glow and dreamt of his time in his kitchen.

The room chilled rapidly with sunset. I took off my clothes and, shivering, bathed in the half-light, using a sponge and the pitcher of unheated water from my washstand. Soap and fresh clothes destroyed the somberness. It was time to go to Bernac's recital and then to dinner with my friends.

*

The light of dedication and its example — like the light in the kitchen. I lived surrounded by it.

At dinner after the concert, I looked at Casadesus' hands, those hands that were not ashamed to practice the simplest passage for hours. I looked into the faces of Bernac and Gaby and Nadia Boulanger and saw work and sacrifice and devotion. I thought of the years of preparation in lonely rooms before they showed the world the finished product of art's past mastery.

After dinner we walked to a sidewalk café near the palace where we sat under an awning and drank the unripe beer they served in postwar France. From an overhead speaker, Edwin Fischer's performance of the Beethoven *Emperor Concerto* sang out into the darkness of cobblestoned streets. The bitter fragrance of Casadesus' pipe tobacco permeated the chill night air.

Students, exalted by beer and Bernac's concert, talked too loudly about music — about Schoenberg, Krenek and Stravinsky while in the yellow lamplight Beethoven surrounded us.

Casadesus glowered at them and muttered about "the little respect they have for music." He leaned across the table and touched my hand with his pipe stem. "Why do you stay here and listen to this conversation?"

"God knows," I said.

"You should be out finding yourself a wife. You should marry now. At your age you should spend all your time making love . . ."

His wife said, "But since when do you stick your nose into other people's business?"

Casadesus puffed his pipe benignly. "It is better to make love than to discuss theory, my friend. You learn more about art and truth that way. I don't understand why you stay here. If I were you I'd go back to —"

"Why do you stay here?" I asked.

"Because I'm old. It's my duty. I'm now an 'educator,'" he sneered at the word. "But you — you are young. I don't understand why you don't leave this silly conversation — get up and walk away . . ."

"Because he wants to hear the Beethoven, perhaps — in peace and without your interference," Madame Casadesus suggested pleasantly.

The final cadence of the Beethoven sounded into the night. Bernac rose, stretched and said, "I think I'll go turn in. Come, walk back to the hotel with me."

After saying good night, we returned to the hotel, his hand on my elbow, guiding me.

"You won't find what you're looking for here, you know," he said casually. "That's what Robert was trying to tell you."

"I know . . ."

"You find what you're looking for alone — never in a crowd," he said. "You won't get it from Robert or Gaby or Nadia or me. We can give you a hint perhaps — show you that you work hard and don't despise loneliness — nothing much more. Each of us had to do it alone. It would have been worthless, commonplace, if we hadn't."

We remained silent until we entered the hotel courtyard.

"Can I ask you something?" he said.

"Of course . . ."

"Your eyesight . . . why do you keep it a secret?"

"You just said you had to do it alone. If I told, I'd be in the midst of a crowd."

"I see. Will it get worse?"

"Yes."

"Soon?"

"Yes — it goes fast now."

I heard him make a clucking sound and felt his hand drop away from my elbow as though the touch suddenly burned him.

Mail lay under the door when I entered my room. I picked it up and carried it to my table. With the reading glass, I studied the top letter from Marie-Bruno Hussar, O.P., written from the Dominican *Couvent St. Jacques* in Paris. Friar Marie-Bruno told me that he had received extraordinary permission to have me visit him during the novitiate, and that he would expect me early the next month. "I can see you during my free time. Your stay here will be a good transition between Fontainebleau and the studies you will make at the Abbey of Solesmes."

At the end, he added: "My poor friend, why are you so determined to be brave? Bravery of this sort is nothing more than a mask. You must work toward finding a way that will not require masks . . ."

*

Insomnia. I sat on the edge of my bed in pajamas and drank a glass of red wine. The diluted amber light of a single globe surrounded me as I listened to the silences of the hotel.

Sleep was a waste. I put it off, wanting it but fighting against it. I felt I should later begrudge every moment passed in darkness that might have been passed in light.

But the wine drugged my heart and intestines, and sleep pressed heavily. I turned off the light at the wall switch and walked barefoot across the wooden floor to my bed.

I was almost asleep when footsteps rumbled on the stairs. The hope that someone might be coming to see me rose like panic in my chest. But if some friend should come and see no light under my door, he would go away. I hurried to the wall and raked my hand across it to flip on the switch.

With my ear against the door I listened to muffled voices.

"I hope this will be all right for tonight. Tomorrow I can put you in a much nicer room downstairs." I visualized the proprietor, a fat middle-aged man who smiled constantly.

"I'm sure it'll be fine," a woman said in a full mature voice. A man mumbled agreement.

A key grated in the lock and I heard the door bump against the thin wall that separated their room from mine.

"Here are towels. I think you'll find the bed comfortable. The w.c. is directly across the hall. Good night, and may you rest well," the proprietor said.

I turned off my lights and listened to the proprietor shuffle heavily down the stairs.

"Are you tired?" the man asked from the adjoining room.

"No . . ." the woman answered tentatively.

I listened to their footsteps, to the sounds of unpacking, to the silence, realizing that this was the way I would know all things in the future, by sounds.

They talked little. I judged them to be a couple long married who no longer needed many words to communicate. The ease of their silence extended to me.

In darkness, seated on the floor with my back to the wall, I followed their movements.

Keys and coins jingled and I knew the man removed his pants.

The woman coughed and almost immediately sniffed. Shod footsteps became the padding of bare feet.

I imagined how it was — the two of them alone in the room as they had been alone in countless rooms during countless past nights. They prepared for bed.

Water gurgled into a glass. A moment later the glass thumped against a saucer when it was replaced.

Bare footsteps moved to the door.

"All right?" the man asked.

"All right," she said above creaking bed springs.

I heard a click. He walked toward the bed cautiously now, his cadence altered by darkness.

I sat motionless and listened to them settle into bed. I thought of them lying side by side under the same covers, relaxing. Did they lie on their backs, I wondered, or face to face? It did not matter. What mattered was that they were there together, sharing the warmth.

Cold air poured through my open window, chilling me, but I was reluctant to move. The invisible scene with its overtones of confidence and sharing stirred me to my deepest hungers. A middle-aged couple went to bed, as they did all over the world in all times; but at that moment they showed me something essential to the heart. My longing was fixed on this quiet thing of drifting off to sleep in dim awareness that part of myself slept beside me.

———————————————————————————→

For the next few weeks, I visited the home of old pre-war friends, the Jacques Duthoos, in Tours, where I had lived as a student during my adolescence.

The blurring and headaches came more frequently. Because the Duthoos were people of great kindness, my presence was painful to them. Each time I ran into furniture, I raged with embarrassment and they stood silently by. I made them miserable, despite their protests of delight to have me.

I wanted almost desperately to go somewhere where I could make the transition into blindness in solitude. Hopefully I wrote a letter to Marie-Bruno of the Dominicans in Paris, asking him to seek permission for me to return there. I felt a great substructure of weakness within myself and believed that the monastic routine would provide the strength and calm to make it bearable, even though I had no intentions of becoming a Catholic.

Meanwhile, I spent more and more time away from the house. I revisited old haunts where I had spent such happy years in my adolescence. Tours was a city of parks and fountains and many bridges over the rivers, a city steeped in history. Every cobblestone gave up its echo of the past, recalling the kings of France and some of her saints, recalling Ronsard and Balzac and Rabelais. I walked as I had done countless times as a lonely schoolboy, under a radiant autumn sun where they had walked and saw what they had seen.

Each day, late in the afternoon, I bought a sack of chestnuts, as much for the pleasure of talking with the vendor as for eating them. We became friendly in the casual way of people who meet frequently. He was from nearby Chinon — "that's where Rabelais came from," he said with pride.

It occurred to me that I had never seen a blind man in Tours, a

city of some 60,000 inhabitants. I asked him about this one afternoon.

"There are some, Monsieur. Pitiful things. One of them lives in
my neighborhood, over near les Halles."

"What's his name?"

"Who knows? They call him *l'Aveugle*. That's all I've ever
heard."

"How long has he been blind?"

"I've lived in the quarter thirty-five years now. He's been that
way ever since I can remember."

"Do you think he'd talk with me?"

"Oh, he's grouchy as hell. You might have to buy some of his
junk first."

"He's a vendor?"

"A beggar, really. He begs postcards, books — any kind of
trash. Then hawks it on the street."

I left him and walked through the old quarter, where balconies
of houses dating from the thirteenth and fourteenth centuries almost touched overhead across the narrow cobblestone streets.
These streets converged on les Halles, a large open square where
executions had once been held, a market place that dated from the
Middle Ages. At this hour of the day it was crowded with workers
returning to their homes from work. I saw no one who might be
l'Aveugle.

I went into a dingy cafe and shouldered my way through the
aperitif drinkers toward the bar. The barman told me *l'Aveugle*
had a room in a corner house "three doors down."

I drank a glass of sour red wine and walked out into the sudden
chill of the square. The sun hung like a cold blue orb above the
bakery shop, filtered of color by the haze of smoke from cooking
fires.

The entrance to the house "three doors down" was so low I
had to stoop. Inside, I slowly raised my head to a somber foyer a
yard square, with a door on each side and stairsteps ahead. I tried
the door on the right. It opened into a black hole of a foul-smelling
w.c. I knocked on the door to the left and it opened a crack.

"Pardon, Madame. I'm looking for *l'Aveugle*."

"Mount the stairs, then, Monsieur. Last door on the right."

I felt my way along the dark hall of the upper landing. At the last door, I heard the sound of a news broadcast from a radio — strange sound in a city where radios were not common and in a quarter where they would be expensive luxuries. I tapped on the door. Footsteps shuffled within and stopped on the other side of the door.

"Who is there, please?" I heard an aged voice, soft and covered, a strangely cultivated voice; not the sour tones the chestnut vendor had led me to expect.

"You don't know me. But I should like to talk with you."

"I'm ready for bed. Do you want to buy something?"

"Yes . . ."

"You are alone?"

"Yes . . ."

"One moment, please."

His footsteps moved slowly away from the door. After a time he called me from across the room. "You may come in now."

I opened the door, prepared to hate what I saw, expecting a view of poverty and blind disorder. Light from his window showed me an immaculately clean and cheerful room. Even the stale, filthy odor of the hall was obliterated by the fragrance of lavender water.

L'Aveugle, an elderly and stooped man, with white hair and thin aristocratic features, finished tying the belt of an expensive red-and-black striped silk robe over his white brocade pajamas. His skeletal feet were encased in red leather house-slippers of an expensive cut. I thought I had got into the wrong room, but then he spoke: "Talk, please, so I know where you are."

"Yes sir. I'm right here."

"You must excuse me. I retire early."

"Please . . . I shouldn't have come so late."

"What do you wish to buy?"

"Perhaps a book . . ."

"I'll show you what I have," he said gently. I watched him kneel and drag a box from under his bed.

"Sit down if you wish. There's a chair by the window," he said.

I glanced out to dusk light on a small and cluttered courtyard behind the house. Across the way, sallow lights were turned on in other rooms and shutters were being closed.

On the table beside me, the radio's light gleamed, downstreaking the oil cloth with yellow. I had obviously interrupted his supper. Half-eaten on a plate lay slices of buttered bread and salami. A tall bottle of unlabeled red wine stood beside a partially filled glass.

The old man stacked books on his bed. His clothes, neatly folded over another chair near his armoire, contrasted oddly to his splendid night apparel: they were the ragged, filthy clothes of a pariah.

"Should I close your shutters?" I asked. "It's getting dark."

"Yes, please," he said, lifting an armload of books and carrying them to the table.

As I closed the shutters to a view of twilight on rubble, I wondered how I should ever get back to the Duthoos.

"There, you may find something interesting," he said. "Are you a scholar?"

"A student. Yes sir."

"You talk like an educated man."

"So do you, sir."

"I learn it all from the radio," he sighed. "In the evenings, for years, I have come home and listened to the radio until time to sleep. I'm a slave to that machine," he laughed. "Without it I would have gone mad long ago."

I asked his permission to turn on the light.

"Of course. I forget others must have electricity when it gets dark," he apologized. "There's a new bulb there. I always turn on the light when I close the blinds."

"You have some sight then?"

"No . . . it's just that I cannot bear the idea of sitting in the darkness. Though I have never seen it, I like the idea of light."

I lifted a large book to the drop-light and examined its title.

"Do you find anything?" he asked.

"I don't know," I said.

"Read the title to me, will you?" he asked. "I never know really what I have."

I deciphered the large printing. "*Pages Choisies* of Pierre Louÿs."

"Really?"

"Yes. And here's *Balthazar* of Anatole France. And here's Maeterlinck's *La Grande Porte*."

As I continued through the stack, I became aware of a mood of intense pleasure in the old man. I saw the scene as though detached from it — the two of us sat at his table under lamplight on a cold autumn's evening. He leaned forward, an expression of concentration on his seamed face, his blue eyes alive but focusless.

My attention was jerked back to the volume in my hand, an obvious piece of pornography. I flipped through to glimpse hazed drawings of sexual orgies and then set the book to one side.

He heard the page-flipping and the rustle as I placed the book on the table.

"What was that one?" he asked quickly.

I told him and watched his face tighten with anger. "They give me these things. I have no way, no way of knowing what they are, you understand. They think it amusing to give me these things. Twice I've been selling obscene cards without knowing. All right if some man wants to buy them. But I'm afraid to show my supply to women or children, afraid they'll see something like that and judge me a hawker of filth."

"Couldn't you get someone to go through them for you?"

"Who? I am alone. I have no one in the world." He hesitated a moment. "Can I tell you something, Monsieur?"

"Of course."

"You're the first person who's ever read these titles to me. You can't imagine what it means to me. Twelve years ago a letter came for me. I carried it for days, not even knowing who it was from. I could have asked someone in the street, but you get timid about such things." His voice thickened slightly. "Finally, do you know? — I took it to St. Martin's and asked one of the Fathers to read it for me. I'm a free-thinker, not a Catholic, but I took it there. He read it for me. It was a tax notice. Since then, until tonight, no one has read a word to me. I get everything from the radio, Monsieur."

His frail body trembled with an emotion that astonished me. "It is cold. I'm sorry I have no fire," he said shakily.

"Shall I go on?"

"Please."

"*Hölderlin* by Stephan Zweig."

"Who was Hölderlin?" he asked in a thin voice. His trembling rose to a paroxysm.

"A painter, I think."

"Would it be asking too much, Monsieur . . . yes, of course it would," he sighed.

"What?"

"If you would read me just one line . . . a sentence anywhere."

Without my reading glass I could not hope to decipher the body text. "The light is too poor, I'm afraid," I said, feeling my own voice grow unsteady. "I could come back tomorrow and read to you."

He nodded his head as though he accepted the disappointment but did not believe me. I struggled with a page, holding it almost against my eye, but the lines were fuzzy gray streaks.

I heard the question within me: "My God, is this the way it is? Is it so bad that a man goes to pieces at the emotion of having a few book titles read to him? — that he begs for a sentence, any sentence from a book?"

"There are other scabrous books here," I said. "Do you want me to separate them?"

"Please . . . if you would."

I arranged them in separate stacks and placed his hand on the stack nearest him. "There are the books you'd not want to show women or children."

"It is foul of them to give me these things," he said with dignity and hatred. "They think it's amusing."

I chose a book I thought he would probably not sell to anyone else: *Les problèmes non résolus de la science*, by Haslett, and asked him the price.

"Thirty-five francs," he said cautiously.

I counted the money into his beggar's hand that protruded from the sleeves of his princely robe.

"Will you have a glass of wine with me?" he asked.

I accepted and watched him pour, quite expertly. He held his finger over the lip of the glass and judged its fullness by pouring until the wine touched his fingertip

He did not clink glasses at the toast, as would most people of the quarter, but offered it like an aristocrat, in a raised gesture, and said: "To your good health."

"To yours," I answered and sipped at the wine.

He gazed toward me, his eyes a blare. "What brought you here, I wonder?" he asked, his voice deep in his throat.

In the background, the slick-jazz music of a Paris orchestra bounced against the room's stone walls.

"I don't really know, Monsieur," I said.

"You didn't come for a book though. Did you?"

"No sir."

"Did you come to see a blind man?" He leaned toward me, his face covering my entire field of vision, consuming me.

"Yes sir . . ."

The jazz raked across us.

"Why?" his voice exploded the word, softly, as though he dreaded the answer.

I wished for silence. The room needed silence. But we heard the cheap upsurge of saxophones and clarinets.

"Because I hoped to learn something from you."

"Learn from me? What, for example?"

"How you do things? How you live? What it's like? . . ."

He drew back as though I had slapped him. "Good night, Monsieur," he said with dignity.

"You don't understand," I said. "It wasn't morbid curiosity."

"What then? A sociological study? — How a blind beggar —"

"No . . . no . . . Believe me."

His voice sharpened with resentment. "Why should you want to know what it's like to be like me?"

"Because that's the way I'll soon be," I answered with equal sharpness, throwing it into his face.

He blanched and the flesh crumpled around his mouth. No matter what reassurances he might give me, I knew the truth of his reaction at that moment on his face. He was visibly, severely stunned.

"I know nothing about it, nothing at all," I said. "I've never even talked with anyone who's had such an experience. I thought I could get an idea of what it was like . . ."

His voice cut in, rasping and far too loud. "How old are you?"

"Twenty-six."

"A child. God damn. A child. Are you married?"

"No sir."

Music from the radio filled the silence between us:

> He was a beautiful sailor boy
> Who brought into port my fullest joy

the woman sang militantly, savagely.

The cold penetrated our clothing. Both of us trembled uncontrollably.

"You have a family?" he asked more gently.

"In America, yes."

"Will you have more wine? We can talk."

"I'm keeping you up — and it's so cold."

He rose to his feet and stood motionless for a long time, supporting himself with one hand on the table.

"Have you had supper?" he asked without opening his eyes.

"No sir."

"Ah," he smiled and slapped his hands together to create a different atmosphere. "Then I tell you. Let's eat. I have blankets. We can wrap up. Come, we will enjoy ourselves, eh? We will talk all night if you wish. It's not really so bad, you know. When one thinks of it, it's not really so bad. You see, I have nice things — nice room, a radio. I'm king here."

The discomfort dropped from between us. We were two people safe in a closed room, separated from the rest of the world by the night. We had something in common, so deeply felt that it destroyed all barriers.

"I tell you, I have good clothes in that armoire," he boasted. "Someday I may have a friend, someone like you perhaps. And he'll take me to a nice restaurant for dinner — one of the really fine places."

"I'll take you . . ."

"Would you?" he cackled with pleasure, as a father at some gesture from his child. "I'd pay for it, of course. Now —" he grimaced and reached for the radio, but drew his hand back. "Do you like this music?"

"God no. I've been wanting to change it myself."

"Good. Tell me if I come to something you like. And there are blankets in the armoire if you'd not mind getting them. You are at home here."

He spun the dial and stopped on a woman's chorus from England. They sang a bouncy, madrigal-like arrangement of a religious song.

"It's nice, eh?" he said. "Do you understand the words?"

"Yes sir. Hold Jesus, dear Jesus, in your arms like a lamb."

"*Merde*," he whispered. "It sounded like it might be something." He turned the dial again. "There, that's good, I know."

A jubilant sequential passage from a Handel violin sonata turned the atmosphere festive.

I placed one of the blankets around his stooped shoulders. He fingered the table edge and drew his chair around to the correct angle before it. Wrapped in the other blanket, I took my seat while he cut slabs of bread and salami for me.

We fell easily into conversation about blindness, not agonizing this time, for the pleasures we felt in one another's company, in drinking the wine and eating the food, overrode the somberness of our subject.

"I can teach you," he laughed. "I'll make you the most accomplished beggar on the continent. There's nothing else we can do in a provincial town. No jobs, not even the humblest. But begging is fine as long as you don't believe what you're doing. You must live two lives, keep your self-respect even when you act as though you had lost it completely."

The idea of becoming the old man's begging protégé excited my imagination.

"You are intelligent. You would learn quickly. And there is much to learn — an entire new way of living. The worst thing is the loneliness. A blind man needs a great friendship, even more than he needs a woman. I've never had a friend, but you must have. The loneliness is too terrible otherwise. When I was younger, I thought of taking a wife — one of those women who pledge themselves to marry only the maimed or disabled. But at the last moment I couldn't. Self-respect becomes the only important thing — it saves your life, really. I would have to marry a woman I won right, who wouldn't be reserved for me like a pension check just because I was blind. Can you imagine what that would do to a man? — to know that a woman slept with you not because she loved you but because she loved God!"

"Yes sir . . ."

"If you give in on one point like that, you're defeated. They have won."

"Who's that?"

"They — those out there — the sighted ones. They want you to be a certain way — they castrate you of self-respect thinking they help you. Sometimes I hate them, Monsieur . . . in their arrogance and superiority. But it's stupid to hate them. And sometimes a saint voice breathes in your ear for just a moment — out of all the clutter of sound — and then the love for humanity comes back. You will experience this. It is a great mystery to me. I am not a man of faith. I hate pious unction. But when you are blind people will reveal themselves to you, knowing you can never identify them. They will show themselves to you as they never would to another. Most are ordinary, dull. But you come quickly to see that some are saints and some are satanic. I have had elderly men and women, Monsieur — I could smell their dentures — with the odor of incense from Mass or Benediction fresh on their clothes, whisper to me — things that only Satan could utter."

His distinguished face hovered before me, his eyes closed, the long wrinkles of his cheeks deeply shadowed in lamplight. "And again, others smelling the same, have shown me hints of the most extraordinary graces . . . souls like the sunlight." His voice dropped to a dead tone: "What do you do about women? Do you go to whores? I ask you this because when you are blind everything changes. Everything is either crushed or it becomes slightly exaggerated. It takes a certain hardness inside you — a callousness — to go to the whores. What will you do about sex?"

"I've wondered about that myself," I said.

"That's the great trap," he said. "You see me? I am a puritan. We blind people almost have to become that way. But you can avoid this horrible sickness if you know about it in advance and can guard against it. We can't evade the sexual impasse like the sighted can. It is such a burning point with us that it turns us puritanical. I believe it's the worst of our handicap. I realize it now, but I'm too old to change. I know better in my mind, but I can't persuade my body and my heart. I freeze with loathing for everything that brings sex to my attention. When I was younger, I had a great craving for love. It is difficult to explain it to you. A person with sight can see in a glance that someone has affection for him. He sees a thousand indications of it — he even has a sort of union with everyone he sees. With us, all of that is gone. We know people only by their voices. And the voice doesn't really tell much. It comes out of the air. When it is tired, it sounds exactly the same as when it is sick or angry or disgusted. It is not enough. We unite by touch. And you can't go around touching people the way a sighted person can go around looking at them. When no one touches you, you crave even a handshake, the feel of something human. With a friend you can have that. He will throw his arm around your shoulder or nudge you in the ribs. Even that is enough. But without it, you crave . . . you crave . . ."

He pushed the wine bottle over the oilcloth toward me. I took it and filled our glasses.

"You think I exaggerate? No, it is a very great thing. You thought nothing of putting the blanket around my shoulders just now. To me it was — *Dieu*, how could I begin to tell you . . ."

He realized only then that he had not offered me butter for my sandwiches. He hastily brought it out of a small upright cupboard with gauze-covered doors beside his chair. I noted his accuracy in reaching for it.

"I judge everything from the location of the radio," he explained. "I know just how many centimeters to the right of that sound I keep my butter. You will learn these things. Indeed they are the least of it. It is the affections that present the problems. Do you know what my name is?"

"No sir . . ."

"I've lived in this quarter almost fifty years. Not a soul knows my name. Not that I would keep it a secret. God no, I should like to hear my name called. They never think to ask. You see, I am not an individual — not Pierre or François or Charles like the rest of them. What do I hear when I walk down the street? *Bonjour, Monsieur l'Aveugle*. I have no name — only a condition. I am known, but not for who I am, only for what I am. I tell you these things not to complain, but to show you what you must do. You must become more a man than blind — overpower the condition of blindness with some individuality. And you must find some way not to kill your love. People don't understand about this. What are you, sitting there? To me you are nothing, really. But if I touch your hand, you become something. There is something terribly wrong, isn't there, something terribly wrong?"

He drank from his glass, more rapidly this time. Then he raised his skeletal hands to massage across his forehead, hiding his face.

From the radio I heard an announcement that Marguerite Long would be soloist in the recording of Mozart's *Concerto Number 23 in A*. Almost immediately the opening measures of this ravishing music poured out into the room between us.

With his face still covered, the old man spoke, his voice somehow catching hints of serenity from the music. "I'll tell you something terrible, because you'll feel these things, too. When I was young like you, this craving for affection got so bad I went to the prostitutes. Do you know why? Not because of sex, really, but because there, at least, someone would touch me. I'd get so desperate I'd try to buy affection. I searched for some true warmth when they put their arms around me. And I never, never once found it. Their embraces were no more real than if I'd laid in a mannequin's arms. I hated them for it. Each time, I felt sick because there was never that special touch or that soft expression in their voices. Each time I swore I would never go back. And always I did. Always I hoped. Finally, I realized I would never have the peace of affection unless the gods sent me either a real wife or a real friend. I started hating what is really good, because it hurt so desperately. I was virile, but I blocked sex out of my life long ago because I could never feed it with the affections. By itself, without affection, it is worse than nothing. I killed it like one kills a well-loved animal who will otherwise torture you by starving to death before your eyes. But one can't really kill it, you know," he added into his hands. "At night, sometimes in summer even now, I pass the park and hear lovers. I imagine them with their arms around one another — and taking all of that for granted, perhaps not even feeling half of the touches. I feel like going to them and shouting: 'Do you know what you have? Do you know what it means to be able to touch someone?' . . . " His voice trailed off as though he could find no further words to express the immensity of it.

I felt his despair in my own belly, mingling with the long and moving phrases of the Mozart and with the rich odor of salami.

"It's strange I can talk about this at all," he said. He dropped his hands and smiled uncertainly. "I tell you these things because you must not be cheated the way I feel I have been cheated. No, that's not it. It's because you are here, and there's warmth in you. To me, for these few moments, it's almost as though you were the friend I've never had. I can talk to you about sex or love without that feeling of nausea because there is safety in here between us. Do you understand that?"

"I think so," I said and drank again, my fourth or fifth glass.

"Did you have enough to eat?"

When I assured him I had, he rose to his feet and began stacking the dishes. He wrapped the bread in a piece of cotton toweling, lifted my glass, felt that it was almost empty and replenished it.

The Mozart absorbed our attention as it entered the slow movement, piano and orchestra in a dialogue of contemplative tenderness. He stood with one hand on the table, the blanket around his shoulders, his head slightly raised, staring toward the ceiling. His hand on the table began to shake as though he were struck with palsy.

"Could I ask you something?"

"Of course," I said.

"You are the first person who's ever visited me — who's ever been easy with me. There may never be another . . ." He hesitated. An awkward silence settled between us.

"What is it?" I asked finally.

"I'm afraid it might offend you . . ."

"I doubt it," I laughed.

His voice rattled deep in his throat. "Would you let me feel how your face is?"

His tone of intense dread and longing sent shock through me.

"Certainly," I said.

"It is not repugnant to you?"

"Not in the slightest." I removed my glasses and lifted his hand to my face.

His fingertips were like ice to my flesh, timid and trembling.

"It's very moving to me," he apologized. Then his touch became more certain as he explored my temples, my forehead, my jaws and around the front to my nose and lips. I smelled the faint odor of castile soap and salami on his hands. His face bore the sharpened stamp of total absorption.

"Is your hair blond?"

"Brown . . ."

"Your eyes?"

"Greenish-blue, I think . . ."

"They are deep sunk."

"Yes sir."

His fingers, hard as sticks, moved over my head to the nape of my neck again and again, trembling less. His features relaxed as though a vast calm entered him. His hands drifted reluctantly away and rested on the table.

"I could teach you to be a good beggar," he said.

"Thank you . . ."

"You could live here with me, perhaps."

"I honestly wish I could. But I'm leaving soon. And after I lose my sight, I'll have to return to America to attend schools for the blind."

"I see . . ."

"In fact, I'm afraid I have to be going now. I'm visiting friends here. Only I'm not sure how I'll get back. I can't see enough to get around after dark."

"Then stay with me," he said eagerly. "The bed is double. I sleep quietly. We could talk all night if you wanted to."

"My hosts will surely become alarmed if I don't return," I explained.

"Well, if you feel you must go, I can take you there. I know the town well. Where do they live?"

"Rue Jules Simon, number twenty-three."

"An elegant part of town," he said in disappointment. "You are a rich man?"

I felt overtones of humiliation that he had dared suggest a rich man become his pupil, live with him, be his friend.

"No, I'm sure I'm much poorer than you are," I reassured him.

He talked rapidly while he changed into his ragged day clothes.

"I hope you realize what this has meant to me. I have had a visitor, Monsieur. We have dined and drunk together at my table. Do you know that during all my years here — nearly half a century — I've never before had someone for supper? Do you know that I never before touched a grown man's face? And I never shall again. I know that. It's too much to hope that another will come here as you did, and then stay for a time as you did. You, my poor friend, are the one big thing that has ever happened to me. I know you won't believe it. But it's true. Come, I'll take you home now."

With his left hand clutched around my arm above the elbow, he guided me down the hall to the accompaniment of light tapping from his heavy stick. "Fine now," he whispered. "A few more steps and we are at the stairs. There. Step down. Careful."

Despite the chill, we walked slowly, far more slowly than was necessary. We strolled past massed houses from which no light showed. We talked softly, as friends with no barriers between us, speaking to express the pleasure we felt in one another's company.

"Here we are, young man," he said at last. He squared me gently so that I felt the high metal grill gate that led into the Duthoo courtyard against my back.

"How did you ever know to stop exactly at this spot?" I asked.

"All the *virtuosi* are not in the concert halls," he laughed. "I know that twenty-three is the Duthoo mansion. And I know that the Duthoo mansion is set back from the street with a garden in front, whereas the mansions on either side are set on the street, with gardens in back. So when I hear my cane tap with a hollow sound, I know we are where we should be . . ."

I realized I had forgotten my book, but said nothing about it. He would probably never know, and he might be able to sell it again.

"Can you see anything at all?" he asked.

"Not in this darkness."

"You are like me now," he said tentatively. His hand descended my arm and came to rest in my hand. It was time to say goodbye.

Neither of us could think of anything to say. No easy words came. I felt him tense beside me. His breathing rasped suddenly.

"What is it?" I asked uneasily.

His fingers contracted like wires around my hand. "I hate it for you," he groaned. "We don't think it's so bad when it happens to us. We get used to it. Then we see it happen to somebody else. Then we realize how horrible it is. There's no way . . . no way . . ." His voice ground out the words in despair.

He released me suddenly and his cane tapped wildly away. For a moment I thought of going after him. But at that speed, and without his skills, I knew I could never catch him. I leaned against the grill, felt frost on the iron bite into the back of my head and listened to his cane dim into silence. A sullen pressure filled my throat and I hoped I should not have to talk with anyone before I got to my room.

Mounting the dark stairs, it occurred to me that he never did tell me his name, and that he did not know mine.

Three letters lay on my bed in my room. One from my parents in America, cheerful, filled with confidence. I thought of *l'Aveugle* with no family to protect him from the raging loneliness that afflicted him.

The next letter, from Marie-Bruno, informed me that they would be unable to have me come and stay, since the rule allowed for the visit only of retreatants for brief periods. He went on:

Now the calm tone of your letter allows me to dare to speak to you of the manner in which you might accept this loss of sight. You are being given an opportunity to offer a great sacrifice to God, and thereby to grow in spirit. If you can accept this, abandon yourself to God's infinite dynamism, in a short time you will surely enjoy peace and the knowledge of how to find God in this darkness.

It is not easy. It might even be impossible without the grace of God. The secret is in this, that we can not make progress if we try to follow our own inclinations; but we must rather seek God's will, even where it most conflicts with our desires. This in a very great love, in a very great docility, until our every thought, our every action and reaction even, is attuned not to ourselves but to the God within us.

I sat on my bed and read the letter again and again, noting that

Marie-Bruno had not forgotten to print a large script, far different from his usual miniature writing.

I recognized with some regret that for somene else these would be words of infinite wisdom. But I could no more fix my attention lovingly on God than I could on the wallpaper of my room. Even the thought filled me with intimate embarrassment. God meant nothing to me, to my great sorrow. He was an idea, the comfort of my youth, a myth worthy of my respect, nothing more.

The third letter was from the guestmaster at the Benedictine Abbey of Solesmes, telling me they could offer me a vacant cell for a visit and that the Father Abbot would be happy to receive me; and that I would be allowed to work in the *Paléographie Musicale*. My years of dreaming about someday studying in this great citadel of learning were about to be realized.

I went to bed full of uncertainty and lay there in half-dreams in which the old *Aveugle* mingled. This was another move. Should I really go? Would it not be wiser — at least kinder — to stay here and learn from the old man, offer him the consolations of friendship? But no, I had made myself a promise years ago — always to take the new step. That alone decided me to leave, to abandon all I knew here in this well-loved city and go there to the unknown. As my body gathered warmth beneath the covers, Solesmes absorbed all my thoughts. I heard in imagination its silences, the great bells, the chants drifting down endless corridors of the cloister . . .

The next day I took a last walk along the tree-lined ramparts of the Loire River. Thoughts of *l'Aveugle* preoccupied me but I decided against seeing him again. We had said everything last night. Another visit would be painful for both of us.

Late in the afternoon the sky filled with thick black thunderheads. I turned back toward the Duthoo home, guided by the towering Gothic spires of the ancient Cathedral Saint-Gatien. First heavy drops of rain smacked against the cobblestones as I arrived in the cathedral square. Here, trees and buildings were reduced to miniature by the nearness and massiveness of the church. Lightning flickered constantly, pinpointing the ornate façade in greenish light against the black skies.

I hurried inside and mingled with the crowd. Long queues

formed at each of the little upright coffins they used for confessional booths. They were all there — men, women and children,
the wealthy and the poor — for Saturday evening confession.

I gazed at them through the dim light and wondered. Their
world, their home life, their ethics, their way of looking at things
— all of that lay behind the fog of mystery to me. Were they at
all like me? Did they have the same flashes of frightful temptation;
did they harbor the beast in their bellies? If so, how could they
pour out such filth into the unseen ear of the confessor?

A few prayed in the central portion of the church, their figures
dwarfed by the vast heights. My hungers stirred painfully toward
what they had found, but my mind congealed against it. In the
building's gloom, lighted here and there by clusters of votive lamps,
the intensity of prayers pervaded the atmosphere.

I felt alone and under an almost magnetic compulsion to enter the
black-curtained confessional box. I rejected the idea but it returned
insistently. After all, the priest would never know who I was and I
should never know who he was. I would be in the dark talking to a
voice that represented wisdom and faith. I would be speaking to a
person vowed never to divulge what he heard. I had no one else in
the world to talk with.

Then a statement from Gide came to mind. Referring to a group
of nuns, he had observed how they cherished the pearl of their
faith, never realizing it was a false pearl. He had added that as long
as they did not realize it was a false pearl, perhaps it had the same
value to them as a real one. I turned and walked away from the
confessional, past statues of saints mounted on giant pedestals that
loomed above me, past a young woman whose face was blank with
prayer. I felt my body hang about me as an encumbrance; my feet,
cold and sweating in my shoes, walked on removing me from contact with the false pearl. I strode toward the normalcy of cobblestone pavements and the noise of the world outside. But where
could I go? I saw the world as nothing but an endless dusk leading
me down a thousand alleys which I already knew ended nowhere.
They ended nowhere unless one had a kitchen, a family, a bed and
the brains and hearts of others to share.

The idea of returning to the Duthoos and sitting at a glittering
dining table repelled me. I should not be there. They were a fam-

ily sufficient unto themselves. The picture of them without me was better than the one with me.

My footsteps slowed and I sidled into an empty pew.

A veiled woman lighted votive candles at a nearby side altar. A cough reverberated in the obscurity. Drawing my coat more tightly about me, I shuddered. Odors of age and stone and humanity combined into a stench that stifled the spirit. I looked on the backs of kneelers who worshipped the pearl. Each stone of this immense structure had been laid centuries ago with devotion to the same pearl. Generations had worn the stone floors down with their footsteps. They had mumbled the same prayers, confessed the same sins, wasted how many energies and hopes on the false pearl?

I sat for a time in the rustling silence, and I felt myself drowse when the thought quietly settled in me. How did Gide know? True, I shared his belief, that the pearl was false. But how could we know? Did we, ourselves, possess the true one? If so, why were we so tormented? Marie-Bruno had said that the experience of faith teaches. Not having possessed this pearl, how could we know what it might teach or if in truth it were false?

The picture of myself was suddenly thrown coldly in my face. I saw a young man going blind, it is true, but clinging to all that was pathetic in it, mourning because of a faith denied him. He played the classic role after all, even while sincerely thinking he struggled against it. He cast his last lingering glances at the world, vacillated endlessly for fear of compromising his precious intellectual integrity.

I felt blistered by self-contempt and embarrassed to catch myself in a falsity of which I was not even aware. But now, the self-indulged pathos shone clear and cheap in all its noble trappings of tragedy and sacrifice. I got up and stomped out of the cathedral, relieved to have been shown myself, even in such a brutal way. Filled with an upsurge of energy, I sloshed through the downpour to the *bureau de tabac* and bought a package of strong black cigarillos.

I returned to the Duthoos' and sneered at my room which had been the locale of so much sadness. Stripping off my soaked clothes, I switched on the radio and plopped down in a chair. Rain

gusted against my window, not the sad rain of the past weeks, but
the pleasant rain of my youth, accenting elements of shelter and the
taste of butter cookies near the hearth. The BBC Third Pro-
gramme faded in over the warming hum of the radio. I listened a
moment while an elderly British poetess chewed the crystal of her
verses. Cutting her off in the middle of a squawk, I turned the dial.
The needle paused at Radio-Paris where a massive-voiced soprano
bellowed *Depuis le jour*.

". . . tergiversation . . ." the British poetess enunciated pleasantly as I passed her station again.

A full-bodied performance of Bach's second *Brandenburg Concerto* bounced into the room. I sank back in my chair, overwhelmed by the vigor and sanity of this music. It filled me with a
jubilance that brought tears from my eyes. I lighted one of the
strong cigarillos and let its aroma mingle with the Bach. So I would
be blind. With such music and such smells, I could state it bluntly
and laugh at it. So I would be blind. So, by all rights I should have
been dead, buried somewhere in the Pacific. So, this was a new life,
given free.

When the Bach ended, I switched off the radio and listened to
the rain-filled silence. I heard the children's muffled voices and
footsteps downstairs and smelled a lamb roast.

Dinner was festive that night. I drank much wine and ate with
good appetite and joked with the children. It was a time of change,
influenced by the Bach, the rain, the cathedral. I felt contempt
for sadness. That was all right in the ordinary run of living. A man
had to try to get a little of everything in his one life and be sad if he
were deprived of some of it. But with me, it was different. If I
should consider that I was killed back there, dead and gone, then
my life was done and I no longer had to look for my little of everything. The years to come had been given me to live an experience
which I was free to color any way I chose. I was no longer bound
to the ordinary reactions. However it might go, I should have no
regrets. If I should be reduced to begging in the street then I
should enjoy the feel of hot pavement beneath my shoes and the
odors of asphalt and automobile exhausts. Good or bad fortune
were equally attractive when viewed in such a context. Hunger
was as interesting as satiety? A life without sight as interesting as a

life with sight? Who was to say different? Society? The bulk of humanity? But they were living their first lives, cautiously aware that someday they would die. They had everything to lose. They could not take the risks. But I had been through death, had my insides burned out by it twice. I was living a second life, freed of those cautious awarenesses. I had nothing to lose. I could take all the risks.

PASSION AT TZINTZUNTZAN

→

Tzintzuntzan, once the capitol city of the Tarascan empire, is now a quiet village on the highway between Morelia and Patzcuaro in the Mexican state of Michoacán. It lies near the shore of Lake Patzcuaro in a valley high in the Sierra Tarascas mountains. Each year the people relive the events of Holy Week in the streets and compounds with a sense of reality that becomes almost hallucinatory.

The villagers prepared silently for the Passion when I arrived Holy Thursday morning. A hundred yards off the main highway, stone walls enclose the six-acre compound of the sixteenth-century Franciscan Monastery of Solitude. I entered through the arched gates and walked past giant olive trees planted by Spanish Franciscans 400 years ago. Near the back wall, the original monastery stands, as do the original church and a more recent one.

An elderly priest, Padre Ernesto Tovar, occupies the monastery's crumbling magnificence alone now. I found him seated under cloister arches in a courtyard brilliant with flowering trees and shrubs. A barber shaved the octogenarian priest and trimmed his white stubble of hair in preparation for the events to come. Father Tovar graciously confirmed our prior agreement that I was to photograph the Passion as part of a proposed cultural history of the Tarascan civilization. "I have told my people to cooperate with you," he said.

"May I look around?" I asked, nodding toward the abandoned upstairs portion of the cloister.

"Of course. This is your home."

I wandered through the second floor cells and corridors, my feet stirring dust. Odors of stone and age surrounded me. Ghosts of the past hovered over the ruin, telling me that this was once a center of Franciscan learning where friars copied manuscript books on mathematics, philosophy and theology; where they painted frescos on the courtyard walls depicting the Sacraments.

Drawn to these ghosts, I felt glaringly out of place and time as I opened my case of splendid cameras with their precision optics, set up tripod and photographed the peeling frescos.

It was soon done, but I could not leave. I turned at the stairway and walked back down one of the corridors to the last cell at the end. I seated myself on a stone niche carved as a kind of chair against the wall and looked out the hole that had once been a window. Mountain peaks rose in the background. In the foreground below, children played beneath tall jacarandas that were covered with blue blossoms. I sensed some strangeness. Something was not natural in the sights and sounds. It came clear. The children made no sound. Nothing made any sound. Birds were hushed. Except for breeze-stirred leaves, silence brooded over the land. Christ was away, beyond sight and sound, on the Mount of Olives.

Guards, dressed in white, with faceless blood-red hoods and belts, rode their horses through the narrow village streets below my window. They searched for Christ. The horses' muffled footsteps, like the sounds of heartbeats, deepened silence rather than broke it.

Occasionally, in the distance, an oboe-like Tarascan shepherd horn sounded its plaintive call, flooding the sunlit countryside with melancholy.

Terror insinuated itself implacably into the atmosphere despite the brilliant light, the profusion of flowers and the crowds of Tarascans who streamed toward the compound from neighboring villages. The genius of the terror sprang from the silence, the strange shepherd call in the distance, the growing awareness that Christ, invisible to us, was being searched down.

Outside, I sat on the church terrace to change the film in my cameras. Across the compound, Barabbas, in sackcloth and chains, and Judas — both wearing ghastly pink masks — strutted among the olive trees. Judas waved a long black sack of coins. Children ran from the two villains. Soon, most of the children had gathered around me. We spoke in smiles, making no sound. Their handsome faces shone with curiosity about my cameras, but they were too courteous to examine them overtly.

A brief flowering of sighs and gasps caused me to look up from my work. Judas and Barabbas sauntered toward me. Since their designs were obviously on me, the children did not run. The two elbowed their way arrogantly through the crowd. Barabbas rattled his chains and gestured in a mute plea for money. I looked questioningly at the lad beside me. He stared soberly, giving no hint what I should do. Barabbas became more insistent, placed one hand on my shoulder and pushed me back on the ground. He tried to force a bottle of tequila into my mouth. Grit rubbed into the back of my head. The pink-masked man held my cheeks with one hand and rammed the corked tequila bottle against my mouth with the other. We struggled in silence. I pushed him back, finally, and reached for my wallet. When I took out the peso for Barabbas, Judas reached down and snatched a five-peso note. Both hurried jauntily away.

The children eyed me with expressions of sorrow and reproach. The youngster nearest me whispered in my ear that it was evil to give money to Judas. I whispered, apologizing but making the point that I had not given it, Judas had stolen it. Nevertheless, they made me feel the guilt of being one of those who paid Judas to betray Christ. I had contributed my part of the thirty pieces of silver. To exonerate myself in their eyes, I decided to go take the money away from Judas.

The crowd followed as I hurried after the two men. They were busy terrifying children under a large tree near the old original Church of Solitude and did not notice our approach. By gesture I demanded my money. Barabbas grabbed the back of my neck and shoved the tequila bottle against my lips again. Judas held his sack of coins high and pushed against me with his free hand. When I would not leave them, Judas caught my arm and guided me into the empty church. He pointed to a chalked sign which said that any money given to any of the actors of the Passion would go to the church. I nevertheless made him take the five pesos from his bag and put it into the alms box.

The children no longer regarded me with fear. I had corrected the error. I was back on the "right side." The hypnotic effect of time and place again became apparent. We were so involved that I found it difficult to realize that this was essentially an *ad libitum* play. I felt split, part realizing this was the twentieth century, part eerily involved in the event 2000 years ago This latter was so predominant that I was astonished to feel anything so banal as hunger and rest room needs while the greatest event in Christian history advanced toward its climax. Yet hunger was there, and heat and thirst. A thick, reddish dust, stirred by the crowds, hung over the compound. Vendors had set up stands under the trees. They sold melon slices that were covered with crawling brown bees; and hard pastry sandwiches topped with a pink icing that represented the blood of Christ. I ate a crumbly sandwich and drank tepid apple cider.

Awareness of Christ permeated the compound, and yet we were as the crowd must have been then — wondering where He was. Soldiers prepared His cell, a dark cubbyhole in the church wall.

Padre Tovar told me that Christ's role is always a voluntary one. Each year a young Tarascan offers to suffer the ordeal. He would, the priest explained, go through all of Christ's physical agonies, with the exception of the final sacrifice when the human is rushed to a hospital and a famous *Cristo* with movable arms and legs is nailed to the Cross. This year's volunteer would spend the night standing in his cell, without food or water. The next day he would undergo Christ's agony. About half of the Christs actually died from the ordeal, the priest stated. The town's citizens paid the hospital bills of those who survived.

Late in the afternoon, guards pushed and shoved Christ mercilessly into the compound. We had not witnessed the kiss of Judas, as the crowd 2000 years ago had not witnessed it. It was strange to see it as the people must have seen it rather than as the Gospels recount it. We glimpsed the magnificent figure of a young Tarascan Christ, his hair long and matted, his face radiant with dread and expectation.

I heard English being spoken and glanced around, surprised to hear words in any language after the hours of silence. An American family had come to witness and photograph the event. Their twelve-year-old son moved to my side, eyed my cameras, showed me his own fine instrument and began to shoot pictures.

When the guards and Christ were within a few feet of us, they halted. A guard slipped a crown of viciously real thorns onto the Christ's head, carefully, gently. Then he gave the crown a sharp hard blow. With a dull pop the thorns pierced the flesh and blood poured down into the Christ's face. The young Tarascan did not wince. He was steeled for the torture to come. But the rest of us winced, though there were no outcries.

"That's enough for me," the American mother said, taking her son firmly by the arm and guiding him away. They left quickly. I think it was not the cruelty of the scene so much as the incredible illusion that this man was Christ, that we were participating in the real Passion, that this went far beyond the niceties of play-acting. As such it was an unbearable agony for the spectator as well as for the victim. It shriveled the heart with dread.

Following the trial and condemnation, they dragged Christ to the small cell and locked him up for the night. Red-hooded guards with faceless masks stood watch behind their spears. Some of the crowd remained outside the cell door, praying. Others went into the two churches and knelt in the barren candlelit interiors. Dogs howled in the distance. The Tarascan shepherd horn sent its desolate call through the moonlit night. We remained suspended in time, waiting for the hours to pass, some kneeling like frozen statues in the church, others in the courtyards among the trees. Some women sat against the high compound walls, cradling their sleeping children who were wrapped in woolen shawls against the chill night.

At midnight I walked toward the monastery where I intended to sleep on the floor of one of the cells. But someone had locked the doors. I moved toward a lighted house in town to ask if I could rent a room. A small group gathered under the light, full of concern. But no, there were no hotels in Tzintzuntzan, they explained. I asked if I could sleep in the jail. No, it was filthy. With many apologies, they found a mat for me, regretting that it could not be a bed; and I arranged to sleep on the floor in a spare room of a neighboring house.

The next morning, the family served me breakfast of scrambled eggs, tortillas and coffee in a beautiful old kitchen that opened out to a courtyard crowded with flowers and children. The morning was overcast and misty. While eating, I watched through the window as barefoot Tarascan girls, with shawls over their heads, walked past in the street. I tried to imagine how it must have been here when Tzintzuntzan was the capitol of the Tarascan empire and the home of its emperors — a city of 100,000. The small village of 500 gave little hint of its important past. Across the street, the Tarascans had sacrificed in one day 600 slaves, as an act of mercy, to keep them from falling into the hands of the Spanish conquerors. Here, the Spanish "butcher," Guzmán, had tortured the last of the Tarascan emperors to make him give up his people's treasures; and then had him dragged through the streets tied to the tail of a horse until he was almost dead, and publicly burned him at the stake as a warning to the Tarascans never to hide their valuables from the Spanish. All of this was done, they said, for "the greater glory of God and Spain." Here, too, the Franciscan Fray Juan de Cordura wrote scathing denunciations of his fellow Spaniards for their degradation of the Tarascans, repudiated the Spanish and lived with the Tarascans.

"If only they had sent only the Franciscans and left the others in Spain," the Tarascans lament even today.

When I stepped out into the street, the sun had broken through clouds. The air was fragrant with wood smoke from breakfast fires. The radiance of early morning intensified the unspeakable horror of the events that were destined to take place that day.

I entered the old church as a group of men were carrying the famed life-size statue of the crucified Christ out a side door into a courtyard. I watched them deposit the figure gently, with its upper portion on a sawhorse. They began dusting it off, and wherever they dusted, they kissed the body. A large, elderly, tough-looking matriarch sent them away and took over the work. When she bent over to kiss the body, I prepared to photograph. She commanded me not to make any photographs. I explained to her that I had Father Tovar's permission, that I did this in reverence, to show the world how the people of Tzintzuntzan observed Holy Week.

She gave a snort of disgust and said I would have to pay her to photograph the Christ.

"Why?" I asked. "Does the Christ belong to you any more than He does to me?"

This amused her. The old ladies love a good, slightly insulting argument.

"You pay or you don't photograph. The money goes to the church."

"I intend to give Padre Tovar a contribution," I said. "I certainly don't intend to pay for every shot as I take it. And when I do pay, I'll give it to the priest, not to some old woman." We understood one another, and liked one another. She almost smiled at the quality of my insult.

"Then you don't photograph," she announced grandly. "Why don't you just edify me by going to some other land?"

"Why don't you just edify the world by bending down and kissing the Christ so we can show the world what a pious person you really are," I said.

"Pooh — never — not without money."

"All you want from your relationship with Christ is money. That is not good. No, I wouldn't photograph you at all. Will you step away, so I can photograph the Christ?"

She gazed at me through slit eyelids, repressing a smile.

"Oh, hell, what do you want me to do?" she asked grudgingly.

"Now you are being amiable," I laughed. She shrugged good-natured defeat. I approached close to the head of Christ, which was at the level of my hips on the sawhorse.

"Bend down and kiss the figure," I said.

"How?" Her eyes glinted, with no trace of malice left in them.

I leaned over to demonstrate. My lips almost touched the statue's cheek when her doubled fist smashed hard against my temple, knocking me back against the wall. The blow stunned me. She folded her arms and stood majestic, her smile suppressed behind wrinkled lips.

"Who do you think you are?" I shouted, struggling against my humiliation and rage. "You think you own Christ . . ." I advanced toward her. She shook her finger slowly from side to side and stared me down.

"Only Judas kisses Christ's cheek in this season."

I looked at her dumbfounded as it came to me that she had saved me from being Judas. Gratitude replaced my anger.

"You are not Judas, I hope," she added.

"I hope not, too. Thank you for preventing me from acting like him."

"Kiss the body," she said, "but not the cheek." Her triumph was total, but not unkind. She could afford to be magnanimous now that she had shown that a simple Tarascan hill peasant carried the Gospels in her very veins and heart and instincts as part of even her most spontaneous reactions, whereas the *gringo* outsider carried them only in his head and could forget them.

Moving into the compound where the crowd gathered, I approached the cell in which Christ was sequestered and took out my cameras. Even though the guards had been told to cooperate with me, they reacted as guards might have in Christ's time. They hoisted spears menacingly. I thought they were posing and prepared to shoot. When I brought the camera to my face, I felt the sharp end of the spear bruise hard into my abdomen. The crowd gasped as I bent double with pain. Recovering myself, I explained in whispers that I had the priest's permission. Behind their red hoods I could detect neither consent nor understanding. I raised my camera again. A spear crashed into the lens guard, knocking it aside. Again, through my anger, I realized they were living their roles. My permission to photograph them meant absolutely nothing.

The crowd, who hated the captors and guards of Christ, were with me. Once more I lifted the camera. The spear banged the side of my head. I reached up, grabbed the point and jerked it so hard the guard fell to the ground. I tossed the spear to one side, photographed the other guard and waited for the fallen one to get to his feet.

The crowd murmured approval as the faceless guard struggled to his feet and I stood my ground against him. But my sympathies were with him. I was overwhelmed with my own sense of guilt at altering historical truth in this manner. Two thousand years ago no photographer had thus embarrassed Christ's guards. My actions distorted the truth of the day, changed it from what it should have been. The pain in my abdomen came from his attempt to right the distortion. I could only respect him for it. Disheartened, he retrieved his spear and resumed his stance as guard.

From across the silent compound our attention was drawn to a man's loud voice ordering guards to bring Christ to him. With a cynicism that chilled us, he added: ". . . and don't fail to give the Master my distinguished regards."

The centurion on horseback and foot guards approached the guarded door. They opened and dragged out a haggard Christ, his face streaked with dried blood from the crown of thorns.

They shoved him toward the opposite side of the compound. There he was ordered stripped and flogged. The guards took him into the inside courtyard of the cloister, undressed him down to a white loincloth and whipped him relentlessly until every inch of his visible body trickled blood from the fine-line lash cuts. He received the blows in numbed silence.

When he was returned to the compound, the crowds cried for him to be crucified. Pilate argued with them, finding no fault with Christ. They demanded that Barabbas be set free and Christ killed. Pilate conceded, washing his hands, and turned the victim over to the mob.

They clothed him in purple, slipping the silken garment over his body. Immediately the blood seeped through to darken the cloth.

With a heavy wooden cross loaded onto his shoulders, the young Tarascan Christ began his long walk through the olive trees toward Calvary. The crowds separated to let him pass. I waited in a good position to photograph him. When he approached, I stepped into the path and began walking backward in front of him. Barabbas, who gleefully preceded the Christ, swung his heavy chains hard against my legs. A guard knocked me off balance. When I stopped to rub my leg, Barabbas brought his chain down across my shoulders and neck. As I photographed, Barabbas continued to chain whip me brutally across the back. Some of the crowd moved forward to defend me, but I waved them back. I concentrated away from the drubbing and photographed the Christ, his face hazed with pain in strange repose. I photographed the crowd of men and women, their eyes forlorn with tenderness and grief. Again, I burned with the embarrassment of my intrusion. Cameras did not belong in the Passion.

Christ fell faint in the red dust. I forgot myself, hurried to help him up, but was restrained by a spear in my belly. Intense silence surrounded all of this activity. The shepherd horn drifted over us from far away, accompanied by savage thuds as the guards beat Christ until he staggered to his feet.

I knelt where I was, in his path, to get a close-up. The chains pounded against my back. I lost my balance and fell on my stomach. Christ was almost on me. His eyes were dazed. I froze, fearing he would stumble over me. I rolled on my back and reversed position trying to scoot out of his way. As his foot touched mine, he stopped. His glassy eyes cleared. He looked down at me patiently, intelligently, and with an expression of such sorrowful love that I felt devastated. Brutally, I reminded myself that this was not Christ, but a Tarascan youth playing a role. It did no good. The illusion was too powerful. During this instant of hesitation, I realized that my instincts as a photographer were functioning, that I was working the camera, photographing first his face and then his blood-blackened feet. Then I rolled to one side and out of the way, into the feet of the bystanders. As he passed, the frightful stench of the dying Christ filled my nostrils, odors of sweat and souring blood. This too, I told myself, is how it must have been, with the dust, the stinks, the dogs and chickens underfoot, the women weeping, the men torn with pity, the children almost unconcerned, the drink vendors, the total degradation of the God-Man. A weird, implacable madness carried the scene forward in the slow rhythm of tragedy.

I filmed the almost nonchalant cruelty of scene after scene as Christ fell and was flogged to his feet to continue and fall again. A piglet crossed his path. At one moment when the Christ stood reeling, unable to take the next step, a hen came and pecked the dried blood on his feet, almost invisible in the red dust.

At the point where tensions could no longer be borne, an exquisite, white-clad Tarascan girl, representing the Virgin, detached from the crowd and ran in a great floating motion toward Christ.

His eyes again cleared. He knelt on one knee and received her into his arms. She embraced the blood and stench. All action stopped. The madness vanished from the crowd. The gesture was so filled with tenderness that even Christ's eyes filled with tears that diluted the blood on his cheeks. Barabbas stopped swinging his chain. Judas faded away into the crowd, his money bag jingling softly. Anger was defeated in us.

Gently the guard pulled Mary from Christ's embrace. She was led away weeping while Christ tottered forward. The crowd followed with dead hearts, obliged to go through the final portions of the walk to Calvary but wanting now for it to be finished. Again and again he fell. Again and again we heard the thuds. Again and again we felt the sickness of heart that must have been felt by those who witnessed it 2000 years ago. Our minds wandered. We became aware of the sun that blared down on our skulls, the dust that clogged our noses and dried our mouths, the hunger of the last hours, for the walk lasted until three in the afternoon when the Christ was pushed and shoved into the church. At the rear of the deserted building where the altar had once been, the two criminals' crosses stood illumed by a shaft of light from a side window high in the wall. The young Tarascan disappeared through a curtained doorway and the famed life-sized *Cristo* was carried to the cross that lay flat on the floor.

They hammered the *Cristo* to the cross with enormous brass nails. Then, while the crowd watched transfixed with grief, the huge cross was hoisted to an upright position with snow white ropes.

Muffled sobs threatened the silence. An elderly man walked into the sanctuary, knelt at the foot of Christ's cross, stared up at the figure and with his arms outstretched in a gesture of abandon began to intone a Tarascan chant, slow and flowing as an ocean wave. The silence of the past days was broken. The crowd knelt and joined their voices to the dirge.

It was over. Christ hung there dead before us. I slipped out the side door. The chant resounded through the countryside as I walked away.

The crowd remained in the church to keep vigil. The late afternoon sun shone beautifully over the deserted compound turning purple bougainvillaea blossoms transparent. Dust had settled. Vendors' stands were empty. Chickens pecked crumbs from the ground. As I walked through the gate leading from the compound into the village, the messenger arrived from the hospital where they had rushed the young Tarascan Christ. He would live. He would be in the hospital three weeks, maybe four, but he would live. The messenger rushed to spread the word throughout the church.

Suddenly, as though on cue, roosters all over the valley began to crow. I walked past olive trees pink-leaved from the dust, out onto the main street of the village. A young girl attended a stand where

I bought a glass of lemonade. Neither of us spoke. The chants drifted to us muffled beneath the brilliant stridor of the roosters' crowing. They would chant on through the night until the new sounds of Easter and the mood of Resurrection were accomplished. For this year, the Passion at Tzintzuntzan was over.

CURRENT TRENDS IN CENSORSHIP

The history of censorship is a history of abuses. Beginning as an attack on pornography, it traditionally grows into a passion to suppress whatever offends the censor's religious, political and other beliefs. Before long, the censorial fog surrounds art, ideas and scholarship. These patterns, with some new developments, characterize recent censorship activities.

A rather curious thing has happened. Smut-hunters have often bridled their urge out of fear they would be considered bigots, fanatics or prudes. Now, however, extremist political groups have announced that obscenity is part of the communist conspiracy to destroy America's morals. Incipient censors, freed from their inhibitions, can indulge their smut-hunting instincts and call it patriotism.

That endearing word *smut* embraces all the nuances of such terms as *pornography*, *obscenity* and *vulgarity*. Some revealing definitions have been given us this year by censors. Typical of the quality of censorship is Mrs. Earl Oltesvig's definition of pornography as "any description of prostitution or licentious behavior" (a dictionary definition). "On this basis," the Michigan censor added, "*The Good Earth* is definitely pornography."

In Texas, a new "obscenity" law was passed by the state legislature on June 16, 1961. It states that "the word 'obscene' is defined as whether (sic) to the average person, applying contemporary community standards, the dominant theme of the material taken as a whole appeals to prurient interests."

This definition, an adaptation of the current United States Supreme Court standard, presents problems. The terms are far from legally precise. What precisely is an "average person" and what are "contemporary community standards"? And since it is axiomatic that censorship appeals to the prurient interest of many smut-hunters, could not censorship itself be banned as "obscene"?

Presumably, the Supreme Court made the standard elastic in order to allow works of serious intent which contained passages of erotic realism some freedom from censorship harassment, while providing a trap for hard-core pornography.

Censors, fearing they could not ban the books they wanted to ban through due process with this new law, simply intensified their efforts to get the books removed by illegal or extralegal means. This resulted in a rash of coercive censorship that threatens to become oppressive. A work not legally removed, but merely forced off the shelves by the manipulation of public opinion, has no legal means to defend and clear itself. Any private group can deprive the reading public at large of any work or idea which the private group can force into disrepute.

No one questions the right of any group to censor whatever it wishes for the members of that group, so long as such censorship does not deprive the public of access to the material, since such material might be offensive only to some particular sectarian belief or principle. But this is a far cry from current tactics whereby such groups effectively censor works to the point of making them unavailable. When this is accomplished through police cooperation by way of pressures or threats against booksellers, censorship becomes a dangerous instrumentality.

Fears that Texas was moving in the direction of censorship without due process were aggravated when Henry Miller's *Tropic of Cancer* arrived thirty years late in Dallas bookstores. Civic leaders and the police got the book "voluntarily" removed from public sale. Charges of police censorship and book-burning were voiced. So far as Texas was concerned, this book, even though it had a large body of serious critical opinion in its favor, was condemned without trial.

The Miller book became the *cause célèbre* of the year. By June, 1962, *Tropic of Cancer* had been effectively banned from distribution in over half the country. Its publisher, Grove Press, had undertaken to defend arrested booksellers, but there were still some sixty criminal cases pending.

An issue of great concern is involved here. The issue is not whether *Tropic of Cancer* is a masterpiece of American literature; rather it is whether an author of Henry Miller's artistic integrity (or any author for that matter) is entitled to the protections afforded by the Constitution of the United States.

The book was brought to trial in the Superior Court of Cook County, Illinois. Judge Samuel B. Epstein's decision of February 21, 1962, read in part:

> The Court is committed to the principle expressed by the majority opinion in the Roth case as follows: "The fundamental freedoms of speech and press have contributed greatly to the development and well being of our free society and are indispensable to its continued growth. Ceaseless vigilance is the watchword to prevent their erosion by Congress or the States. The door barring Federal and State intrusion into this area cannot be left ajar."
>
> Censorship is a very dangerous instrumentality, even in the hands of a court. Recent history has proven the evil of any attempt at controlling utterances and thoughts of our population. Censorship has no fixed boundaries. It may become an oppressive weapon in a free society.
>
> In the words of Justice Douglas in the Roth case: "I have the same confidence in the ability of our people to reject noxious literature as I have in their capacity to sort out the true from the false in theology, economics, politics or in other fields."
>
> Hard core pornography, it is agreed, has no social value whatsoever and does not enjoy the protection of the First and Fourteenth Amendments to the Constitution of the United States, but literature which has some social merit, even if controversial, should be left to individual taste rather than government edict.
>
> The constitutional rights to freedom of speech and press should be jealously guarded by the courts. As a corollary to freedom of speech and press, there is also the freedom to read. The right to free utterance becomes a useless privilege when the freedom to read is restricted or denied.

The court found that *"Tropic of Cancer* is not obscene as defined in the law and that interference by the police in its free distribution and sales should not be enjoined."

In a word, law enforcement agencies have been placed in the odd position of arresting men who have broken no laws but who merely distribute works offensive to some citizens.

Once the alleged connection between "four-letter" words and

the communist conspiracy was established in the minds of the censors, they launched into an often absurd attack against books used in schools. According to their thinking, if dirty words are part of the communist conspiracy, then so are many ideas.

"Books in schools — particularly the 20th century classics — receive short shrift and administrators are often reluctant to do battle in behalf of their library and classroom use," says the March, 1962, issue of *Freedom-to-Read Bulletin*.

Most prominent in attacking textbooks and what Dr. Lewis Allbee called "twentieth-century library trash" have been veterans' groups and "venerable-lineage societies," plus such newer bodies as the White Citizens' Councils, the John Birch Society, the National Indignation Convention, and Texans for America. Their lists, which are often identical, embrace everything from Plato to this century's distinguished thinkers and artists.

History, music and English texts are under attack, not on the grounds that they are untruthful or obscene, but often because they are tainted with that mysterious quality called "un-Americanism." It must be understood what they mean by "un-American." Their attacks usually contain such terms as "pro-New Deal," "pro-UN," "soft on communism," and "subversive."

Though the stigma of un-American or subversive, even when used in such an irresponsible manner, can and does effectively damage careers and endanger teaching positions — to say nothing of respect for ideas — an example will show the extravagance with which the terms are used. One of the textbooks contained folksongs of many lands. Among them was an Israeli folksong with instructions that it be sung "with spirit." The objection stated that "U. S. children should not sing *with spirit* the national songs of any other country such as Israel."

Censorship centering around schools and authors whose works are used in the schools contains some basic fallacies which can be stated bluntly.

(1) Every obscenity law must stipulate that the work be considered *as a whole*. A work cannot legally be held as an obscene libel merely because it *contains* certain words or phrases. At one time, smut-hunters banned most of the world's literature by going through books and making lists of all "offensive words and

phrases." Laws that permitted this piecemeal evaluation of a work were called "containing statute legislation." This was declared unconstitutional in the United States Supreme Court decision in *Butler v. Michigan*. Censorship activities in Texas have invariably returned to the practice of excerpting words or phrases with the view of denouncing the work because it *contains* them. Works *containing* ideas that offend group prejudices are also banned on this basis. We have witnessed again and again the spectacle of people "opposing" books, even in court, without having read them. A list of words or ideas was enough to convince them. The Texas House committee investigating textbooks decided after weeks of testimony that it would accept no further statements unless the witness had actually read the books he condemned!

(2) The long history of censorship has involved the problem of what to judge — the work or the creator of the work. The general consensus of scholarly and court opinion has been that one considers a work on its own merits — not on the basis of the author's character or personal beliefs. One does not condemn an otherwise unassailable work merely because of some distaste for the author. Americans recall attempts to ban the music of German masters during World War I. We have, however, seen recent censorship revert to the unenlightened ethic. The Daughters of the American Revolution in Mississippi condemned a whole mass of books, admitting that though they had nothing against the books, the authors were "unfit" to be read in the South. To be unfit, in one instance, the author had only to lecture at George Washington Carver High School. Patriotic censorship relies heavily on impugning the work's worth by impugning the author's character. To be considered suspect by such groups, an author needs only to have lived. He can be "suspected of disloyalty" for the most absurd reasons.

(3) The censoring groups are placed in an odd position when they claim loudly that they are maintaining a civilization based on what they call "the Christian Ethic," but accomplish this by the unethical and un-Christian means of smear, logical fallacy and intimidation.

(4) Censorship of the patriotic type is often anonymous, and almost always based on self-evident facts or secret documents. It is sufficient to read some of these "secret reports based on secret doc-

uments" (which no one produces in evidence) to suspect everyone in America, with the possible exception of J. Edgar Hoover and Kate Smith, of criminal subversion.

(5) Censorship groups who engage in the suppression of art, literature and scholarship on the grounds they are fighting communism indicate that they would protect us from one form of totalitarianism by imposing on us another. They suggest that we preserve our liberties by subverting our freedoms.

In general, censorship activities have met with public approval, even glee. Censorship is seen by many as the answer to "subversive smut." Therefore any censoring groups, using no matter what repressive means, which profess to rid us of smut and subversion are "on the right side." If in the process they deprive the public of access to art, scholarship and literature, of the freedom to read, that is regrettable, they say, but we are in an extreme emergency and must submit to extreme measures.

Censorship has grown powerful in this atmosphere of massive suspicion and fear where everything that is not openly, even blatantly, patriotic is suspect. Note, too, how these patriotic groups have destroyed the public's respect for art, scholarship and literature by the most systematic repetition of damaging innuendo, e.g., "Modern art is a communistic device to weaken America" . . . "Our liberal pinko intellectuals." The patterns are old and crude, but effective.

In view of the reasoning behind current censorship pressures, one can only deduce that impoverished minds and purified vocabularies will help America win the battle against communism. And one wonders where the subversion truly lies.

Here is a brief rundown of current censorship activities.

An art dealer in California has been arrested for "obscenity" because he displayed a copy of Michelangelo's "David" in his shop window. Presumably the work was considered "as a whole" and found to be obscene "according to prevailing community standards." One recalls the Reverend Wesberry's remark when he was a member of Georgia's censorship board: "I don't discriminate between nude women — whether it's art or not. It's all lustful to me." If "prevailing community standards" represent such an attitude, does this not mean the suppression of every great work of art that shows the human body undraped? Have we sunk so low that in our judgments of obscenity we no longer contradistinguish between cheesecake and classic works of art? Have we not also arrived, in our Christian purity, at the fallacy of seeing as evil what God obviously created as good? — in fact the image of God Himself? If this represents "prevailing community standards," then this is not too bad for Michelangelo, but too bad for us.

Is this an exaggerated example? One searches in vain for one that is not exaggerated.

Perhaps one nearer to us. In Houston last year, Mrs. Fay Seale, who identified herself as a member of the John Birch Society, led an attack against *Living Biographies of Religious Leaders* and *Living Biographies of Great Philosophers*, by Henry and Dana Lee Thomas. School Superintendent H. D. Schochler threatened to burn the religious book, but finally contented himself with the less drastic expedient of simply removing it from the library. Mrs. Seale objected to the book of philosophers' biographies because it contained *Plato*, who, as we all know, is part of the communist conspiracy to destroy morals.

"I haven't read Plato in a long time," she told a reporter, but she recalled he "talks about communal living and free love and such." Plato in her view also suffered from guilt-by-association: he was a student of Socrates, whom "the people poisoned for ideas he was spreading." With reference to Plato's communal living and free love "ideas," she informed the *Houston Post*: "I can't help but believe that this is one reason we have so many sex maniacs walking around." She did not explain how she herself escaped her reading of Plato unscathed. The *Milwaukee Journal* commented: "The suggestion that school children are rushing to read Plato or read about him is startling. Educators everywhere ought to find out how Houston does it."

In September, 1961, the outlawed "containing statute" technique came to light in Midland, Texas. Attacked and pressured off school library shelves because a brochure listing the obscene words contained in them aroused the city's ire were *Andersonville*, MacKinlay Kantor; *The Grapes of Wrath*, John Steinbeck; *Laughing Boy*, Oliver LaFarge; *Of Time and the River*, Thomas Wolfe; *The Big Sky* and *The Way West*, A. B. Guthrie, Jr.; *Marjorie Morningstar*,

Herman Wouk; *1984*, George Orwell; *Brave New World*, Aldous Huxley; and *The Portable Steinbeck*.

The case attracted a large delegation of citizens to a meeting on the subject. A frequent comment was: "You have over ten thousand books — why can't you toss those ten out?"

At this meeting, attorney Reagan Legg, who said he was "opposed to the books," nevertheless expressed confidence in the trustees. John Bragg, a member of the audience, delivered a "stinging denunciation" of the books. He was followed by more than sixty persons who stood up one at a time and identified themselves as being opposed to the books. One of these, the Reverend John Click, said the books "have no place in our schools."

Almost identical lists got the books temporarily removed from libraries in Amarillo and Odessa.

Testifying before the Textbook Investigating Committee of the Texas House, Mrs. Roy T. Moore of Midland explained why these books were attacked. They were, she claimed, "written and distributed as part of the communist conspiracy to lower the morals of youth." The Associated Press flashed the report around the world.

Another highlight of the same hearing featured the Reverend Ralph Wright of Midland in selected readings from *Andersonville* that contained "four-letter obscenities." Shortly after he had begun his reading, another minister "jumped to his feet and asked Mr. Wright to stop" — not out of respect for the law that a work must be judged *as a whole*, alas, and not out of respect for literature, but because ladies were present.

Such incidents have been widespread this past year all over the United States. It should be noted that wherever officials and newspapers have taken a firm stand, the opposition has quickly subsided. School officials in Midland, Fort Worth and Amarillo have succeeded in restoring most of the "twentieth-century classics" to the bookshelves.

Some of the more disheartening cases involve attacks against history and other textbooks by a group calling itself Texans for America. This group has offered vast lists of picayune objections to a number of history books, but their main target has been *This Is Our Nation* by Paul F. Boller, Jr., and E. Jean Tilford, published by Webster. We will focus on this for a moment.

J. Evetts Haley, speaking for Texans for America, began with the fallacy of attacking author Boller, whom he accused of having the liberal's "usual obsession with democracy." Surely, a strange sort of crime. Later, using anonymous letters (which contained the exact wording of Texans for America objections), opponents of this book indulged in vicious character defamation, safe behind their transparent anonymity. They charged that Dr. Boller had been affiliated with "communist front organizations," but of course did not name them or document the charges. This is a typical tactic. One recalls Edwin A. Walker's recent blast at a State Department official who was allegedly "close to the communists." It turned out this official attended two communist rallies, out of curiosity, at the age of fifteen. The fact that he has been an active anticommunist since apparently did not count.

My own research into charges anonymously brought against Dr. Boller revealed absolutely nothing to merit this kind of smear. The point here is once again clear — although Texans for America brought many objections against the book, they virtually admitted that "no indication of this (Dr. Boller's questioned loyalty) is given in the book." They denounce the book because they do not like the author's liberal political views.

The quality of their objections to the book is revealing:

Texans for America say that the book is friendly to the United Nations.

They object to material on American Indians, whose contribution to America, they say, "is practically nil."

They object to mention of the Salem witch hunt; call it "overemphasis on this one particular morbid aspect."

They say the authors seem to have an "affinity for Roosevelt."

They object to a cartoon depicting the purchase of Alaska from Russia in 1867. Alaska at that time was called "Russian America" and because that expression appears in the cartoon of the period, TFA say the authors are trying to prepare American students for a "Russian America."

They object to "overemphasis" on the slavery problem.

They object to mention of Crispus Attucks, a Negro who was killed during the Boston Massacre of 1770.

The concluding objection, TFA item 70, concerns references in the text to Sherwood Anderson, Maxwell Anderson, Stephen Vincent Benét, Ralph Bunche, Aaron Copland, Theodore Dreiser, Bernard DeVoto, Albert Einstein, William Faulkner, Ernest Hemingway, Sinclair Lewis, Eugene O'Neill, Willa Cather, Carl Sandburg, "and many more!"

Texans for America object to any mention of these names in a history textbook because "recognized authorities on subversion have pointed out that *statements, associations* and *affiliations*" (italics mine) of these writers "have called their loyalties into question." One wonders what kind of "recognized authorities" question loyalties with such promiscuity. One also wonders how a historian could discuss American literature without mentioning Dreiser, Cather, O'Neill, Sinclair Lewis, Faulkner, Hemingway, or Sandburg; and what patriotic service would this omission perform for the student?

A close look at the objections shows that TFA rarely question the truth of the historians' findings. No, they object to points of emphasis, inclusion and exclusion. One can pick almost any work to pieces in this manner. They demand that textbooks be slanted toward purely "nationalistic history." They require the historian to alter or "edit" historical facts to conform to their group prejudices. If he does not, he will suffer character defamation and possible financial reprisals. This could become a punitive form of censorship if it caused the product of years of work to be nullified.

Haley's credo is this: "The stressing of both sides of a controversy only confuses the young and encourages them to make snap judgments based on insufficient evidence. Until they are old enough to understand both sides of a question, they should be taught only the American side." An eloquent statement, particularly the part about "snap judgments based on insufficient evidence."

This begs the question, however, since most of their objections concern not controversial points, but historical fact. TFA demand the truth be truncated wherever it reveals an incident of weakness or error in our national past. In effect, they require the historian to abandon the science of history and become an amateur therapist, or at least a propagandist to pump into the young a spurious and hard patriotism; and what is more, a patriotism that never wavers from the narrow harmonies of extreme conservatism.

And what about the young? Are high school students really subverted by so-called "four-letter obscenities" that they have heard all their lives? Are they really so fragile they cannot take nourishment from truths that make other men strong? Will they not later resent and completely distrust their education when they discover it was designed as a therapy? Will they not feel cheated that truths were deliberately kept from them? Will this not turn that cheaply-sponsored patriotism into no patriotism at all?

This is only a small segment of the censorship picture, but it perhaps indicates some trends, some need for concern on the part of thinking men. Censors have gained a tremendous and willing following among those who oppose "smut subversion," and who do not realize what the censors are really preaching: that delinquency is the product of art and subversion is the product of truth.

PRUDE AND THE LEWD

→

Obscene, lewd, lascivious, filthy, indecent, and disgusting — these are the six adjectives connected with censorship. No two persons agree on their precise definition, as Ernst and Seagle point out in their book *To the Pure*. The League of Nations was unable to arrive at a legal definition of obscenity, the most frequently used adjective of all.

In the new wave of censorship that is sweeping all English-speaking countries, we are seeing familiar patterns repeated. Beginning with the laudable purpose of suppressing pornography, censorship historically ends up by engulfing more and more works of legitimate value and by spreading beyond the realm of creative literature to technical and philosophical works as well.

In this process, since no one has ever defined obscenity in a satisfactory manner, the general test is based on Chief Justice Cockburn's ruling in the case of *Regina v. Hicklin* in 1868:

> The test for obscenity is this: whether the tendency of the matter charged as obscenity is to deprave and corrupt those whose minds are open to such immoral influences, and into whose hands a publication of this sort may fall.

This sounds reasonable enough, but it only takes a moment's study to see that it actually means nothing insofar as legal precision is concerned, since it is predicated upon unascertainable, indefinite standards. For who can say whether the tendency of such and such a work is to deprave and corrupt one person, not another? And how does one determine who exactly are those "whose minds are open to such immoral influences"? And, of course, who is to know "into whose hands a publication of this sort may fall"?

This evaluation is supported by the decision of Judge Curtis Bok in *Commonwealth v. Gordon*, Philadelphia, 1949:

Strictly applied, this (Cockburn's) rule renders any book unsafe, since a moron could pervert to some sexual fantasy to which his mind is open by reading the listings of a seed catalogue. Not even the Bible would be exempt . . . Who can define the clear and present danger to the community that arises from reading a book? If we say that it is that the reader is young and inexperienced and incapable of resisting the sexual temptations that the book may present to him, we put the entire reading public at the mercy of the adolescent mind and of those adolescents who do not have the expected advantages of home influence, school training, or religious teaching. If the argument be applied to the general public, the situation becomes absurd, for then no publication is safe.

The Cockburn test is still used as the basis for censorship legislation and for the judging of a work as obscene. A number of states have statutes which define as obscene "any publication *containing* obscene, immoral, lewd, or lascivious material tending to incite *minors* to violent or depraved or immoral acts, manifestly tending to the corruption of the morals of youth." (Emphasis added.)

This again sounds admirable, except that under this ruling virtually every major author, including Nobel and Pulitzer prize-winners, has been banned from public sale as obscene. It is even more faulty than the original Cockburn statement and appears to be a clear violation of the rights guaranteed under the First and Fourteenth Amendments to the Constitution of the United States in that it: (1) prohibits the distribution of any book to any member of the public because of the hypothetical effect the book might tend to have merely on minors; (2) permits books to be banned merely on the basis of *containing* questionable passages; (3) offers no express definition of what constitutes obscenity, and therefore many passages of legitimate realistic description can be proscribed merely on the basis of differing tastes.

Few people realize the far-reaching aspects of the statement: ". . . any publication containing obscene, immoral, lewd, or lascivious material." Art, in order to have any influence on man's understanding, must exist whole. Unless a work be considered as an entity, there is obviously no way of judging its validity. Isolated words and phrases torn out of context from the Bible, for example, sound exactly like those same words and phrases lifted from some pornographic book, and on the basis of merely *containing* such words and phrases the one is as subject to banning as the other. This is essentially what happens. So-called objectionable words and phrases are copied out of context, a list of them is handed to the censor, and he is obliged to decide the obscenity of the work on the basis of whether or not a fourteen-year-old child should be allowed books *containing* such words and phrases. The answer is as obvious as the process is puerile. It is like taking a photograph of the navel of Michelangelo's "David" and asking someone unfamiliar with the entire figure if he would like to have his fourteen-year-old daughter see a statue containing such realistic details.

In his testimony before the Gathings committee, Inspector Herbert Case, in charge of the Detroit police department's censor bureau, stated: "We in our municipality feel that the law and the statutes and everything are intended to protect the adolescent, the weak, and susceptible." This, again, is admirable, but it becomes vicious when the adult public is denied the right to any book on the basis of its possible harm to the "adolescent, the weak, and susceptible," and in passing it might be added that the Detroit blacklist reads like a *Who's Who* of our most respected novelists. Yet you can still walk into hotels and drugstores and buy the same old "Violent Honeymoon" and "Midnight Passion" trash because publishers have simply deleted the objectionable words and phrases. Actions such as Detroit's succeed effectively in banning everything except the innocuous and the mediocre.

Judge Learned Hand in *United States v. Kennerly* ruled that this type of obscenity test would "reduce our treatment of sex to the standard of a child's library in the supposed interest of a salacious few" and "forbid all which might corrupt the most corruptible." Accordingly, authors of the caliber of Faulkner, Hemingway, Mauriac, Huxley, Greene, Dos Passos, Zola, and even Boccaccio, plus many others, are being branded as pornographers and their works dismissed as "obscene."

Although, as we shall see, all censorship can be lumped together, since all of it commits the same errors and is based on the same fallacy of juvenile behavior, it is necessary to point out that there are three general types of censorship currently practiced in the English-speaking world.

First, there is the police censor who derives his authority to ban books from such statutes as the one I have discussed. An assigned policeman goes through new books, or reprints of old ones, and rejects from public sale those which he thinks might conceivably harm the young, the weak, and susceptible. He is often "aided" in making up his blacklist by lists furnished him by religious and sectarian organizations. Then there is the censorship board, such as that in effect in Georgia, where a three-man group of private citizens does the filth-hunting. And finally there is the so-called hidden censorship, consisting of religious and civic leaders, leagues for and against this and that, which use a technique of pressures on bookshop owners in somewhat this manner: A representative of the group visits the local bookstores, presents them with lists of works which the group finds objectionable, promises them a plaque of cooperation if the blacklisted books are removed from sale, and indicates that lists of cooperating and non-cooperating stores will be published. Thus, through furnishing lists to tired police censors and to bookstores, these groups apply very effective censorship, replacing the "due processes of law" by extra-legal pressures to attain their ends. This practice is followed by many religious organizations of laymen, such as, for example, the National Organization for Decent Literature.

No one would deny the right of any sectarian group to discourage its members from reading books which are offensive to it, but such a prerogative becomes vicious when it is used to deprive others, who are not members of that particular group, from access to work to which they have a perfect right, according to the legal standards of the United States. Speaking of this, Victor Weybright, in his testimony before the Gathings committee, said:

> The fact that these groups act from the best of motives does not alter the fact that their attempt to pose such extra-legal standards is a clear infringement of the right of the reading public to select for itself what it will read. When the action of local or sectarian groups takes the form of pressure applied to distributors and dealers, whether or not with the assistance of local law-enforcement agencies, it becomes a secondary boycott which may be actionable as an illegal restraint of trade.

Censorship, by depriving the community of the right of access to serious works because it cannot distinguish pornography from realism, thereby commits mankind to a cultural and ethical hari-kari. The list of abuses is far too long to be presented here, but it must be apparent that wherever these censorship drives have started they have invariably spread to works that could not conceivably be considered obscene. In one English community recently, *The Decameron* was banned along with trash such as *Foolish Virgin Says No*. In another English community, a novel highly respected in America and Europe was banned because, according to the censor, "there is an insidious, sneaking Roman Catholic propaganda in it which I detest." The censor added that he would keep it "even from septuagenarians," which somewhat removes us from the criterion, false though it may be, of "the young, the weak, and susceptible."

The difference between pornography and the legitimate and necessary treatment of evil in literature is one which appears to escape these censoring agents. Every great artist, whether he is conscious of it or not, in some way illuminates the mystery of evil. But the pornographer wallows in evil, illuminating nothing. Unable to distinguish art from pornography, the average censoring body simply denies that the distinction exists . . .

There is, then, particularly among the clergy and religious groups of all sorts, a growing clamor based on good intentions and a total disrespect for accepted artistic standards, which denounces anything not totally innocuous as "contemporary" or "new," with the implication that it depraves our children — or they presume it does, for it is odd that none of these youths has ever been presented in evidence as having been corrupted by banned works of literary stature. No, what is "new," of course, is the idea that we can no longer exercise parental control over our children. We do not ban essentially adult products in the pharmaceutical lines, we do not ban alcohol and cigarettes on the basis of our not desiring our fourteen-year-olds to use them. It is therefore intriguing that in what concerns literature and art, parental control mysteriously vanishes and we must deprive everyone of these works, which range from the Latin classics through Shakespeare and Shaw and the real contemporaries, some of which are admittedly adult fare, sometimes even the fare of scholars, theologians and scientists — as the recently banned *Phallic Worship*, a noted work in its field — on the formula of their possible harm to our children.

And what about this juvenile corruption of which we hear so much? Where does the problem really lie? It lies squarely in the home, the school and the church. By the time the corruptible youth reaches an age to understand what he is reading and to be sensitive enough to it to be corrupted, his background training and moral development will have already been fairly well established; and if this has been properly done, art, no matter how realistic, will serve for him the same function it has for all men in the past: the dissemination of truth and the creation of perspective and compassion.

Blaming truthful art for juvenile corruption is like blaming one's mother for original sin — the harm will have been done before either enters the picture. Does not this banning, making literature the scapegoat, indicate only one thing: defeat within the home? Another very new thing, of course, is that you build resistance to temptation by hiding it under a barrel. The legitimacy of these new ideas is richly indicated by the juvenile crime rates, which are high in banning countries and low in those where great art, and frank art, is a part of daily life under the guidance and control of parents. This is indisputable. Too many bishops and saints were reared on works now subject to banning. Cardinal Newman said:

> We cannot have a sinless literature about sinful men, and nothing is barred per se.

Huntington Cairns, one of the most astute critics of censorship in this country, observes:

> In general such men (police censors) have had little or no contact with science and art, have had no knowledge of the liberty of expression tacitly granted to men of letters since the beginnings of English literature, and have been, from the point of view of expert opinion, altogether incompetent to handle the subject.

How much less qualified as experts are those chosen at random from church and community groups on the basis of some fervor to "clean things up." This cleaning is producing an error of national proportions of which the average layman is more or less unaware.

Leon Bloy ascribes the error to two causes: ". . . the astounding unintelligence of modern Christians and their deep aversion to the beautiful." More detailed causes might be these:

That a problem of the most profound significance is attacked in its most superficial aspects;

That the censors appear innocent of any awareness of the supreme importance of art in the maintenance of a culture, particularly when that art offends some cherished prejudice, and are therefore willing and glad to sacrifice highly regarded works "to the good cause."

It has always been so, and there is little hope that the cycle will not again complete itself without going to an extreme that will make the demands for freedom of press and pen the subject of bitterly fought battles; for the public is always late in realizing that between the two evils, the prude does it ultimately greater harm than the lewd person. The prude and the bigot are what they are precisely because they lack qualities of prudence and understanding. Moral virtue, behind which they hide, is impossible without these intellectual virtues of prudence and understanding which direct man to the *proper means* of achieving his goals. Power, then, in the hands of people who are currently embracing censorship with neither prudence nor understanding, must inevitably result in abuse. Seemingly admirable motives obscure the true damage caused by such people until it reaches commanding dimensions — dimensions which it is now reaching in our English-speaking countries.

To the author, viewing this situation, it is indeed a source of some confusion that tempts him to throw up his hands and say: "What's the use? What's the use when such innocents are waiting to pounce on the lowest elements within a work without viewing those elements in the light of their function or treatment?" Pascal long ago described this tendency:

No, no, if they are great it is because their heads are higher — a thing which we cannot see if we look only at their feet which are on the same ground as ours.

But to some, this situation in itself is a challenge, a challenge to discover how in this most advanced of all technological ages, when

the degree of literacy is higher than ever before, how in this en-
lightened age a whole mass of people can have reached such a pitch
of fervor over such a patently self-destructive ideal. Here, for the
author who would illuminate the mystery of evil, is an evil of magni-
tude.

NOTES ON SMUT-HUNTERS

→

The responsible person seriously concerned with the question of pornography is distinguished from the smut-hunter by a certain discretion of the intellect that prevents him from seeing as intrinsically evil many things God obviously created as good. For example, he does not confuse nudity with provocative stripped-down nakedness, never confuses classic Greek sculpture with cheesecake. Sex, for him, is not synonymous with sin. More importantly he understands that innocence is not based on non-knowledge of evil, but on non-love of evil; and that heroic innocence, in fact, encompasses a profound knowledge of evil. He knows that the innocence of the saint is not grounded in ignorance but in knowledge. Unlike the smut-hunter, he feels no need to glut himself on every four-letter word or nudie photograph in order to deal with the problems of pornography in society, since he knows, of course, that the mere existence of such terms or pictures does not necessarily constitute pornography.

*

Smut-hunters invariably present an obscene spectacle, and almost always an absurd one: the obscene and absurd spectacle of good men and women whose noses are poked into every conceivable source of obscenity in order to ferret it out for the purpose of protecting society from the very thing that has proved such a fascination to the smut-hunters themselves. If they were as aware of the obscenity of their actions as they are of the obscene elements of human language, they would, if honest, quickly censor themselves into oblivion.

*

I have never yet met a smut-hunter who admitted that his constant exposure to the "lewd, lascivious, obscene, salacious and pornographic" had for one moment menaced his body or soul. No, he invariably pursues his smut-hunting apostolate to protect the rest of mankind from the kind of "appalling dangers" that have never apparently endangered him.

*

Their preoccupation with purity is so obsessive that their very minds and tastes appear to cry out unhappily from a location in the geometric center of all human genitalia. So do their ethics which are as vagrant as the urges of human sensuality. Is their concern for purity a pharisaical mask? In truth, all they ever reveal is a vast preoccupation with impurity.

*

They read more filth than the victims they seek to protect. They immerse themselves in filth to further the cause of purity. If you want to feel completely depraved, get a smut-hunter to show you the collection of pornography he has gathered to prove how widespread these materials are. One Chicago cleric, founder of an organization of smut-hunters, reportedly claims to have the country's largest collection of dirty books and films, and invites interested, concerned or skeptical adults to come and see his private showings. No audience at a stag party gets half the show that is regularly given when smut-hunters meet to show one another and the public their latest "discoveries." I have wondered why police do not raid the illustrated public lectures given by professional smut-hunters before audiences all over this country. Since these are usually under some religious auspices I suppose the police feel it would be somewhat like raiding a church service. My wife attended such a lecture on a church-sponsored series and returned home dazed. She said she felt as though she had been pietistically raped.

*

Apparently you cannot be a smut-hunter unless you are deeply suspicious of all mankind. All smut-hunters are, by nature, suspicious. They constantly suggest that the kind of reading they do from high and pure motives is done by the rest of mankind from base and prurient motives.

*

They dedicate all the energies of their septic minds and septic consciences to the task of keeping ours antiseptic.

*

They are especially suspicious of all writers, except of course the biographers of St. Thérèse of Lisieux. To feel really comfortable and loved in their presence, a writer must have written at least one article on the Little Flower. They are even suspicious of all non-Little Flower religious writers. Look at Graham Greene and Mauriac, for example. They wrote some pretty nasty stuff, they'll say. The implications are immediately clear to those "in the know." All writers are not only unprincipled and oversexed hacks who will do anything for money, they are also either conscious or unconscious dupes of this gigantic conspiracy to wreck humanity by destroying the morals of youth through the clean or dirty portrayal of *lust*, God forfend. At the deep core of this insidious conspiracy lurks the master fiend, a half-Jewish, half-Negro commie bastard who birthed at midnight on the bare soil of some Vodka field in Soviet Russia, is now serving as a Justice of the United States Supreme Court, and is secretly involved in the plot to fluoridate our good pure water. All writers are seduced by their natural depravity into obeying his will. They've always been that way. You can't trust a writer. Even the Desert Fathers wrote some raw, raw things, especially St. Jerome who lusted even into advanced age, which proves that if you get your morals wrecked as a youth you just never get over it.

No, that is too much. It would be a rare smut-hunter who had read St. Jerome or any of the Desert Fathers. Such reading would nullify the smut-hunting mentality.

*

Semanticists, jurists, philosophers and theologians have long searched for valid criteria by which to judge pornography. The smut-hunter sees it clearly and simply. "Any normal man *knows* when something is dirty," he usually says, implying always that only smut-hunters are truly normal, among other things. One of the best-known professional lecturers on this subject, in a private conference for Catholic theologians, explained his infallible criteria for detecting pornography. He contended that you could be sure a work was pornographic if it contained any passages that gave you "a kind of feverish feeling in the cheeks and a grinding feeling in the stomach." Although his definition was felt to lack something in theological precision, he demonstrated by showing his collection of pornographic materials, presumably so that the distinguished theologians might gain empirical knowledge of the indicated physiological responses in themselves in order to judge the validity and universality of these criteria. When he died shortly thereafter in the midst of his arduous lecture tour, one of the theologians promptly diagnosed the death as stemming from occupational causes: "undoubtedly too much grinding of the stomach."

THE POULENC BEHIND THE MASK

⟶

During a telephone conversation with cellist Zara Nelsova I learned that Francis Poulenc had died in Paris.

The scene from the second act of Poulenc's *Les dialogues des carmélites* immediately absorbed my attention. In it, the Mother Superior dies, writhing in agony, crying her doubts about her faith. Did Poulenc die that way, too? He had already died that way once. The death scene of the Mother Superior had been a direct translation into music of his own agony.

He had written me:

> My God, you cannot know the anguish. God knows if I shall ever complete *dialogues des carmélites* because I am very ill. It is my stomach. Cancer. In spite of my doctors' reassurances that there is nothing wrong with me, I fear that I will never be able to work again. Will you ask the Carmelite Fathers of Dallas to make a novena that I recover my health and that I may be able to glorify God and the blessed martyrs of Compiègne with my music? I am in terrible fear. Will God take into account my poor efforts — the Mass, the religious motets? Will He at least see them and me kindly, as another bungler, a *jongleur de Notre Dame?* Please locate a good peasant priest to help me. The priests who are considered "intelligent" exhaust me.

I promised him the novenas he requested, and asked permission to send a noted Dominican, Father Gerald Vann, to help him. ("He is a master of souls. You can put yourself in his hands.")

Poulenc wrote immediately:

> Please, no. I feel bludgeoned by the intelligence of Dominicans. A Dominican would make me lose the remnants of my poor faith in five minutes. No, send me a poor, ignorant parish priest —

someone who is good and who will not beat me to death with theology.

This correspondence had been initiated when Discalced Carmelite Fathers at Mount Carmel Seminary in Dallas had asked me to inquire about Poulenc's opera *Les dialogues des carmélites*. And although I had met Poulenc in France — we had been neighbors in Tours in my school days and had encountered one another at concerts in Paris after World War II — he did not make this association. He answered my query as though I were a stranger, a friend of the Carmelites. He poured out his agony in a way that I am sure he seldom did to anyone face-to-face.

In his letters, he adjured me to silence until after his death. The correspondence reveals a Poulenc who does not coincide with his popular public image, or even with my own personal impression of him.

Everyone knew Poulenc by sight during the prewar years in Tours. He wore an odd green hat at all times, and it was rumored he never removed it, even in the house. We schoolboys would remark with distaste that he was *très bizarre* but a great pianist, which, of course, excused everything.

After the war, I was back in Tours, in a room in Jacques Duthoo's *Château de Belles Ruries* where I practiced on an old pedalless Pleyel piano that had been desecrated by the Nazis. Poulenc was to come for lunch that day. None of us looked forward to it. He was too cloying, too precious. He hovered about one with an air of solicitude, almost tenderness, like a puppet being manipulated by a Cupertino or a Neri; as an unfortunate joke that never came off. It left one with an oversweet taste and always an undercurrent of panic, of suspected tragedy under all of this — of some man helplessly trapped behind a mask.

But none of this appeared in his letters. They were straight — the cry of a heart that could no longer waste time with the mask.

All that your Carmelites are doing for me overwhelms me, and I feel unworthy [he wrote in a letter dated September 10, 1954]. I don't know if I have told you all the truth about my case. Here it is in a few words. After months of personal sorrows, overwork and voyages, I felt myself gravely ill. The doctors continued to reassure me. I want to believe them but doubts have gnawed at me for days and nights, and still assault me. Alas, these doubts concern not only my physical self. The most terrible pain has been to feel my faith fail at the very moment when I have such need of it.

Now, miraculously, you and your Carmelites have extended help and become a source of extraordinary consolation. Tell them that I am constantly aware of their help and that it is a great balm to me. I have begun the orchestration of the first act of *Dialogues;* but I must give my nerves time to gain health before I undertake the second act. I hope Heaven gives me the strength.

How wonderful it must be to have a faith without fissures. It is true that many saints knew difficult hours — and I am so far from ever being a saint! I hope God will take into account my religious works . . .

This was followed by another letter from Amsterdam, dated October 11, 1954, in which the depression had returned.

Forgive my silence, but I find myself so unworthy of your letters and your concern that I hardly dare write you. I am a poor sinner and I am in a state of the blackest neurosis. I can no longer play the piano. I can no longer work. I have such contempt for myself. I came to Holland to give three concerts in the hope a change might help. But the loneliness is so hideous that I cannot stay in my room. I wander over to the hall, seeking contact with any human, talking with strangers. I have truly the impression that I am the Devil's puppet. Only outside of my room can I find any calm. Redouble your prayers for me, I implore you, and may Heaven help me to sleep again, to work again, to forget, to pray. I am two men now, and Poulenc despises with all his strength the too-vulnerable Francis.

I want so much to finish my *Carmélites,* but how can I find enough peace, how can I sleep? I am ashamed to write you like this, but you and your Carmelites are the only help I have now.

Will God ever forgive me all my follies, all my folly? I want so to honor Him again with a music completely purified of these dregs of trickery and cheapness. I have sinned so terribly, but how much I suffer for it. Pray that my soul be saved from eternal fire because my body and my heart burn on this earth.

Throughout the winter of 1954–55 a calmer tone entered his letters. He was back at work. In April, he wrote:

Thanks to the prayers of all your Carmelites, my health returns. Alas, during this nightmare, which clung to me for two years, I almost lost the Faith. All my life I counted on religion to help me die well, and when I had this cancerphobia, my prayers turned to dust. I hope that one day the source of Grace will flow again. For the moment, I feel nothing at Mass. I await the *Ite Missa est* the way I used to await the liberating bell of the lycée.

It is easy for me, the musician, to thank you, the writer and therefore my brother, from the bottom of my heart for having stood by to aid me during these terrible months.

The need to write diminished. A mutually understood silence replaced the flow of letters. Finally, on October 31, 1955, he sent me this brief note: "My opera is finished and will be performed at La Scala in January, 1957. Deo gratias."

The last letter I received from him, dated simply August, 1956, reads:

Forgive my long silence. Yes, the opera is done. It will have first performances at Milan in February and Paris in March. They say it is beautiful. I hope that is true. It is terribly earthy — as I see Bernanos' piece terribly human: Pride; Fear. I hope that the last tableau, a great Salve for the climb to the scaffold, will throw a breath of the Spirit into the hall. May I, like Blanche, at the moment when one least expects it, again take my place among the faithful. This word "faithful" is so full of so many meanings.

I cannot fix my thoughts enough to pray. They vagabond over the years of my childhood.

Some months later, one of the Carmelite Fathers telephoned to tell me the N.B.C. Opera was scheduled to premiere *Les dialogues des carmélites*. I drove with another of the Fathers to the Provincial headquarters in Oklahoma City. Since television sets are not permitted in Carmelite houses, a group of us were given permission to watch the performance in a friend's home.

None of us had seen the score of this work or heard any of the music. All were trained musicians, however, and we were deeply involved, through our contacts with the composer and also because the work concerned the martyrdom of Carmelite nuns at Compiègne.

The first act — yes, a strangely Mozartian, flamboyant but elegant composition. It excited us but did not move us.

Then came that remarkable second act where the Mozartian felicity suddenly evaporates at the scene of the Mother Superior's death. She gasps with pain, clutching her abdomen. She cries out her doubts. This is the tortured Poulenc of the letters. His own agony transforms the music. Some of his very phrases are in the Mother Superior's mouth. This is the "terribly earthy" portion of which Poulenc had such fears.

We sat transfixed in the darkened room until one of the monks rose and walked quietly into the kitchen for a glass of water — anything to break the unbearable spell that Poulenc had created. Seldom in art has a creator trusted himself to create so intensely from the depths of his own entrails.

Here and in the last act Salve, Poulenc had known how to shed his mask.

We heard nothing from him after that. He no longer needed to write those anguished letters. His music told us where he was going. A splendid Gloria for soprano soloist, chorus and orchestra echoed through the world's concert halls a few years later.

But the Poulenc of the public mask remained on view to the world — the bounder, the fop, the wit, the exquisitely vulgar and jaunty Francis. He continued to refer to himself as "half-monk, half-bounder," all in hiding the half-monk part even while he wrote music that revealed it for all to hear. But few heard it.

Jean Casadesus sat in my studio a few months after Poulenc's death. "All of Paris's musical world was there for the funeral," he said. "You should have seen it. It was grotesque, a farce, but somehow fitting, as though Poulenc himself had designed it for a comic opera. A real *blague*. There were all of those great musical figures. And then a great mob of painted and effeminate young men swarmed in. Even his funeral had an air of the ridiculous. It was a typical Poulenc finale," Jean concluded with a pained laugh.

Haunted still by Poulenc's obsession with pain and suffering, I associated his death with the earlier death in the second act of *Les dialogues des carmélites*.

"How did he die?" I asked Jean.

"It was completely unexpected. He just dropped dead. Suddenly. A heart attack."

The funeral might have been a typical Poulenc finale. Yet, it was not the real one. The real Poulenc finale, his final composition, was performed for the first time recently. A religious work, *Sept répons des ténèbres*, almost shocked by its depth and serenity. In it, for the first time, one finds no hint of the old mask. In it, Poulenc no longer despised the "too-vulnerable Francis." Both somehow fused into the music, allowing the composer to succeed in doing what he had so long desired to do: "to honor Him with a music completely purified of those dregs of trickery and cheapness."

Notes on Recordings of Poulenc's Religious Works

Poulenc wrote his first religious work, and one of his finest, in 1937. In August of that year, his friend, the composer Pierre Octave Ferroud, was killed in an automobile accident. Grief-stricken, Poulenc retired to the religious sanctuary of Rocamadour in the Dordogne where he composed his *Litanies à la Vierge Noire de Rocamadour* for a cappella chorus. It is recorded on a Pathé-Marconi disc DTX 247, and on a Gregorian Institute disc S–205.

In 1937, he composed his *Mass*. In 1939, he wrote the *Quatre motets pour un temps de pénitence*. These austere works, which Poulenc compared to paintings by Mantegna, have been magnificently performed and recorded on Angel 36121.

When the painter Christian Berard died in 1949, Poulenc composed his extraordinary masterpiece, the *Stabat Mater*, based on a thirteenth-century hymn by Jacapone da Todi. This work, for orchestra, chorus and soprano soloist is perhaps the most accessible and most profound (with the exception of the *Sept répons*) of all Poulenc's religious music. It is superbly performed and recorded on Angel 36121.

Les dialogues des carmélites is recorded on Angel 3585 C/L.

Gloria in C is radiantly performed on Angel 35953.

Other religious music, such as *Quatre motets pour un temps de noël* and the *Salve Regina*, recorded in Europe, have not made their appearance in American catalogues.

MARTIN LUTHER KING

———————————————————————————————➤

Mrs. Rosa Parks, an attractive young seamstress, walked to a corner bus stop in downtown Montgomery, Alabama, on her way home from work. She was too tired to pay much attention to Christmas festoons that late afternoon of December 1, 1955.

Boarding the Cleveland Avenue bus, she took the first seat in the "Colored" section. Mrs. Parks was physically tired, but she was also tired in a deeper way, tired the way Southern Negroes get tired — tired of a lifetime of being discriminated against.

When the bus filled, the driver ordered the four Negroes who occupied the first row in the "Colored" section to give up their seats to white passengers. Since such demands were common in segregated communities, three of the Negroes immediately obeyed. Mrs. Parks hesitated. She saw that every seat was taken. If she complied, she would have to stand while a white male rested in the seat for which she had paid her fare. She felt the tiredness, the unbearable tawdriness of being forever second-class, and she quietly refused to move. The bus driver had her arrested. She was jailed on a charge of disobeying the city segregation ordinance.

Ordinarily, this would be an insignificant incident. Such sour notes occasionally disturbed the "wonderfully harmonious relations" Southern whites claimed to enjoy with Negroes. Severe punishment usually righted the matter and discouraged others from making similar unharmonious mistakes.

But this time, no. The accumulated resentments of past slappings, cursings and unjust arrests had reached an explosive pitch in the Negro community. Smoldering indignation flared into massive protest over Mrs. Parks' arrest. The young seamstress had unknowingly touched off a revolution that was to catapult a local minister, twenty-seven-year-old Martin Luther King, Jr., from obscurity to world prominence.

The Reverend Dr. King, recently out of Boston University, had come to Montgomery to accept his first pastorate a little more than a year before the arrest. His whole life appears, in retrospect, to have been a preparation for the role he was to assume in Montgomery, and later in other areas. Dr. King, himself a Southerner, had spent years pondering the philosophy of nonviolent resistance as it related to his religious beliefs and to the problems of oppressed minorities. Now he found himself in a locality that was engendering a revolution. Conclusions he had reached in the calm of his meditations were to be tested in a laboratory of harshest reality — the reality of man in crisis, man capable of behaving at the brute level.

King detests being given credit for the great social revolution that held the world spellbound for the next year. He points out that he did not start it, and once started certainly it was the product of cooperative effort. But without his presence and his long preparation to assume his leadership role, without his vision and his willingness to set an example of heroic charity, the story would have been different. Nevertheless, Dr. King seldom acted without consulting his colleagues in the ministry and other leaders of the Negro community; and wherever we mention King in these pages, we intend to imply also the actions and counsel of his colleagues.

The Reverend Dr. King's task was gigantically difficult in two principal areas.

First he had to inspire and persuade his fellow Negro citizens to channel their outrage and their energies of revolt away from violence toward an absolute Christ Ideal of behavior — behavior that appeared hopelessly idealistic under the circumstances. They must do battle to gain for themselves and their children rights of which they were being defrauded under the "System."

. . . In Montgomery, the Negro community had reached a point where the System's inequities were no longer bearable. "Actually," Dr. King explained, "no one can understand the action of Mrs. Parks unless he realizes that eventually the cup of endurance runs over and the human personality cries out, 'I can take it no longer.' " [1]

Martin Luther King's first problem, then, was to inspire his peo-

---

[1] Martin Luther King, Jr., *Stride Toward Freedom* (New York, Harper, 1958), p. 44. This and the quotations from the same book which follow are reprinted with the permission of Harper & Row, Publishers, Inc.

ple not only to persevere in their battle for freedom but to limit themselves to a single weapon — the weapon of Love: to return love for hate; to embrace a truth strange to modern ears but which the Negroes' life had uniquely prepared them to understand — that unearned suffering is redemptive.

He asked fifty thousand people to do that rare thing — to make themselves subservient to an ideal (the Christ Ideal) in the face of opponents who made ideals subservient to their prejudices.

The Reverend Dr. King's second problem was to place the Christ Ideal in firm opposition to segregationists who were persuaded that they themselves acted from the noblest Christian motives and who felt it wholly within the framework of Christianity to smear, terrorize, kill or do anything else to protect the traditional Southern Christian System from anyone who sought to alter it. Jacques Maritain has brilliantly summed up the religiosity of racists:

> God is invoked, but . . . He is invoked *against* the God of the spirit, of intelligence and love — excluding and hating this God. What an extraordinary spiritual phenomenon this is: People believe in God and yet do not know God. The idea of God is affirmed, and at the same time disfigured and perverted . . . [This] is not less anti-Christian than is atheism.

Maritain concludes that this general paganization has resulted in man's placing his hope in force alone and in the efficacy of hate, "whereas a political ideal of brotherly love alone can direct the work of authentic social regeneration: and it follows that to prepare a new age of the world, *martyrs to the love of neighbor may first be necessary.*" [2]

The rarity of Martin Luther King's experience lies in the fact that he not only arrived at essentially the same philosophical conclusions but that he was given the opportunity to demonstrate them in his actions, in his willingness to love and to die not only for the good of the Negro, but for the good of all men.

This is some of the background of a revolution that was to show the world man bombing and beating his neighbors on the one hand

[2] Jacques Maritain, *Scholasticism and Politics* (Garden City, Doubleday, Image Books), pp. 23, 29.

and man praying for and confounding his opposition with love on the other hand.

The principal figure in this drama, Martin Luther King, Jr., was born in Atlanta, Georgia, and spent much of his life there. His father, whom Louis Lomax calls one of the most imposing men he has ever met in his life, was the pastor of the Ebenezer Baptist Church in Atlanta. The elder King bitterly resented and resisted the indignities of segregation. As a sharecropper's son he had met all the brutalities of discrimination at first hand and had begun to strike back at an early age. "I don't care how long I have to live with this system," he said, "I will never accept it."

Dr. King recalls riding with his father one day when the older man drove past a stop sign. A policeman pulled up to the car and said, "All right, boy, pull over and let me see your license."

"I'm no boy," the Reverend King replied indignantly. Then, pointing to Martin, he said, "This is a boy. I'm a man and until you call me one, I will not listen to you." [3]

As pastor of the Ebenezer Baptist Church in Atlanta, where he presided over a large congregation, the elder King had great influence in the community and, as his son observes, "perhaps won the grudging respect of the whites." In any event, the fearless and outspoken father was never attacked physically, a fact that filled Martin and his brother and sister with wonder as they grew older. Martin's mother, an educated and cultivated woman, herself the daughter of a minister, helped provide a warm and secure home in which she and her husband did everything in their power to minimize the crippling effects of discrimination on their children.

Some have contended that Martin Luther King, Jr., growing up in relative comfort and security, never knew the deep, bruising resentments that were the lot of most Negroes; and that his doctrine of love came with a certain facility and was not, in fact, a triumph over hate. But no one not totally insensitive could escape the essential ravages of the System. By the time he had reached his early teens he had been marked to his depths by these bruising resentments.

> I had grown up abhorring not only segregation, but also the oppressive and barbarous acts that grew out of it [he wrote]. I

[3] King, *op. cit.*, p. 20.

had passed spots where Negroes had been savagely lynched and had watched the Ku Klux Klan in its rides at night. I had seen police brutality with my own eyes and watched Negroes receive the most tragic injustice in the courts. All of these things had done something to my growing personality. I had come perilously close to resenting all white people.[4]

This was young King's state of mind when he entered Atlanta's famed Morehouse College in 1944. A strongly athletic, physically robust, life-loving youth, he evidenced no obvious vocation for the ministry, but his concern for racial and economic justice was already substantial. Under the stimulus of such thinkers as Dr. Benjamin Mays and Dr. Samuel Williams it became far more profound. At Morehouse, he read for the first time Thoreau's *Essay on Civil Disobedience*. "Fascinated by the idea of refusing to co-operate with an evil system, I was so deeply moved that I reread the work several times. This was my first intellectual contact with the theory of nonviolent resistance." [5]

By 1948 his vocation had crystallized. At Crozer Theological Seminary, he began a serious intellectual quest "for a method to eliminate social evil." In addition to his regular studies, he spent a great deal of time reading the works of social philosophers. Soon he had reached the conviction that "any religion which professes to be concerned about the souls of men and is not concerned about the social and economic conditions that scar the soul, is a spiritually moribund religion only waiting for the day to be buried." [6]

The young seminarian absorbed the social and ethical theories of the principal thinkers, from Plato and Aristotle down to Rousseau, Hobbes, Bentham, Mill and Locke.

During this period he began to despair of the power of love to solve social problems. The precepts of Christianity were not for the market place, could not compete against the evil means Christians themselves were willing to employ in order to win their battles.

Then one Sunday afternoon he heard a sermon by Dr. Mordecai Johnson, President of Howard University, who had just returned

[4] *Ibid.*, p. 90.
[5] *Ibid.*, p. 91.
[6] *Ibid.*, p. 91.

from a trip to India. Dr. Johnson's talk on the life and teachings of Mahatma Gandhi exercised an immediate and profound influence on King.

As the seminarian delved deeper into the philosophy of Gandhi, his skepticism concerning the power of love gradually diminished,

> and I came to see for the first time its potency in the area of social reform. Prior to reading Gandhi, I had about concluded that the ethics of Jesus were only effective in individual relationships. The "turn the other cheek" philosophy and the "love your enemies" philosophy were only valid, I felt, when individuals were in conflict with other individuals; when racial groups and nations were in conflict a more realistic approach seemed necessary. But after reading Gandhi, I saw how utterly mistaken I was.[7]

In the Gandhian emphasis on love and nonviolence, King perceived the method of social reform that he had sought so long.

During the years that followed, King began to develop his synthesis; to apply the Gandhian principle to the elemental problems of the segregated Negro. True pacifism, he felt, was not nonresistance to evil, but nonviolent resistance to evil. "Gandhi resisted evil with as much vigor and power as the violent resister, but he resisted with love instead of hate." [8]

The crucial point, with King, lay in his growing conviction that

> it is better to be the recipient of violence than the inflicter of it, since the latter only multiplies the existence of violence and bitterness in the universe, while the former may develop a sense of shame in the opponent and thereby bring about a transformation and change of heart.[9]

The love ethic of Christ, the Gandhian method and philosophy for applying that love ethic, the Sermon on the Mount, a firmly established hierarchy of values — all of these elements anchored in a realistic knowledge of man that countered false optimism, evolved through King's years of graduate study at Boston University into

[7] *Ibid.*, pp. 96, 97.
[8] *Ibid.*, p. 98.
[9] *Ibid.*, p. 99.

the philosophy that was to play such a positive role in the Negro revolt. A brief summary of the principal points of this philosophy reveals that:

Nonviolent resistance is not "passive resistance" — it does resist.

It does not seek to defeat or humiliate the opponent, but to win his friendship and understanding. The effects of nonviolence lie in the creation of a harmonious community, while the effects of violence lie in bitterness.

It attacks forces of evil rather than persons who happen to be doing the evil. "We are out to defeat injustice and not white persons who may be unjust," King told the people of Montgomery.

The nonviolent resister must be willing to accept suffering without retaliation. "Rivers of blood may have to flow before we gain our freedom," Gandhi had said, "but it must be our blood." If going to jail is necessary, the nonviolent resister enters it "as a bridegroom enters the bride's chamber." [10]

Nonviolent resistance avoids not only physical violence but also "internal violence of the spirit." As King often said: "The nonviolent resister not only refuses to shoot his opponent, but he also refuses to hate him." And again: "Love, *agape*, is the only cement that can hold this broken community together. When I am commanded to love, I am commanded to restore community, to resist injustice and to meet the needs of my brothers."

Dr. King's "love-*agape*" is disinterested love. He makes it clear that he is not referring to some sentimental or affectionate emotion.

> It would be nonsense to urge men to love their oppressors in an affectionate sense. Love, in this connection means understanding, redemptive good will . . . It is a love in which the individual seeks not his own good but the good of his neighbor.[11]

In 1954, after twenty-one years of uninterrupted schooling, Dr. King ended his formal training. He had created a positive social philosophy but it remained an intellectual accomplishment, untested; and he had no plans to put it to the test.

Dr. King had offers of two churches in the East, and three colleges had extended invitations to attractive posts. While he was

[10] *Ibid.*, p. 103.
[11] *Ibid.*, p. 104.

considering these offers — whether to move into pastoral work or into education — he received a letter from the officers of the Dexter Avenue Baptist Church of Montgomery expressing an interest in him. This interest soon culminated in a firm offer of the pastorate.

Dr. King considered the available possibilities. Though he had a real love for the South, he loathed the idea of returning to live under its segregated System.

Too, he had recently married and had to consider his wife in this decision. He had met and courted the beautiful and gifted Coretta Scott while she attended the New England Conservatory of Music in Boston. But Coretta was also from the South, from Marion, Alabama. They discussed the matter at great length. A serious musical career for Coretta would certainly be easier to pursue in some Northern city. But Coretta was a brave and dedicated woman who was to prove herself extraordinary in the future turbulence. They reluctantly decided that their greatest service could be rendered in the South; that they had a moral obligation to return — "at least for a few years."

*

Dr. and Mrs. King were well established in the community when Mrs. Parks was arrested for refusing to give up her seat on the Montgomery bus to a white man.

Early the next morning, Friday, December 2, 1955, E. D. Nixon, an outstanding civic leader, telephoned Dr. King.

"We have taken this type of thing too long already," Nixon said. "I feel that the time has come to boycott the buses. Only through a boycott can we make it clear to the white folks that we will not accept this type of treatment any longer." [12]

A meeting of Negro ministers and other community leaders was called for that evening in Dr. King's church. Plans for the boycott were laid. Dr. King noted a strong atmosphere of unanimity and enthusiasm rarely typical of such gatherings.

During the weekend, every effort was made to get into contact with as many Negro citizens as possible. Preachers announced the message: "We can no longer lend our cooperation to an evil sys-

[12] *Ibid.,* p. 45.

tem." Mimeographed leaflets were distributed throughout the community. The news spread.

On Sunday evening, at home with their two-week-old daughter, the Kings discussed the prospects of success. Would the people have the courage to follow through? Would they fear reprisals? Would they act, or would they, as so often in the past, fall back into apathy, fearing that the System was too firmly entrenched?

They agreed that if they could get sixty percent cooperation, the protest would be a success.

The Kings awoke earlier than usual Monday morning, December 5. They were fully dressed by 5:30. The hours stretched ahead. Would the boycott be successful? What would happen at Mrs. Parks' trial, scheduled for later in the morning?

A bus stop only a few feet from the Kings' house made it convenient for them to watch the opening stages of the drama from their front window. The first bus would pass at 6 A.M.

Dr. King was in the kitchen drinking a cup of coffee when he heard Coretta call, "Martin, Martin, come quickly!"

He hurried into the living room and joined Coretta at the front window.

"Darling, it's empty," Coretta said.

The South Jackson line, which ran past their house, usually carried more Negro passengers than any other in Montgomery. The first bus was always filled with domestic workers going to their jobs. A second bus passed — empty. A third, empty of all but two white passengers.

"Instead of the 60 percent co-operation we had hoped for," Dr. King wrote, "it was becoming apparent that we had reached almost 100 percent. A miracle had taken place. The once dormant and quiescent Negro community was now fully awake." [13]

A strange scene for the Old South city: buses drove about empty, with motorcycle police as escorts; Negroes walked or hitched rides to work. Unconventional transportation was seen — men riding mules to work, horse-drawn buggies. The sidewalks were crowded with laborers — many of them elderly people, "trudging patiently to their jobs, sometimes miles away." The atmosphere turned festive. They began to cheer the empty buses. Children sang out: "No riders today," whenever a bus passed.

[13] *Ibid.*, p. 54.

Events moved rapidly that day. Mrs. Parks was found guilty of disobeying a city segregation ordinance. She appealed the case.

At an afternoon meeting of Negro community leaders, the Montgomery Improvement Association (MIA) was founded to guide and direct the protest. Dr. King, to his astonishment, was elected president. The MIA board included ministers of all denominations, schoolteachers, businessmen and lawyers. These realists wondered if the Negro community could sustain its fortitude and enthusiasm under such hardships; whether they should allow the boycott to continue, with the risk that it might "fizzle out" after a few days, or discontinue it while they were victorious.

They finally decided to let the mass meeting — which was only an hour off — be their guide. If the meeting were well-attended, they would continue. If enthusiasm appeared lacking, they would call the protest off and use its victorious tones to bargain for better treatment.

Dr. King tried to find a few moments of quiet to prepare his talk for the rally. This speech would be of crucial importance. It needed to be militant enough to keep the people aroused and yet moderate enough to keep their fervor within controllable and Christian bounds. He knew that many Negroes were victims of a bitterness that could easily turn to violence.

When Dr. King approached the Holt Street Church, where the rally was to be held, he saw cars lined up on each side of the street for blocks. A crowd of thousands had gathered.

The opening hymn was "Onward, Christian Soldiers." Dr. King says, "When that mammoth audience stood to sing, the voices outside swelling the chorus in the church, there was a mighty ring like the glad echo of heaven itself." [14]

When prayers and scripture readings were over, Dr. King was introduced. Television cameras began to shoot from all sides. The crowd grew silent.

After telling the story of what had happened to Mrs. Parks, he spoke of the long history of abuses that Negro citizens had experienced on the city buses, of which they were the chief patrons. And then this Ph.D. plunged into the heart of his talk in the eloquent language and rhythms of his people:

[14] *Ibid.*, p. 61.

But there comes a time that people get tired. We are here this evening to say to those who have mistreated us so long that we are tired — tired of being segregated and humiliated; tired of being kicked about by the brutal feet of oppression. Tired. Do you hear me when I said TIRED? Now we have no alternative but to protest. For many years we have shown amazing patience. We have sometimes given our white brothers the feeling that we like the way we are being treated. But we come here tonight to be saved from the patience that makes us patient with anything less than freedom and justice.

Dr. King then spoke briefly about the legal and moral justification for their actions. He compared their protest to methods used by the Klan and the White Citizens Councils, showing that "their methods lead to violence and lawlessness. But in our protest there will be no cross burnings. No white person will be taken from his home by a hooded Negro mob and brutally murdered. There will be no threats and intimidation."

He concluded with the cautions, urging the people not to force anyone to refrain from riding the buses.

Our method will be that of persuasion, not coercion . . . Love must be our regulating ideal. Once again we must hear the words of Jesus echoing across the centuries: "Love your enemies, bless them that curse you and pray for them that despitefully use you." If we fail to do this our protest will end up as a meaningless drama on the stage of history, and its memory will be shrouded with the ugly garments of shame.

The audience responded with shouts of enthusiasm. After a moment, Dr. King quieted them and made his closing statement:

If you will protest courageously, and yet with dignity and Christian love, when the history books are written in future generations, the historians will have to pause and say, "There lived a great people — a black people — who injected new meaning and dignity into the veins of civilization." This is our challenge and our overwhelming responsibility.[15]

[15] *Ibid.*, p. 61. Cf. Louis Lomax, *The Negro Revolt* (New York, Harper, 1962).

Dr. King described that historic evening as "indescribably moving." As he drove away, he told himself that the victory was already won, no matter what struggles lay ahead. "The real victory was in the mass meeting, where thousands of black people stood revealed with a new sense of dignity and destiny . . . That night we were starting a movement whose echoes would ring in the ears of people of every nation; a movement that would astound the oppressor, and bring new hope to the oppressed. That night was Montgomery's moment in history." [16]

That night also was Martin Luther King's moment. In effect, everyone there realized that he was calmly making himself the target for the racists' fury — fury that implied not only physical violence but also the more cunning and devastating techniques of character assassination.

But he did not stand alone. Others, notably the Reverend Ralph Abernathy, stood beside him at all times. And the people? They persevered in a crusade that lasted until victory was won a year later. Under the leadership of Martin Luther King and his colleagues, they discovered the invincible weapon of nonviolence and were transformed from a cowed and resentful people to a united, hymn-singing, fearless community. They walked for freedom, day after day, month after month. One elderly woman summed up the whole spirit of the movement. Asked if she were tired, she said: "My feets is tired, but my soul is at rest." [17]

With rare exceptions, the white community, including the police and the civic officials, indulged in their customary obstructionist tactics. Unconcerned about clearing themselves with history, they carried on a program of harassment and reprisals against the Negroes. But most of their strategy backfired, because the Negro had changed. He was no longer afraid. He no longer considered it a disgrace to go to jail. He accepted blows, curses, stares of hate as marks of honor. The white community was bewildered by this drastic, inexplicable change, and the racist elements grew more outraged. But everything they did was countered by the singing, laughing, praying Negro.

[16] King, *op. cit.*, pp. 64–70.
[17] *Ibid.*, p. 10.

Typical of this change is an incident involving the Ku Klux Klan. This hardy group, clad in their white sheets, decided to stop the "foolishness" by marching through the Negro section. Always before, when the Klan had marched, the Negroes had cleared the streets and remained invisible. But this time they rushed out of their houses, lined the sidewalks, chattered, waved and cheered as they would at any parade. A sinister demonstration was turned into a festivity. The Klan made no more marches.

The deep irony of the situation did not escape the world. As the months passed and the white community sought in every legal and illegal way to suppress the Negro, as the bombings and beatings increased, the world was given the spectacle of a self-styled "superior race" behaving in a manner far inferior to the behavior of the so-called "inferior race."

The world's eyes focused on Martin Luther King, Jr. This young man had committed himself and his people to Christlike behavior. No matter what they did to him, he had to prove himself exemplary or the whole structure would crash. And yet King himself has never hidden his humanity, his human fears and weakness; he has never played the saint, never indulged in angelism, never assumed the ascetic role. He is a young, healthy family man, deeply in love with his wife and children, deeply fearful for their safety.

Dr. King keeps his intimate spiritual life to himself. He will not discuss it. But his actions have spoken eloquently, and because they have, his philosophy has spread and nonviolence has become the weapon by which the American Negro is gaining his freedom.

What were these actions? Perhaps a single one typifies King's heroism. After months of constant harassment, telephoned threats, assaults, when every day his friends wondered if he would live until the night, Dr. King had somehow managed to survive with a ragged set of nerves. One day a reliable white friend told him that plans were being made to assassinate him. At a mass meeting shortly afterward, King told the people: "If one day you find me sprawled out dead, I do not want you to retaliate with a single act of violence." [18]

He went into a depression of fear, fear of his own inadequacy

18 *Ibid.*, p. 133.

before the task. "It seemed that all of my fears had come down on me at once. I had reached the saturation point," he said.

That night he reached a point of personal crisis and cried out in desperation to God: "I am here taking a stand for what I believe is right. But now I am afraid. The people are looking to me for leadership, and if I stand before them without strength and courage, they too will falter. I am at the end of my powers. I have nothing left. I have come to the point where I can't face it alone." [19]

The admission calmed him. Three nights later, he went to a mass meeting at the First Baptist Church. A member of his congregation, Mrs. Mary Lucy Williams, came to the parsonage to sit with Coretta and the baby.

The sound of the explosion at his home was heard many blocks away, and word of the bombing reached the meeting almost instantly. Noting the agitation among some of his colleagues and their worried looks cast in his direction, Dr. King guessed that the disturbance concerned him. He called Reverend Abernathy and asked what was wrong.

"Your house has been bombed."

Dr. King controlled himself and asked about his wife and baby.

"We're checking on that now."

Dr. King managed to hide his agony. He interrupted the collection and told the audience what had happened. He urged each person to go straight home and asked them all to adhere strictly to their philosophy of nonviolence, no matter what might be the result of the bombing.

Rushing home, he saw hundreds of people with angry faces in front of his house. Many were armed.

> The policemen were trying, in their usual rough manner, to clear the streets, but they were ignored by the crowd. One Negro was saying to a policeman, who was attempting to push him aside, "I ain't gonna move nowhere. That's the trouble now; you white folks is always pushin' us around. Now you got your thirty-eight and I got mine; so let's battle it out."

Violence was in the air.

[19] *Ibid.*, p. 134.

Dr. King ran into the house and dashed toward the bedroom, where he saw his wife and child uninjured. "I drew my first full breath in many minutes." He learned that when Coretta and Mrs. Williams had heard the bomb land on the porch, they had run for the back of the house. If they had gone to the porch to investigate, they would surely have been killed.

His wife's composure, her lack of bitterness, steadied Dr. King. He returned to the front of the house to try to calm the crowd. There, he found the Mayor and the Police Commissioner, both of whom expressed their regrets. One of King's colleagues spoke up to them.

"You may express your regrets, but you must face the fact that your public statements created the atmosphere for this bombing. This is the end result of your 'get-tough' policy."

The crowd grew and began to get out of hand. Dr. King stepped up and asked for order. He assured them that his wife and baby were all right.

> If you have weapons, take them home; if you do not have them, please do not seek to get them. We must meet violence with non-violence . . . We must love our white brothers, no matter what they do to us. We must make them know that we love them. Jesus still cries out in words that echo across the centuries: "Love your enemies, bless them that curse you and pray for them that despitefully use you." This is what we must live by. Remember, if I am stopped, this movement will not stop, because God is with the movement. Go home with this glowing faith and this radiant assurance.

When he finished there were shouts of "Amen" and "God bless you." And again: "We are with you all the way, Reverend."

Martin Luther King looked out over the throng and saw tears on many faces.[20]

Through physical attacks, jailings, framed-up assaults on his character, Dr. King has continued to lead and inspire not only "his people" but men all over the world. As Louis Lomax remarked, he is like a St. Paul, going from place to place inspiring his people to

[20] *Ibid.*, pp. 136–138.

nonviolent resistance against injustice and then returning to suffer with them.[21] In the market place of harshest reality he proved his thesis: that the Christ Ideal is not only a valid way, but in the case of the American Negro in Montgomery, Alabama, was the *only* way to insure victory: that the highest idealism is the ultimate practicality.

[21] Lomax, *op. cit.*, p. 92.

MY NEIGHBOR, REVERDY

→

In my schooldays in France before the war the great poets and painters were our heroes. The regimen of a French *lycée* is almost monastic in its strictness. We were not allowed to leave the enclosed grounds, rarely heard a radio, and almost never saw a newspaper. For recreation we read books and studied paintings, and our discussions centered in an awakening awareness of sex and art. The Latin and Greek classics, Molière, Racine — these were our background, and our most heated enthusiasms brought forth the names of Braque, Vlaminck, Chagall, Matisse, and Derain in painting, and of Rimbaud, Apollinaire, Claudel, and Reverdy in literature.

When I returned to France in 1946, the famed American painter, Abraham Rattner, asked me to deliver gifts of clothing to some of his friends.

One of them was the poet, Pierre Reverdy. I was excited at the prospect of doing this legendary figure some small service.

At that time, Rattner wrote me this thumbnail sketch of him:

> The purest of the French poets. Not a self-pusher. Refuses to encourage publication of his work. One of the pioneer cubist group along with Max Jacob, Apollinaire, Braque, Picasso, etc. Fiery temperament, discourses beautifully. Tender, considerate, sensitive, gentle, warm — also violent.

Reverdy was in Paris when I delivered Rattner's package of clothing to his home in Solesmes.

A few months later, I returned to study with the Benedictine monks of Solesmes. Once again I called on Reverdy and once again he was gone — this time to the hospital, put there indirectly by our good deed in taking him the new clothes.

Madame Reverdy explained quickly at the gate, without inviting me in. He had worn the new clothes to Paris. There, in the foyer of his hotel, a friend had introduced him to a communist. The communist had sneered at his clothes and called him a *capitaliste*. The aging poet had answered with a blow to the communist's jaw. It had broken his arm.

"Pierre came back here," Madame Reverdy said. "He is so stubborn. The arm got worse, but he wouldn't allow me to call a doctor. Then Picasso stepped in and took charge. He made arrangements with doctors in Paris, got Pierre a hospital room. He bullied Pierre into going — threatened to hire thugs to carry him bodily. Heaven knows how long he'll be there," she concluded.

A few days later, one of the monks came to the paleography room and said that Madame Reverdy wished to see me downstairs in one of the *parloirs*. I was surprised, since I had learned that she was a solitary who spoke to no one and left her home only to come to the abbey for Mass and Vespers each day.

She asked me if I would telephone Braque in Paris for her. "They'll know how Pierre is getting along. Here is fifty francs. No, I insist on paying for the call. Pierre would want me to. When you have talked with them, will you come and tell me?"

Madame Braque said that Reverdy was getting along fine, and now had a phone in his hospital room if we wished to call him direct.

I felt that Madame Reverdy would surely prefer to make the call herself. When I went to their little house at the end of the road leading up to the abbey, she asked me in — but nervously, suggesting she "guessed" it would be all right with Pierre.

"You must understand. Pierre receives no one except the gardener of the monastery. He leads two lives — one as an unknown farmer here in Solesmes, where those who know his real identity guard the secret; the other in Paris, among his friends. Only special friends are ever allowed behind these walls. The rest have to see him in Paris."

I promised I would not reveal to the people of the village who their neighbor was. She relaxed and finally said, "Yes, I'm sure Pierre would want you here. I'll write and ask him for certain."

Within a couple of days the problem of whether I should be allowed in their house or must remain at the gate had been solved. She had a letter from her husband, instructing her to have me telephone him each day at the hospital and then to carry the news to her. She read part of the letter, as though to reassure me: "You will receive him, let him warm himself by the fire and offer him hot tea or coffee."

I assured her that I did not want to impose, that I would gladly call him and then bring the news and talk to her through the grill of the gate. But she would not hear of it, and kept waving Pierre's letter in the air in a rather pathetic way — as if it were a command neither of us could afford to question.

So it was arranged. I looked forward to the visits because the winter was glacial — fuel was scarce and there was no heat in my cell at the abbey — and for an hour each afternoon I could sit before their stove and have a hot drink.

I learned that Pierre had the artist's passionate obsession with freedom. As a youth, he had refused to go into business with his father — a wine dealer in Narbonne. He wanted to be free. "He was poor," Madame Reverdy said, "but that had no importance. Liberty was the only thing that counted with him. He took jobs as a copy editor and proofreader for publishers. But even at that, it was only substitute work — nothing regular. He worked mostly at night. He'd work three nights a week and earn forty francs. That was enough. When he left work — around two or three in the morning — he'd go to his room and start writing by gaslight."

During World War II, when the Germans occupied his home, he became silent. He created nothing at all. And when they left, he refused to live in the house they had occupied. He sold it and converted an old stone grange into their living quarters. He had rebelled, Madame Reverdy explained, against all restraints, anything that would put a damper on his creative freedom and turn him into a slave. And yet, ironically, he had ended up overwhelmingly aware of his slavery, his slavery to freedom itself.

The stone grange had been made into one large room with two small sleeping alcoves and with a kitchen off to the side. A single window looked out on Pierre's garden and orchard, and the whole was surrounded by a high stone wall. We sat before a small wood stove which had been installed in the brick fireplace. Around us, in the large room, on chalk-white walls, hung two bright and serene Braques, an important Leger, and Picasso's portraits of Reverdy and St. Thérèse of Lisieux.

"Pierre dies of loneliness here," Madame Reverdy said. "His work is all from his great loneliness. It is perhaps a good thing he had to stay in the hospital. There he has friends who come to see him . . . Braque, Picasso, Borés and the rest. But he broke with Borés. Listen." And she picked up a letter she had just received from her husband.

Borés came in while I was talking to Griffin on the phone. When I hung up, he had to know who it was. I told him it was an American friend. Then he said, in that sarcastic, nasty sweet way of his: "Me, I don't much care for Americans." That was enough. I kicked him out. No, I decided then and there. I told myself I'd put up with Picasso's Spanish moods all my life; and I'm too old to have another Spanish genius for a friend, no matter how much I admire his painting. I told him *merde* for good luck and never to talk to me again.

I apologized for being the cause of that rift.

"You don't know that crowd," she laughed. "By tomorrow Borés will be loving the Americans — they will have a great reconciliation. They fight and make up — always. Those Spaniards. But they are sweet people. I remember when we were in Paris. Juan Gris would come in the evenings with his guitar and we would drink strong coffee and have music. We were too poor to have anything else."

"Did you know Maria Blanchard?" I asked.

"Oh, very well. I know little of painting, but I know that she was a very great artist. She was gentle and sweet with me. I think her temper was only panic. She was poor and exploited by those who recognized both her genius and her naïveté. She was in a cage and couldn't get out."

Each day I used the telephone at the abbey and called Reverdy. He spoke in the warm, thick accent of the *Midi*. Always he asked me to reassure his wife that everything was going fine, even though he did not hesitate to admit to me privately that he was dying of pain, that the hospital was peopled by sadists.

"But tell her — be certain, will you?" he pleaded, "that I am well and improving. I suppose it is all right since my friends won't rescue me from this nightmare."

And when I consoled him about the pain: "The pain . . ." he

would groan. "I am too old to suffer such pain. It is agony, my poor friend, agony. But you must not worry. Tell my wife to buy you a beefsteak and cook it outside on the ground, on the little grill. Have a good meal for once."

"But I can't deliver such a message to your wife."

"Tell her. I insist. If you don't, I'll be obliged to write her, and in such agony, that would be a cruel thing to make me do."

A few days later I came down with malaria. When I regained consciousness, I had a letter from him, written in pencil on cheap notebook paper:

My dear friend, I learn this moment by a letter from my wife that you have fallen ill at Solesmes. I am very worried. I hope that the fevers will already be subsiding when you receive this word. Here, I have at present, some cognac that I can't drink because I'm running a temperature. I'm even sorrier now not to be at Solesmes. I should have been able to take care of you. I'm about as good at nursing the sick as anyone I know — which isn't saying much. Tell my wife for me — my letter to her has already gone — to make you some good coffee, very strong, and to buy a bottle of alcohol. If you drink the alcohol along with the coffee, it should do something. And my entire library is at your disposition. As soon as you are able, give me your news. Yours P.R.

Shortly afterward, Madame Reverdy came to the abbey to tell me that Pierre would be home the following Wednesday evening and wanted me to come to lunch on Thursday.

"You must come in through the kitchen door," she said. "That will give him time to get from his chair and greet you standing up."

"But he doesn't have to stand up to greet me," I protested.

"You don't know Pierre," she said. "He plans on making a great thing of this greeting. He wrote full instructions. He says he is very fond of you in spite of the fact that you are obviously intelligent in that educated way he detests. He says you have a warm heart in you and if you stop studying soon enough, you may be able to conserve it." She shrugged her shoulders as though not entirely understanding the connection herself. "His greeting is apparently part of his great plan to divert you from your studies."

On Thursday, I waded through snowdrifts toward their house. I don't know what I expected — an old man with ferocious eyes, perhaps; a sneering man — I didn't know. I did know that I was at last to meet one of the heroes of my youth — a great poet.

When I walked in, a powerfully built, square-shaped man stood in the middle of the room with both arms outstretched and a smile as open as the sunlight. He looked like anything but what I had expected. He was dressed in a heavy wool robe with a muffler around his neck. His face was hidden behind several days' growth of beard stubble, black with silver highlights. His head was massive, his face dark, his eyes black. In one gesture he was greeting me, shoving me into a chair, pouring wine. He apologized for his beard. "With this arm, I can't shave," he said.

"I'll shave you, if it's uncomfortable," I suggested.

"Ah, good — after lunch, eh?" He lit a cigarette and then looked at me sharply.

"Did you ever shave anyone else?"

"No, but I can learn — surely . . ."

"Do you use the blade or the safety razor?"

"The safety razor."

He decided not to risk it.

The fevers had lingered on. I was weak and gaunt.

"I know about these things," he assured me. "We'll get you well. What you need is plenty of food, plenty of alcohol, and plenty of aspirin."

The cure seemed drastic to me, but there was no question about it — he was in charge.

The first *apéritif* went to our heads. He sat opposite me, smoking and talking. "Tell me about yourself. You roam about the world studying. Why?" he asked gently.

Madame Reverdy, setting the table, glanced at me as though to say that she had told me so, and also with a vague smile which clearly indicated that I would be perfectly within my rights to tell the great man it was none of his business.

"I don't know. What else is there to do?" I said. "I have no particular talent. Until I discover one, I thought I should spend my time studying."

"I know what you mean," he said. "But in my heart I don't

really understand it. I've had to write — from the very beginning. If I hadn't written, I'd have gone mad long ago. My writing is what saved my sanity."

Madame Reverdy called us to table, to a dinner in which neither of us was much interested now. Wine, black coffee, cognac — these were the interesting things. But she reminded him I was sick. He became concerned again. Yes, we must eat. The talk could come later — all through the winter.

That afternoon, we gave his cure a fair trial. By early evening I could do little more than reel back to my cell at the monastery. For days afterward, both of us were violently ill. He sent me a note with his apologies, suggesting that there must have been something wrong with the coffee. The cure had proved infallible for the fevers in his past experience.

When I recovered, I met Madame Reverdy outside the chapel one day and she asked me why I did not come to see them.

"I'm afraid I might interrupt his work," I said.

"Oh, come along," she insisted.

When we got there, he reproached me for having deserted them. I repeated my reasons.

"It takes me a year to think of enough to write in five minutes," he said. "Besides — I do nearly all of my writing at night. I hate the night. I can't sleep. I keep a paper and pencil beside my bed, and when I have insomnia, I write. Otherwise nothing. Come any time."

With this, he brought out an enormous package of papers and undid the string around them. There were scraps of all shapes and sizes, covered with pencil scrawlings — pounds of them — fragments, thoughts, observations. These were later published as *Le livre de mon bord.*

Since my eyesight was failing, I asked him to read me some of them.

"In poetry, the only thing worth saying is that which cannot be said," he would read, making marks on the paper as he went along, talking always with a cigarette or pipe in his mouth. "This is why we have to depend on what passes between the lines."

Later, Jean Duché, of *Le Figaro Litteraire,* was to report a conversation similar to so many we had during those long winter months when we were brought together by the cold and the loneliness.

"Images. Poetry is made of images. People express themselves in images. However, not many have the interior pressure to make of these images a poetic work. I write for them — for everyone," he said, and then added: "That is, I write for no one."

Again, he said that the image is a pure creation of the spirit. It was not born of a comparison, but rather of a bringing-together of two more or less separate realities. He said that an image is not strong because of any element of the brutal or fantastic, but because the association of ideas is distant and exact. "One creates a powerful image, new for the spirit, in bringing together, without comparison, two distant realities of which the *spirit alone* perceives their relationships."

But we did not often talk of poetry. I was a musicologist; not a person involved in the problems of creation, only in their results. And too, like most intensely creative people, he did it rather than discussed it. It was always difficult for me to reconcile the man whom I knew as a friend and neighbor with the works of the poet, so little did the one resemble the other. As a man, I saw each day the farmer or the philosopher, shabbily dressed, ill-shaven, jovial. We would drink wine together and talk about life in America, particularly in the South, which fascinated him. His conversational language was more akin to the barracks room than the ivory tower. Then, when I turned to his poetry, I would find the immaculate craftsman, the connoisseur of nuance, the expresser of the inexpressible, the user of a language of magnificent purity and vigor.

In the early spring, we went on a photographing spree and I made many photos of him. A week or so later, my left eye went out. While I was in Sablé, the doctor bandaged it and I picked up the photographs and returned to Solesmes. I dreaded seeing Reverdy any more, because he was a man to suffer greatly the pains of his friends. But I had to go. I took him the photographs and started immediately talking about them.

"To hell with the photos," he said aghast. "What has happened to your eye?"

I told him the whole thing — that I was rapidly becoming blind.

As I feared, it changed our relationship drastically. He went into a profound depression and took it far worse than I did.

Some days he would read to me — new works by Anouilh, and discuss them with eagerness. Other days, when the weather permitted, he would work in the garden and we would drink wine; but always there was the great pall of sadness which nothing could dissipate. He was careful never to let me see that I was the cause of these depressions, but both his wife and I knew.

Of himself, he turned to another causality — his own imperfections as a poet. If the day were too bad for outside work, he would sit at the window and call himself a *raté* — a failure. His reaction to my blindness tormented him with doubts about himself.

"I've always dreamed of the meteors," he said one day. "Rimbaud, Lautréamont — that's what I should have been. I'm a *raté*."

At such times, he who could not console, needed to be consoled. He would become a desperate, agonizing man, speaking of his slavery, his insomnia, his inability to break the chains of his mediocrity.

For a long time, I remained silent, feeling it was foolish, impertinent even, to cross him. But one afternoon, when he fell into this melancholy and we had both been fortified with a large glass of brandy, I heard myself objecting, arguing with him.

"No . . . no . . . listen," I said. "Is everyone wrong except you? I grew up, and so did the best of my schoolmates, on your work — long before I ever dreamed of meeting you. I have spent evenings in the home of a judge in Tours, listening to him read poetry, and always he ended up with your work — not with Rimbaud or Lautréamont, not with Eluard or Cocteau or Apollinaire. No — with Reverdy."

I heard him snort, and smelled the smoke from his pipe. His face was obscured in shadows.

"You take away a great deal from me when you spit on what has meant so much to me," I said. "You'd be the first to condemn a man for complaining that he was not a Reverdy. And yet you complain because you are not a Rimbaud. When people return to your work again and again, long even after they've memorized it, then you are not a Rimbaud *raté* but a Reverdy *réussi*. You went your own way — a way only you could go. The rest of us thank God you did."

He spoke then, as though he were very tired. "It's hard to believe, you know. It's very hard to believe."

He murmured, talking almost to himself, but telling me a story. "Once a young man came to see me about publishing his poems in a review I was editing. I refused them. Some time later I received a letter from his wife. He'd died of tuberculosis. She told me that *Les ardoises du toit* lay on his bed table . . . that my poems had softened his agony."

He sighed. I drank from my glass. All of the tensions had gone. "It's very hard to believe," he kept saying. "For me, it's very hard."

I understood then the extreme privacy of such a man's work, his doubts and torments, and his almost desperate need occasionally to be reassured of its value.

That was my last visit with him. Within a few days I had lost my sight and left Solesmes to return to America.

In the intervening years, I heard from him rarely. His letters were full of affection and bitterness. He disliked profoundly the "Americanization" of France after World War II.

"A hard irony for me lies in this: when you came to France, we gave you the best that we have and that we are, and you went away with the best of France in your mind and heart; but what have we chosen to take from America? — the jukebox, the hamburger, the fads."

Jacques Maritain wrote me of Reverdy's death:

Raissa and I loved Reverdy profoundly, and we held him to be the greatest poet of our age. I learned of his death when we arrived in Paris in those terrible summer days of 1960 when illness threw itself so totally on Raissa. It would have been too great a blow for her to tell her of the death of our friend — she never knew of it on earth. All that I know is that Reverdy died suddenly, in a few moments, of a heart attack, I believe. He was stricken on his feet, as he was preparing to go out and work in his garden. Pierre van der Meer (who is now a Benedictine monk in Holland) met a monk at Solesmes who saw Reverdy frequently, and what he learned from this monk filled him with admiration and confidence. Reverdy believed he had lost the Faith. In reality, God hounded him constantly. He hungered for God; this great soul had a passion for the Absolute, which even if it never was satisfied, placed him always close to the Divine. (It was also this passion for the Absolute that explained his angers.)

(Jacques Maritain, letter to JHG, Oct., 1961)

My journal notes for that day read:

Reverdy has died. It came as a shock. I said the Requiem for him last evening. My work is filled with the intrusion of my memories of this great poet and longtime friend and neighbor, of the tortured days we spent together at Solesmes huddling against the cold, against incomprehension and the vastness of his bitterness with the Nazi occupation.

Apparently, in the last years, some resignation, if not peace, came to him. Among his last poems, collected in a book called *La liberté des mers*, illustrated by Braque, are these magnificently serene final lines of a life:

Le soir — le rideau déployé referme le paysage.
Les rêves sont partis. Les bateaux à pleins mâts glissent
*   sur l'horizon.*

I can see him in these lines, sitting there motionless, old in years and worn to a terrible fatigue by the batterings of years of feeling too much, too deep; sick with himself for being less than he dreamed man should be; sick with the rest of us for being still less . . . so generous and warm and lonely.

A VISIT TO HUY

→

Sunday, July 12, 1964
In New York City, 7:15 P.M. Leave at 9:50 for Belgium; waiting in Sabena Airlines lounge at John F. Kennedy Airport. Tired and sleepy. Awakened at 6 this morning. Wrote "The Poulenc Behind the Mask" for *Ramparts*. Packed and left home at 10:30 A.M. Due to arrive in Brussels at 9:50 A.M. tomorrow.

July 14, 1964
Arrived in Brussels sick and spent most of the time in bed at my hotel . . . but got some good photographs.

July 16, 1964
Now, in Huy, have spent the day at Father Pire's University of Peace — students from all over the world.

Later — 11:30 P.M.
Am finally settled in my cell here at La Sarte, the Dominican priory. This ancient building, constructed in 1834, on top of a hill overlooking the city of Huy, is like the monasteries I used to know in France — truly poor and simple. I am occupying the cell of a Father Leonard, who is away on a trip. It is a small room, large enough only for a desk, cot and washstand. The ceilings are very high, the walls lined with books. A single window looks out beyond poplars to the lights of the village below. No screens, so the room hums with night bugs. A vast surrounding silence of other cells.

In the corner near the window, a large crock washbowl covers the washstand; it holds a carafe of wash water. The water faucet and toilet are at the end of the corridor.

I feel immediately at home here. Everything begins to relax. A great contentment born long ago (how many years?) in other cloisters returns this silent night in this ill-lighted cell.

Occasionally I hear a footstep. Father Pire never sleeps, so they say. He moves about in his cell across the hall. One of the world's great men, Nobel Prize winner,* Doctor of Theology, Lawyer — 36 years he has lived in this building, in a cell like this.

Am torn with the desire to write . . . to write all of this that is so new and yet so deeply familiar from my past. And at the same time, torn to be still, silent — to allow the experience of simply being here to fill those crusted and calloused places of myself. Great fatigue overwhelms me, comfortable, even pleasant now in this quiet, this poverty, this simplicity.

I bought a bottle of powdered Nescafé and take a long time preparing some in a glass of cold water. There is time here — a sudden luxury.

Odd, if I had these accommodations in a hotel, I would be depressed and wretched; as I was when I was a Negro and could get nothing better.

I told Father Pire tonight: "This seems a planet away from Mississippi."

It is warm tonight, still. Through the open window from somewhere far in the distance below I can distinctly hear an infant squalling. Universal sound, thrice familiar to the heart of any father, familiar to all the nights of men.

All of these hundreds of volumes, many of the large paperbound kind of years ago, yellowed. Some mind inhabiting this cell has read them, pressed their knowledge into his own wisdom. Books in Latin, French, English, German.

July 17, 1964

All day at the University. Very good sessions and tonight a most enjoyable concert by a young Belgian pianist, Patrick Grommelynck, student of Ashkenase — most gifted. Works by Beethoven, Chopin, Bach, Prokofiev.

July 18, 1964

Returned here to the monastery at 4 P.M. to take some photos and do my washing. But there is a water shortage and I was able to wash

---

* Editor's Note: Father Pire received the 1958 Nobel Peace Prize for his work in behalf of displaced persons following World War II.

only one undershirt before the water went off. Very hot and still now at 6 P.M., but overcast, rain predicted for tonight. Vesper bells ring now in the distance and bees hum in this cell. Darkness does not come until after 9 P.M.

Covered with sweat in my shirtsleeves. Electricity in the air. Rain will surely come and bring some coolness.

I run now — or hobble rapidly — to Vespers in the Chapel.

Later

After Vespers, supper in the refectory — butter and bread (one takes two immense slabs of bread which have already been buttered in between), fresh tomatoes, boiled potatoes with raw onion slices mashed into them, a plain omelet, an orange and black coffee.

Even though I learned to eat fast long ago at the Benedictines of Solesmes, I could not keep the pace. I still had a large portion of bread to consume when I noticed the Prior reach for his bell. He waited, watching me. I crammed the bread into my mouth and he rang. I almost choked on it while we stood and chanted the after-dinner prayers.

In the midst of supper the skies turned green, the wind suddenly rose, the refectory filled with a garish glow of lightning. The rain brought a blessed coolness.

The window of my cell is surrounded with some type of large-leafed ivy. Rain rattles against the leaves, so near and clear it is as though it were striking my very eardrums.

In the obscurity of the storm, the whitewashed corridors are dark except for the faint light that penetrates from side windows — a beautiful kind of visual repose, visual silence.

Now the wind and rain subside. Thunder rumbles away toward the distant hills.

Two monks converse in loud whispers, shouting whispers down the corridor. A door squeaks on its hinges, closing. Silence.

The principal speaker today at the University was Father Cornelis, O.P. Marvelously clear exposition of the theory of the Fraternal Dialogue.

Father Pire is careful that the University of Peace *not* appear sectarian in any way — but a University belonging to all men, welcoming all men of all colors and politics and faiths (or no faith).

Today while I was photographing the lecture, he asked me not to publish any photographs of the two Dominican Fathers together. And he deliberately absented himself from Father Cornelis' conferences, as he told me, so as to avoid any suggestion in the students' minds that this might be a Dominican school.

He is most successful. Students from all countries meet, and with no hint of any particular religious or political orientation, learn to dialogue while studying the great problems of our times from medical men, lawyers, philosophers, etc. The accents are on justice and peace — the problems that stand in the way of justice and peace.

More and more I am persuaded that we desperately need such a University in the United States, where great numbers of students could come to learn the techniques of dialogue and the impediments that prevent dialogue. Odd, I am called to Europe to help teach the dialogue, and yet I have never even been asked to speak about dialogue in all of the hundreds of lectures I give in the United States.

Later — 9 P.M.

The wind has stopped. A soft rain falls steadily now. From my window a view of gray sky, black poplars, and shining through their leaves and through the gray mists, lights from the village below. They resemble an upside-down galaxy of stars. The grays of the valley are the same as the grays of the sky at this hour.

July 19, 1964

Overcast sky and a chill breeze at dawn. Mass at seven in the Chapel downstairs. Birdsongs and stillness. Green trees and distant hills seen through haze.

Nerves gradually come to a profound quiet. I feel almost stunned by this healing process and sit dumbly while the curative forces of peace and security work within me. A kind of muted harmony settles like mist over the clash and blare of this past year.

Nature is fully in it — the trees, the body — the washings and shavings and feedings and sleeps. The soul rests in these things now in an almost somnolent state, abiding, not counting the time, not concentrating but merely being. A kind of felicity is glimpsed occasionally. The clangor of church bells resounds with clarity through the hazes of this morning — near and far.

July 22, 1964

Three days of intense work. Press conferences, radio and TV shows, two lectures. Returned here at 10 P.M. with Father Pire, both of us too exhausted to speak; but we discussed again the need for a branch of the University in America.

I do not understand how Father Pire keeps from collapsing. Since the day of the Hungarian revolt six years ago he has suffered a relentless insomnia. He sleeps one or two hours a night. Sometimes he goes for days without lying down. Whenever I go to the bathroom at night, I often see the light under his door, though often he just lies in the dark to rest.

My admiration for him grows each day. For many years he was a renowned teacher of theology until he began his "works" and, as he says, "abandoned the theory for the practice." But he is so unassuming and so open one has to remind oneself who he really is, and how many thousands of lives he has saved from despair.

I have heard he reads detective novels to help pass the sleepless nights, to divert his mind from his work. I am reminded of Madame Alexander Grunelius' remark to me of Jacques Maritain's penchant for reading detective novels to distract his mind long enough to allow him to sleep. This lady, whose château in Kolbsheim (France) is a resting place, a retreat for the world's great intellectuals, said she was amazed at how many supremely gifted thinkers read mysteries for the same reason.

"But they must be poorly written," she explained. "If they are well-written they hold the reader and prevent the sleep."

Later — 4 P.M.

First mail today. What joy to hear from my daughter, Susie. A nice long letter written in different colored inks.

Day of silence and solitude. Profound sense of peace. Contentment to be here. But there is a change in me due to the years. The fragrance of old incense permeating stones of the Chapel would once have opened up in me a flood of reactions. Today it merely adds its part to the calm felicity of the senses. I have rested, written letters, walked about the grounds and photographed. For the first time since my arrival there is no physical pain. The skies are overcast but the light, though soft, is brilliant.

I glance up from this page to see my small Leitz table tripod with its rotating ball head — am struck by the beauty of this flawlessly crafted instrument.

My body calls attention to itself by its lack of pain, by the wonder of this new sense of its well-being. This must be the way most people feel most of the time.

July 26, 1964

Busy but good day. Trip to Liège (Belgium) to see the famous baptismal font in the Église Saint-Barthélemy. The church dates originally from the 11th Century (1010–1015) and the brass baptismal font, one of the world's supreme masterpieces, dates from 1107–1118. The sculptor is unknown, but believed to be Renier, a goldsmith (or silversmith) who died in 1150. In any case, it was a person from Liège. Impossible to describe the marvelous effect of all elements combining into a harmony that leaves me stunned.

Back now at the monastery after photographing a splendid Château-Farm (12th or 13th Century) near Madove.

July 28, 1964, Château de Kolbsheim, Bas-Rhin, France

Nearby, the clock at the church rings midnight. I arrived here yesterday to spend three days with Jacques Maritain. He and Madame Alexander Grunelius met me at the station in Strasbourg, Jacques looking skeletal but chipper. The car would not start, however, so while Madame Grunelius went in search of help, the Alsatian attendant at the parking lot came over and asked us to help him push the car up out of the way. I protested that Jacques should not.

The attendant said, *"Bien, grandpère, restez-là."* ("All right, grandpaw, remain there.")

Jacques replied, *"Le grandpère reste là, alors."* ("Grandpaw'll remain here, then.")

But the outing was too much and Jacques was fainting by supper. He had bought some books, shopped and taken me to a café in town for coffee. He retired immediately after supper. I talked with the Grunelius family until 10 — slept from 10:30 until 10 this morning.

Visited with Jacques between 11–12, took a long walk in these splendid gardens, photographed him and the gardens. He told me of the great care Alexander Grunelius takes with these gardens — the "philosophers' walk" they are called. Grunelius considers it the "vocation of the house" to create an atmosphere of calm — a contemplative atmosphere — for Jacques and the other world-famed artists and intellectuals who come here (and have for years).

We had a good and pleasant lunch. I photographed more in the afternoon — particularly Raissa Maritain's grave, as Jacques asked me to. Jacques then showed me the room where they have arranged the papers and furniture and art objects Raissa loved best — many photographs of their friends, paintings and drawings of Rouault, Chagall, etc., (including a complete *Miserere.*) Jacques asked me to photograph this room and the objects in it.

Then, at my insistence that he let me help him, we worked until supper time (7:30) on the photographs he wants to include in his *Memoirs.*

Immediately after supper he went to bed. I visited again with the Gruneliuses — we talked much of Victor Hammer who helped build and decorate the private chapel here at the château, and is a close friend. I realized suddenly he was the same great printer who has done some of Thomas Merton's works. I was correct. They had copies of all of them. I then told them about Merton sending the Hammer edition of *Hagia Sophia* to Clyde Kennard and how it had softened his death, and that I had even met Hammer with Merton at Gethsemani. Reluctantly cut short this interesting session to return here to my room at 9 P.M. to work on the photos for Jacques' book.

Am quite amazed to see Jacques' good spirits, his delight in things, the sharpness of his wit. We are having a thoroughly good time together. The awful anguish over Raissa's death has finally turned into something no less preoccupying but now peaceful.

July 30, 1964

Returned finally this evening from Kolbsheim. Good to be back in this cell again. But a marvelous visit with Jacques.

Got here an hour ago (8:30 P.M.). Father Pire is not back yet from the University, so I washed two shirts; went to the refectory, found sardines, boiled potatoes, bread and mayonnaise left over from supper . . . I ate well.

When I opened the door, returning to this cell, an odor of strong French tobacco struck me. I smoke so much the room is permeated with the odor.

At Strasbourg yesterday, the Trans-Europe Express was crowded so they refused to take me since I had not made a reservation. I made one immediately for today — spent yesterday evening photographing Strasbourg — a beautiful city. I ate too much because the food was so delicious.

Walked miles over Strasbourg and now my legs ache. But I walked surprisingly well. I never dreamed my legs would hold up for such distances. But it was mostly flat — little uphill walking at all. Here at Huy everything is up and down.

After an immense dinner last night, I sat on a bench at one of the quais under the trees and listened to the water for an hour. Young couples, their arms about one another's waists, passed occasionally, their voices soft and delightful as the summer night air. Listening to them, I felt old — or rather I felt what it is not to feel young. I sat there tired from the afternoon's walk, contented from the supper, and envied them not at all. For a moment this unsettled me, but I realized that if Piedy were here it would be different — we would be doing as they. Only we would not have to leave one another at the end of the evening — we would go right on to bed together.

When one is young, one is self-priming; older, it takes a lot of elements steeped in nature and in the nature of marriage to accomplish the same priming. Much better.

August 1, 1964

It has turned almost cold tonight — about 50 degrees I judge. Light rain splatters against the vines that grow around my window.

Long and hard day's work. Opening of the new (second) session at the University. Father Pire gave a brilliant analysis of the Fraternal Dialogue, in great depth and the simplicity that finally comes out of complexity. I jotted down some of his statements.

"To speak without first listening is not dialogue, but monologue."

"We must distinguish between dialogue between two and a mere double monologue."

"Unilateral declarations published at the same time are simply double monologues. The greatest error is to make people believe that a double monologue is a true dialogue."

"Monologue separates. Dialogue unites."

"To build bridges across chasms that separate us — dialogue."

"Those who oppose dialogue are fanatics. They want only to hear their own monologue and will listen to no other truth than the one they think they possess."

"I firmly believe men can get along together — by accepting and frankly admitting their contradictions."

"Dialogue — to open oneself to the 'other.'"

"Dialogue — to escape the prison of words and prejudiced ideas."

"Dialogue — the spirit of honest disagreement."

"The problem of contradictions — the human cacophony."

Sunday, August 2, 1964

Next Sunday I will be in Texas, a continent away. Here, at 6 P.M., a cold sunlight streams through the window of my cell. It casts a magnificent glow into every corner of these white plaster walls. Church bells from the valley float up faintly to us — the sounds of sunset. Otherwise, a profound hush is softened only by hints of conversations somewhere in the valley and a breeze rustling the trees outside. Moments of profound peace. Soon supper, then Matins and Lauds and then, at 8:45, I am scheduled to lecture to the monks here at La Sarte.

Another magnificently clarifying lecture from Father Pire this morning.

But everything fades as my awareness concentrates on the peace that overwhelms me after the relentless tensions of the past years. It stupefies me. I feel a tremendous pull toward sleep always. I do not resist it, two hour nap this afternoon, waking from time to time to glance out at the sky and the poplars framed by my window, sensing the benevolence of this place and falling effortlessly into sleep again. At four, coffee and a large slice of bread and a banana, alone in the refectory.

My last Sunday here. I'll return surely, but not again in this cell, not again in this cloister because next time I'll bring my family,

God willing, and that will be better but never again the same. So I look at everything with the eyes of a last time, feel everything with that special sensibility.

And my heart looks ahead to the joy of being with my family next Sunday — but with dread of the telephone calls, the constant running in the paths of man's inhumanity to man.

Long, long twilights — from about 6:30 to 9 P.M.

Marvelous light here. At the end of the article he did about me in *Figaro Litteraire* this week, Gilles Lapouge caught it, too. He wrote:

> Now we are in the monastery at La Sarte. Inside the cloister there is a garden, a bush of red roses, the last brilliance of evening sun. I don't know if John Griffin has told me all he wanted to. I suspect not. We could speak for hours. But in this setting where all elements are reconciled, surrounded by the miraculous accord of light on stone walls, John Griffin feels the need to pause, to stop a while.

Earlier in the same piece, he wrote with extraordinary perception:

> Griffin wanders along the banks of the Meuse between Namur and Liège with a metal case containing complicated photographic equipment. What does he photograph? The ancient farms of the region, he says, and I think this is not exactly true. I think he photographs only the gentleness, the peace and the order of these scenes.

In spite of the long sleep and the hours of catching up on rest, one works here; finally much gets done and without great effort. Everything is perfectly organized to let work flow on its own rhythm, naturally, without force or strain.

August 4, 1964 (Feast of St. Dominic)

The monastery bustles this morning and last night with preparations for the great Dominican feast. The usual profound quiet is hardly less silent, but with movement as everything is cleaned and polished. Young monks carry tables to the refectory, others carry great stacks of borrowed dishes (white china with blue flowers, lent for the occasion.) Father Econome, a middle-aged man, carries a huge metal basket of rolls from the bakery down the street. A hazy, almost sunlit, morning — an air of marvelous festivity.

I have just returned from the refectory where I had my breakfast of bread and coffee. Tables are set, place-cards and crystal in place. I note that I am to the right of the Père Abbé — an honor that embarrasses me in view of the numerous distinguished visitors invited today.

Later

A crowd at the Mass. I entered late (not knowing the hour), at the very end, but in time to hear the jubilant Frescobaldi trumpeted out on the organ. Strange — sixteen measures of this music, and I felt all that is in me catch the spirit of the day — almost as a shock to the system — a great joy and suddenly I am in the midst of the preparations for dinner. I go to photograph the proceedings now.

The menu for today's luncheon feast: celery soup, tomato stuffed with small shrimps, broiled chicken, mashed potatoes, sauce, apricot preserves, kidneys and mushrooms and potatoes (again), ice cream and fruit.

Later

Radio, television and press conferences all afternoon. I returned here this evening to dress for tonight's concert — a recital by Jacques Genty and Lola Bobesco, sonatas by Bach, Mozart and Beethoven, performed by two supreme artists. A moving thing — the students dress informally for all of the lectures, no matter how distinguished the lecturer; but they invariably dress for the music with which Father Pire surrounds us — an homage to art.

While I was here bathing — 186 pounds in two quarts of cold water in a washbowl — three young men from Father Pire's home for refugee children called at the little reception room downstairs. When I went down, they asked me for a conference. One, Jewish, orphaned when his parents were sent to Hitler's ovens, told me that war was declared today between the United States and the Viet Cong. I wait alone now for further news with a great weight in my chest.

Listened to the news on a transistor radio. No war yet. United States accused of brinkmanship in Vietnam to distract attention from growing racial crises in America. Trouble in New Jersey and Philadelphia. Announced also the discovery of the mutilated bodies of the three students (Andrew Goodman, James Chaney, Michael Schwerner) missing in Mississippi.

This is the reality. One speaks of men like Father Dominique Georges Pire as though they were dreamers, when nothing could be less true, if this implies a lack of reality. Father Pire lived through the nightmare of occupation in a village where for each German slain, 50 local family-fathers were shot as hostages. The same racism, different version, comes to light in Mississippi with the finding of the bodies. The report says James Chaney (the Negro student) was severely beaten before being shot. Dehumanization of the racists. This is what I go back to, back to the rooms where I must look into the ravaged faces of James Chaney's mother, or Clyde Kennard's mother and how many more mothers of martyrs before we learn to stop justifying our cheating?

Bibliography

SELECTED BIBLIOGRAPHY

⟶

WORKS BY JOHN HOWARD GRIFFIN

BOOKS

The Devil Rides Outside. Fort Worth, Smiths, Inc., 1952. In paperback,
New York, Pocket Books, Inc., 1954. Also published in England, France,
Germany and Italy.
Nuni. Boston, Houghton Mifflin, in association with Smiths, Inc., Dallas,
1956. Also published in France and Germany.
Land of the High Sky. Midland, Texas, The First National Bank of Mid-
land, 1959.
Black Like Me. Boston, Houghton Mifflin, 1961. In paperback, New York,
Signet Books, The New American Library of World Literature, 1962.
Also published in England, France, Germany, Italy, Norway, Holland,
Portugal, Poland, Yugoslavia, Hungary, Czechoslovakia, and Japan.

MONOGRAPHS

*A Report of the Crisis Situation Resulting from Efforts to Desegregate the
School System,* by John Howard Griffin and Theodore Freedman. Field
Reports on Desegregation in the South, Mansfield, Texas; New York,
Anti-Defamation League of B'nai B'rith, 1956.

CHAPTERS IN BOOKS

"Is This What It Means to See?" in *The Spirit of Man,* Whit Burnett, ed.,
New York, Hawthorn Books, 1958.
"Dark Journey" in *The Angry Black,* John A. Williams, ed., New York,
Lancer Books, 1962.
"Martin Luther King" in *Thirteen For Christ,* Melville Harcourt, ed., New
York, Sheed and Ward, 1963.
"Dialogue With Father August Thompson" in *Black, White and Gray* (*21
Points of View on the Race Question*), Bradford Daniel, ed., New York,
Sheed and Ward, 1964.
"The Intrinsic *Other*" in *Building Peace,* Father Georges Dominique Pire,
O.P., Belgium, The Marabou Press, 1966.
"Into Mississippi" in *Honey and Wax* (*The Powers and Pleasures of Narra-*

tive), Richard Stern, ed., Chicago, University of Chicago Press and University of Toronto Press, 1966.

SHORT STORIES

"Miss Henrietta Briggs and Her Metamorphosis" in *Story*, *3*, Whit Burnett and Hallie Burnett, eds., New York, A. A. Wyn, 1953.
"The Whole World In His Hands" in *New Voices 2: American Writing Today*, Don M. Wolfe, ed., New York, Hendricks House, 1955.
"Sauce for the Gander" in *New World Writing*, *3*, New York, New American Library, 1953. Also published in *Communicative Reading*, Otis J. Aggertt and Elbert R. Brown, eds., New York, Macmillan, 1956.
"Wooly" in *Catholic World*, August, 1956.
"Chez Durand" in *New World Writing*, *12*, New York, New American Library, 1957. ("Chez Durand" is a chapter from Griffin's novel, *Street of the Seven Angels*.)

FOREWORDS

Cousin, Gabriel, *Théâtre I*. Paris, Gallimard, 1963. ("Preface to Gabriel Cousin's *L'Opéra Noir*").
Kreyche, Robert J., *God and Contemporary Man: Reflections of a Christian Philosopher*. Milwaukee, Bruce Publishing Company, 1965.
Jones, Penn, Jr., *Forgive My Grief* (*A Critical Review of the Warren Commission Report on the Assassination of President John F. Kennedy*). Midlothian, Texas, *The Midlothian Mirror*, 1966.

ARTICLES

"Withdrawal of the Artist." *The Nation*, May 2, 1953.
"Prude and the Lewd." *The Nation*, November 5, 1955.
"My Neighbor, Reverdy." *Southwest Review*, Spring, 1958.
"What It Means to See Again." *Jubilee*, May, 1958.
"Is This What It Means to See?" (Excerpt from *The Spirit of Man*), *Reader's Digest*, September, 1958.
"Journey Into Shame." (Part I). *Sepia*, April, 1960.
"Journey Into Shame." (Part II). *Sepia*, May, 1960.
"Journey Into Shame." (Part III). *Sepia*, June, 1960.
"Journey Into Shame." (Part IV). *Sepia*, July, 1960.
"Journey Into Shame." (Part V). *Sepia*, August, 1960.
"Journey Into Shame." (Part VI). *Sepia*, September, 1960.
"Journey Into Shame." (Seven part newspaper serial, internationally syndicated). New York, King Features Syndicate, June, 1960.
"The Living Chains of Blackness: Journey Into the Mississippi Night." *Southwest Review*, Autumn, 1960.
"The Men From the Boys." *The Basilian Teacher* (Canada), January, 1961.
"The Cultivated Mind — Guardian Genius of Democracy." The University of Dallas, 1962. (A specially printed pamphlet studying the contribu-

tions of religious institutions to higher education in Texas, 1689–1962.)

"I Passed for Black." *Man's Magazine*, May, 1962.

"Current Trends in Censorship." *Southwest Review*, Summer, 1962.

"On Either Side of Violence." *Saturday Review*, October 27, 1962.

"Lillian Smith's *Killers of the Dream:* A Review." *Southwest Review*, Winter, 1962.

"Scattered Shadows." (Two selections from Griffin's autobiography, *Scattered Shadows*). *Ramparts*, January, 1963.

"The Shine Boy Has the Dream: Some Afterthoughts on *Black Like Me*." *The Texas Observer*, January 24, 1963.

"Martin Luther King's Movement." *Sign*, April, 1963.

"Racist Sins of Christians." *Sign*, August, 1963.

"Dialogue With Father August Thompson." *Ramparts*, Christmas issue, 1963.

"Journal of a Trip South." *Ramparts*, Christmas issue, 1963.

"The Struggle for Racial Justice: What Lies Ahead?" *The Critic* ("Cross Section"), June–July, 1964.

"The Poulenc Behind the Mask." *Ramparts*, October, 1964.

"The Tip-Off." "Mississippi Eyewitness," a special issue of *Ramparts*, Autumn, 1964.

"Arthur Lourié: A Great Composer Rediscovered." *Ramparts*, January, 1965.

"A Visit to Huy." *Ramparts*, August, 1965.

"Maritain Charts a Course Through Change." *National Catholic Reporter*, November 9, 1966.

STUDIES OF JOHN HOWARD GRIFFIN

Blakey, G. Robert, "Obscenity and the Supreme Court." *America*, August 13, 1966. (Reference to the U. S. Supreme Court decision upholding *The Devil Rides Outside* in the case of *Butler v. Michigan*.)

Cargas, Harry J., "Who Is John Howard Griffin?" *St. Louis Review*, May 28, 1965.

Daniel, Bradford, "Why They Can't Wait: An Interview with a White Negro." *The Progressive*, July, 1964.

———. "The Nobel Vision of Father Pire." *Ramparts*, August, 1965. (Discussion of Griffin's association with Father Georges Dominique Pire, O.P., and the University of Peace, Huy, Belgium.)

Dugger, Ronnie, "An Interview with John Howard Griffin." *The Texas Observer*, July 1, 1960.

Fixx, J. F., "South's Other War." *Saturday Review*, April 14, 1962.

Geismar, Maxwell, "John Howard Griffin: The Devil in Texas." *American Moderns*, New York, Hill and Wang, 1958.

Library Journal, October 15, 1952. (Biographical sketch.)

Lomax, Louis E., "It's Like This." *Saturday Review*, December 9, 1961.

McDonnell, Thomas P., "John Howard Griffin: An Interview." *Ramparts*, January, 1963.

McNamara, Eugene, "Prospects of a Catholic Novel." *America,* August 17, 1957.
——. "The Post-Modern American Novel." *Queen's Quarterly* (Canada), Summer, 1962.
Montgomery, Ruth, "John Howard Griffin: A Biographical Study." *Wilson Library Bulletin,* May, 1963.
Süssman, Irving and Cornelia, *How To Read A Dirty Book.* Chicago, Franciscan Herald Press, 1966.
Turner, Decherd, "The Griffin Mosaic." *Town Crier,* September, 1960.